Ground Training for the Private Pilot Licence

Manual Three

PRINCIPLES OF FLIGHT, AIRFRAMES AND AERO ENGINES, AIRCRAFT AIRWORTHINESS AND AIRCRAFT INSTRUMENTS

AOPA PRIVATE PILOT SYLLABUS (AEROPLANES)

TECHNICAL SUBJECTS

This training manual is one of a set of four specifically written to cover the technical subjects section of the AOPA Private Pilot Syllabus as approved by the United Kingdom Civil Aviation Authority.

In this series of manuals the reference information as listed in the AOPA Private Pilot Syllabus is divided into the sections shown below.

Manual One	Section 1	Air Legislation
	Section 2	Aviation Law, Flight Rules and Procedures
		Air Traffic Rules and Services
Manual Two	Section 3	Air Navigation
	Section 4	Aviation Meteorology
Manual Three	Section 5	Principles of Flight
	Section 6	Airframes and Aero Engines
	Section 7	Aircraft Airworthiness
	Section 8	Aircraft Instruments
Manual Four	Section 9	Specific Aircraft Type
	Section 10	Fire, First-Aid and Safety Equipment
	Section 11	Aeromedical Facts

Other manuals in this training series for instructors and students comprise:

Flying Training for the Private Pilot Licence
– Instructor Manual
Flying Training for the Private Pilot Licence
– Student Manual (Part One and Part Two)

Manuals are also available to cover the requirements of the:

Night Rating
Multi Engine Rating
IMC Rating
AOPA Radio Navigation Certificate

Ground Training for the Private Pilot Licence

Manual Three

**PRINCIPLES OF FLIGHT, AIRFRAMES AND
AERO ENGINES, AIRCRAFT AIRWORTHINESS
AND AIRCRAFT INSTRUMENTS**

R. D. Campbell

BSP PROFESSIONAL BOOKS

OXFORD   LONDON   EDINBURGH

BOSTON   MELBOURNE

Copyright © 1979, 1980, 1983,
1985 R. D. Campbell

All rights reserved. No part of this
publication may be reproduced, stored
in a retrieval system, or transmitted,
in any form or by any means, electronic,
mechanical, photocopying, recording
or otherwise without the prior
permission of the copyright owner.

First published in Great Britain by
 Aviation Training Publications Ltd 1979
Second edition 1980
Reprinted by Granada Publishing 1981
Reprinted 1983 and updated to meet new
 syllabus requirements in effect
 from 1983 by Granada Publishing
Reprinted by Collins Professional and
 Technical Books 1985
Re-set and updated to meet new syllabus
 requirements 1985
Reprinted 1986, 1987
Reprinted by BSP Professional Books 1989

British Library
Cataloguing in Publication Data
Campbell, R. D. (Ronald D)
 Ground training for the private licence.
 Manual 3. Principles of flight, airframes
 and aero-engines, aircraft airworthiness
 and aircraft instruments.
 2nd ed. Re-set and updated to meet new
 syllabus requirements.
 1. Aeroplanes. Flying — Manuals — For
 private pilots.
 I. Title II. Aircraft Owners & Pilots
 Association
 629.132'5217

ISBN 0-632-02658-8

BSP Professional Books
A division of Blackwell Scientific
 Publications Ltd
Editorial Offices:
Osney Mead, Oxford OX2 0EL
 (Orders: Tel. 0865 240201)
8 John Street, London WC1N 2ES
23 Ainslie Place, Edinburgh EH3 6AJ
3 Cambridge Center, Suite 208, Cambridge
 MA 02142, USA
107 Barry Street, Carlton, Victoria 3053,
 Australia

Set by Columns of Reading
Printed and bound in Hong Kong

Nothing in this manual must be taken as superseding the Legislation, Rules,
Regulations, Procedures and Information contained in the Air Navigation Order,
the Air Navigation (General) Regulations, Rules of the Air and Air Traffic
Control Regulations, the UK Air Pilot, NOTAMS, Aeronautical Information
Circulars, or the Recommendations, Restrictions, Limitations and Operating
Procedures published in Aircraft, Engines or Systems Manuals and Certificates
of Airworthiness, or any Civil Air Publication or similar document published by
the Civil Aviation Authority.

Contents

Contents vii

Section 7: Aircraft Airworthiness

Section 8: Aircraft Instruments

Acknowledgments

Grateful acknowledgements are made to the Civil Aviation Authority for permitting reproduction of certain material in this manual.

Acknowledgements are also made to those members of the Civil Aviation Authority and Aircraft Manufacturers; to Mr J. Jones MA Cantab, Dr R.G. James ACGI, BSc, PhD Cantab, and to those members of the AOPA Instructor Committee and Panel of Examiners for their advice and helpful suggestions, all of which formed an important contribution to this training manual.

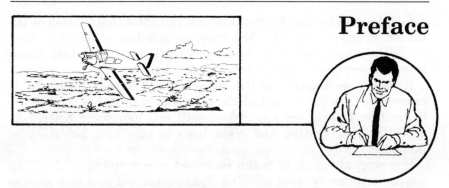

Preface

When a person first learns to fly, his immediate concentration is on learning how to control the aircraft and develop his physical reflexes to achieve judgement in handling the controls so that the aircraft does what he wants it to do.

However, in flying, judgement involves two specific areas, one which relates to the development of physical skills and the other which relates to the making of correct decisions. Lack of judgement in making decisions usually stems from a lack of appreciation or failure to properly comprehend the many items of knowledge which in themselves form the basis of understanding, and without which, the correct decision in handling a particular situation cannot be made without a large element of luck.

In order to operate an aircraft in safety, a pilot will need to develop the elements of skill and good judgement, the quality of these requirements will largely be based on the acquisition and correct application of knowledge. From this statement, the importance of knowledge, when flying, can be appreciated. Once knowledge is gained, the appropriate skills can be developed and the basis of sound captaincy laid.

Probably the greatest difficulty in gaining the necessary knowledge relating to aircraft operation is the number of technical subjects which need to be covered. The pilot must have a sound understanding of all aspects of operating his aircraft and of the environment in which he operates. This means he will need to study and receive instruction in a wide curriculum.

The Civil Aviation Authority is responsible for laying down the privileges of a private pilot's licence, and the number of flying training hours which they consider to be the minimum required for the grant of a licence. In order to ensure that the training you receive embraces all the items considered necessary to qualify you to exercise these privileges, the Civil Aviation Authority also issues a broad but specific training syllabus to cover the requirements of *flight safety*.

The detailed interpretation of this syllabus, however, is normally undertaken by the various individual training organisations, schools, and clubs, and by the Aircraft Owners and Pilots Association of the United Kingdom (AOPA). The training syllabus is therefore very much the responsibility of those individuals with particular knowledge and experience in the training of pilots.

It will, nevertheless, be the responsibility of your instructor to ensure that you have reached the necessary standard of competence in relation to aviation knowledge, skill and judgement before you apply for your written and flight tests to gain your private pilot licence.

However, although it is the combined responsibility of the Civil Aviation Authority, your training organisation and your instructor to ensure you have reached the requisite standard before receiving a private pilot's licence or any of its associated ratings, the ultimate responsibility for flight safety is yours and yours alone. Remember, in the final analysis, it is your knowledge, your skills and your judgement which will either result in a safe enjoyable flight, one made within your limitations and experience, or an unpleasant or hazardous event or worse, one suffered by you and your passengers alike, because these essential qualities were lacking.

The knowledge required by a private pilot concerns many areas and those laid down in the AOPA Private Pilot Licence Syllabus conform to the requirements of the United Kingdom Civil Aviation Authority, which are as follows:

- Air legislation
- Aviation Law, Flight Rules and Procedures (Air Traffic Rules and Services)
- Air Navigation
- Aviation Meteorology
- Principles of Flight
- Airframes and Aero Engines
- Aircraft Airworthiness
- Aircraft Instruments
- Specific Aircraft Type
- Fire, First Aid and Safety Equipment
- Aeromedical Facts

These subjects clearly cover a wide area and therefore to simplify and direct a student's task, the necessary items of knowledge have been placed in four small manuals in a manner which directly follows the layout of the syllabus produced by the Aircraft Owners and Pilots Association, one which has been approved by the United Kingdom Civil Aviation Authority.

The subject presentation follows the sequence of the AOPA syllabus both in the order in which the subjects are listed and in the order in which the items of any one subject appear. A series of progress tests is included at the rear of this manual and this section contains a number of multiple choice type questions which will allow a student to monitor and self examine his learning coverage simply and efficiently.

Learning is achieved in various ways, but generally, two methods are paramount. One, in which reading, thinking and resolving problems plays the primary part, and the other where the person practises and develops physical skills. In flying training, a student will find that both these methods of learning are employed, however, whereas learning is the act of acquiring knowledge, the purpose of it is to obtain a skill or acquire experience.

Therefore, the knowledge gained through studying this manual must be related to the understanding of those factors which concern the practical operation of an aircraft. If this fact is borne in mind throughout the reading of this book, an important and necessary step towards pilot competence will result.

To organise training time efficiently, it will be necessary for a student to know the depth of knowledge expected from him in each of the subject areas, and therefore in the following pages an attempt has been made to embrace both the coverage and depth of the information which is considered essential for the private pilot to understand, in order to develop the necessary skills and judgement required of a safe competent pilot. However, in a manual of this nature, it would not be amiss to cover briefly the best way in which the student should use in his learning programme and a structured guide which outlines a recommended sequence of learning is shown on page xvii.

The reason for including this guide is that, although the subject areas are contained in their individual sections throughout this set of manuals, it would be inadvisable to read and study each page in numerical sequence until the end is reached.

For example, from the early stages of his training, a pilot will, during any one flight, use items of knowledge drawn from many technical subjects. With this in mind, it will be sensible to learn small portions of the various subject areas during any one learning period, e.g. your first learning period would cover the initial information given under several subject headings. Reading across from one subject to another will be in keeping with the way such knowledge is used in the cockpit and helps towards a quicker understanding of what is involved in any one of your training flights.

The guide is only a suggested one and you are free to develop your own sequence and content depending on your own capabilities, the time you have available and your own instructor's advice and recommendations.

A further and important point when reading the subject matter is that your memory retention will be significantly improved by using an organised 'review technique'. This statement is based on the fact that most people forget some 80% of the information they have received within 24 hours of a learning session.

Correct review technique can result in an enormous reduction in the amount which is normally forgotten. For example, a first review of the subject matter learned should take place about 10 minutes after a learning session and this review should be some 10 minutes in length. The following day, a second review of the subject matter learned should be completed and this should last about 5 minutes.

A third and fourth review of 5 minutes at a time should be carried out within one week and this should be followed by a final 5 minute period one month later. After these reviews, most of the knowledge gained will be implanted into your *long term memory* and can then be recalled in the same manner as a person can recall the address of his previous home although several years may have elapsed since he lived there.

Finally, it must be realised that although this type of review sequence may seem an unnecessary chore, its most significant benefit lies in its accumulative effect on the activity of learning, thinking and recall. A person who does not find time to correctly review what he has learned, will continually waste most of the effort he has put into the learning task. On the other hand, a person who has developed good memory recall will be far more likely to arrive at the correct decision at the correct time when the circumstances require it, and as such, he will be able to demonstrate the essential qualities of a good aircraft captain.

Study Guide

Stage 1
> Start by studying from page 5-4, (Principles of Flight), Physics and Mechanics Revision, through to page 5-36, Aspect Ratio.
>
> Read through the guidance notes at the beginning of the Progress tests section and:
>
> Complete Quiz 1, page Q3.
>
> *Note*: An answering sheet is provided at the end of each quiz.

Stage 2
> Study from page 6-3, Airframe Structure, through to page 6-23, Types and Purpose of Control Locks.
>
> Complete Quiz No. 2, page Q9.

Stage 3
> Study from page 5-37, Flying Controls, through to page 5-71, The Stall.
>
> Complete Quiz No. 3, page Q13.

Stage 4
> Study from page 5-72, The Spin, through to page 5-98, The Propeller.
>
> Complete Quiz No. 4, page Q17.

Stage 5
> Study from page 6-24, The Aero Engine, through to page 6-39, Detonation and Pre-ignition.
>
> Complete Quiz No. 5, page Q21.

Stage 6
> Study from page 5-99, Aircraft Performance, through to page 5-133, Weight and Balance in relation to Aircraft Category.
>
> Complete Quiz No. 6, page Q25.

Stage 7
Study from page 6-39, Carburettor Icing, through to page 6-68, Electrical System.
Complete Quiz No. 7, page Q32.

Stage 8
Study from page 6-68, the Variable Pitch Propeller, through to page 6-82, Running Down Methods.
Complete Quiz No. 8, page Q36.

Stage 9
Study from page 7-3, Certification and Documentation, through to page 7-10, Aircraft, Engine and Propeller Log Books.
Complete Quiz No. 9, page Q40.

Stage 10
Study from page 8-3, Aircraft Instruments, through to page 8-36, The Magnetic Compass.
Complete Quiz No. 10, page Q44.

Principles of Flight

Introduction

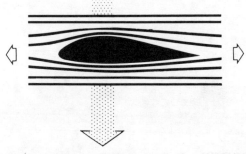

Air is a mixture of gases, and can be defined as a fluid, that is to say, a substance which can be made to flow and change its shape when a moderate pressure is applied to it.

Aerodynamics is the science which involves a study of the action and interaction of forces which act on a body in motion through the air. However, this manual is primarily devoted to the basic aspects of aerodynamics as applicable to an aircraft in flight throught the normal atmosphere, or, put more simply, the *principles of flight.*

Although a pilot does not need a profound knowledge of aerodynamics, it must nevertheless be appreciated that his ability to control an aircraft and arrive at correct decisions during the many and changeable flight conditions to which he will be exposed will benefit considerably from a basic understanding of certain aerodynamic principles. Hence this subject has been included in the private pilot syllabus.

The operational use of the knowledge gained by studying this subject has been covered in considerable detail in the companion manual of this series, *Flying Training for the Private Pilot (Part Two).* Therefore, the information covered in this ground training manual is confined to basic principles.

In order to comprehend more easily some of the terms which are used in this manual, the first few pages have been devoted to a brief review of those areas of physics and mechanics which are related to the principles of flight.

Physics and Mechanics: Revision

SPEED, VELOCITY AND FORCE

When a motor car moves off rapidly, the occupants are pressed backwards in their seats, and if the driver brakes suddenly, they are thrown forward. From this it can be seen that there is a tendency for anything at rest to remain at rest and anything which is moving to keep on moving in the same direction.

These actions can be summarised in Newton's First Law of Motion, (often called the Principle of Inertia), as follows:

> Every body continues in its state of rest or of uniform motion in a straight line unless compelled by some external force to act otherwise.

Velocity is defined as speed and direction, whereas speed is a rate of movement in any direction. A stationary aircraft on flat ground is clearly demonstrating Newton's first law: it will not move because no force acts on it. If this aircraft is moved by the thrust from its engine, a force must have been applied to it, i.e. from the propeller. When the aircraft is flying at a constant speed in a straight line, inertia tends to keep the aircraft moving and some external force would be required to change its flight path.

This first law of motion is therefore useful when interpreting the word *force*, because this word is commonly used to describe the push or pull needed to move an object, whereas Newton's first law more accurately determines force as anything that alters the velocity of a body.

PRESSURE

Force is closely related to the term *pressure*, the latter being defined as force per unit area. Pressure may act in one or several directions and is measured in pounds per square inch or square foot, inches of mercury, kilograms per square centimetre, or in SI units as newtons per square metre.

Natural atmospheric pressure is created by the mass of air surrounding the earth, and although the atmosphere extends upwards from the surface for about 500 miles, the pressure created in the upper regions is minute. Therefore it is the lower layers up to approximately 10 miles above the earth in which the subject material of this manual is concerned.

BERNOULLI'S PRINCIPLE

The science of aerodynamics involves the natural pressures exerted by the atmosphere and the pressures which originate through technology. An aeroplane is able to fly as a result of producing lift. This lift is achieved by creating a differential pressure around an aircraft wing (or aerofoil).

This is produced by giving a wing a certain shape and moving it through the air. As a result of this, the pressure above the wing is slightly reduced and the pressure below the wing is slightly increased. The reason why this occurs is found in the principle expounded by Daniel Bernoulli and can be explained by considering the case of fluid moving through a tube:

Providing the mass flow of fluid remains constant, any restriction in the diameter of the tube will cause the fluid to increase its speed and its pressure will drop. If the mass flow through the tube is increased the pressure drop at the restriction will increase.

A commonplace effect which demonstrates this principle occurs when a door is left slightly ajar. When the volume of air passing through the gap moves fast enough, the door will close on its own accord. This is because the air flowing through the narrow gap suffers a sharp drop in pressure. Figure 5-1 shows an illustration of Bernoulli's principle when using a tube which is constricted at the centre. A tube shaped in this way is known as a *venturi*.

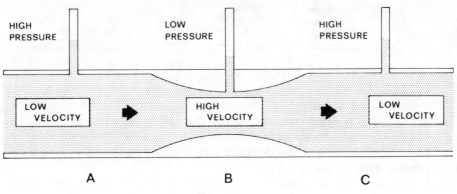

Fig. 5-1

The three small vertical tubes shown in the illustration indicate the change of fluid pressure as it passes through the venturi. In the side portions of the venturi at 'A' and 'C' the fluid velocity is low and is at, say, normal pressure. However, to maintain the same rate of flow at each end of the tube, the flow through the narrow section at 'B' has to speed up and in so doing, it creates a lower pressure.

The shape of an aircraft wing is designed to create this type of pressure change and it can be seen from Fig. 5-2 that it is similar in shape to one half of a venturi tube, i.e. air passing over the top of a wing is forced to speed up, thereby creating a low pressure area and in consequence *lift*.

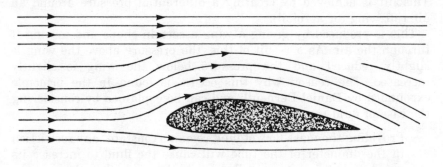

Fig. 5-2

When a wing is directed through the air at an angle as shown in Fig. 5-3, both the pressure below the wing and the speed of the air passing over the wing are increased, thus creating a greater pressure differential between the top and bottom surfaces, and generating increased lift.

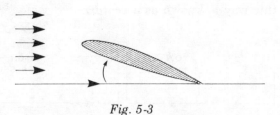

Fig. 5-3

Figure 5-4 relates the increased wing angle to the previously explained venturi effect. Increasing the angle at which the wing is passed through the air (*angle of attack*) is in a sense the equivalent of increasing the size of the restriction in a tube and therefore creates a greater drop in air pressure.

Although the pressure differential created about an aircraft wing by this method is relatively small, the total effect is considerable

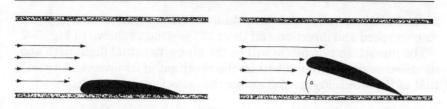

Fig. 5-4

when integrated over the complete area of the wing surface. For example, a typical weight and wing area of a light aircraft could be 2500lbs and 175 square feet. This means that each square foot of wing must support 14.28lbs. Dividing 14.28 by the number of square inches in a square foot (144) reveals that a pressure difference of only 0.099lb per square inch is necessary to support the weight of the aircraft.

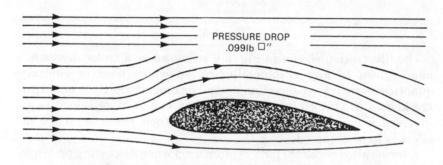

VECTORS AND MOMENTS

If an aircraft is flying in a given direction and if the wind is acting at right angles to this direction, its actual speed and flight path over the

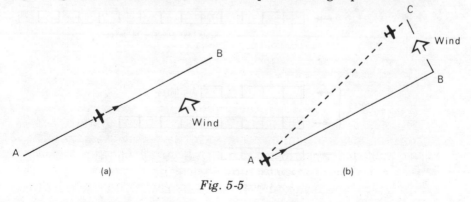

(a)   (b)

Fig. 5-5

ground will be given by the vector sum of the two separate velocities, i.e. its own speed and direction and those of the wind as shown in Fig. 5-5.

The line *AC* in Fig. 5-5(b) will be the aircraft's actual flight path and its speed over the ground will be the resultant of its own velocity and that of the wind. Figure 5-6 shows this effect in greater detail.

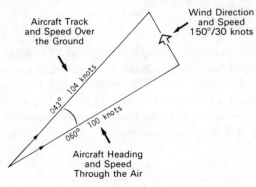

Fig. 5-6

The illustration shown in Fig. 5-6 is known as a *vector diagram*, a name given to any graphic illustration which adds or subtracts quantities which have direction as well as magnitude. Such quantities are known as vector quantities and when two or more velocities are involved it will be necessary to calculate their resultant if the net effect is to be obtained.

A term called *resultant force* is often used when discussing principles of flight and can be illustrated graphically as shown below.

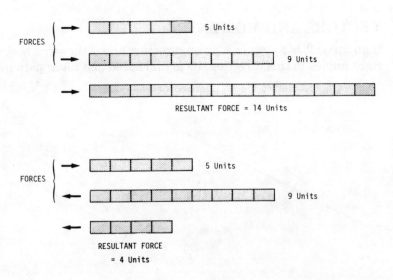

When two forces are parallel, the resultant acts along the same line for both and is equal to the vector's sum of the two. However, when two forces are inclined to each other as shown in Fig. 5-7 the resultant cannot so easily be found by simple arithmetic. This is because the forces have direction as well as magnitude.

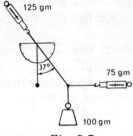

Fig. 5-7

These vector quantities have to be resolved in the same way as finding a resultant velocity. In Fig. 5-7, a 100 gm force is being applied by the weight, and the horizontal spring balance indicates a force of 75 gm. The other spring balance measures a force of 125 gm. This effectively shows the pulling force on the cord is 125 gm acting in a direction 37° from the vertical.

Weights, cord and spring balances apart, the above explanation reveals that the resultant force could be calculated by merely putting pen to paper and using the vector method in the form of a triangle or parallelogram. For example:

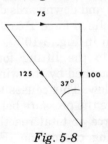

Fig. 5-8

draw a vertical line equal to 100 units and a horizontal line of 75 units as shown in Fig. 5-8. When the two extremities are now joined, a line of length 125 units and a direction 37° is revealed. This triangle of vectors is a basic principle used in air navigation, which, when used employing velocity vectors, is known as a *triangle of velocities*.

Alternatively, a parallelogram of forces can be simply constructed as follows:

draw a vertical line **OA** and a horizontal line **OB**. Because the lines of force **OA** and **OB** have been drawn to scale in their appropriate directions, the line **OC** represents the resultant force being applied.

Similarly when velocities are employed, such a diagram is referred to as a *parallelogram of velocities*.

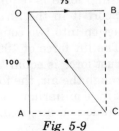

Fig. 5-9

ACTION AND REACTION

Newton's Third Law of Motion is commonly called the law of action and reaction. It states:

> for every action, there is an equal and opposite reaction.

For example, if the propeller of an aircraft pushes a mass of air backward with a force of 625 lbs, the air pushes the blades forward with a force of 625 lbs.

Another term used when discussing principles of flight is *total reaction* and this can be explained by taking an example from everyday life and considering the forces involved in pushing a lawn mower. Initially, the only force exerted is the weight of the mower which acts vertically downwards.

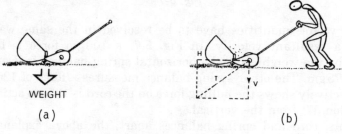

(a)   (b)

Fig. 5-10

When the lawn mower is pushed, the action is set up a horizontal forward force, but the push force will be forwards and downwards due to the handle being inclined at an angle. This inclined force **T** can be resolved into two components **H** and **V** as shown in Fig. 5-10(b).

A further example of this can be applied to the lifting force required by an aeroplane. This lifting force is obtained by the wings when they are presented at an angle to the airflow. This causes the pressure over the top of the wing to decrease while the pressure below the wing is slightly increased. The resultant force or total reaction will be approximately perpendicular to the wing chord line (Fig. 5-11).

An aerodynamicist however, needs to know how much vertical (lifting) force is required to overcome the weight of the aircraft and support it in the air. This can be calculated by resolving the total reaction into two components as shown in Fig. 5-12.

The lift force of 1000 kg will balance the weight and provided the thrust force is equal to the drag produced by the aircraft as it moves through the air, the forces of lift and weight, and thrust and drag will be in equilibrium, i.e. the aeroplane will remain at a constant altitude and airspeed.

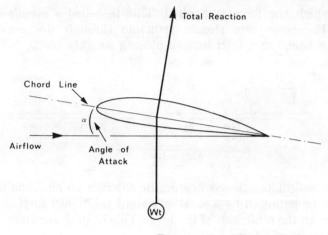

Fig. 5-11

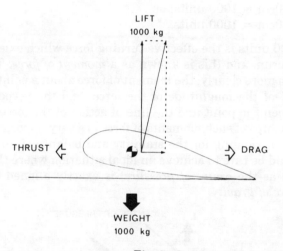

Fig. 5-12

So far, only the effect of forces which act through the same point have been discussed, but if the forces do not act through the same point they can create a turning effect. This turning action has to be considered in relation to the disposition of the four basic forces of *lift, weight, thrust* and *drag,* all of which act on an aeroplane during flight. These turning forces are also important to the distribution of the weight of the passengers, fuel and baggage carried.

The application and use of forces to provide a turning action is a common practice in mechanical devices, for example, the force applied to the pedals of a bicycle. The turning effect of any force will depend upon the amount of force used and the distance from the turning point at which the force is applied. This is called a *simple lever*. Figure 5-13 shows this simple principle through the action of balancing a beam on a fulcrum and placing weights on it.

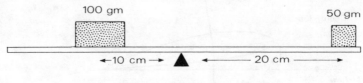

Fig. 5-13

A heavy weight positioned nearer the fulcrum on one side of the lever could be balanced by a smaller weight positioned further from the fulcrum on the other side of the lever. This is an illustration of the *effective moment* of a force, i.e.

10gm × 10cm = 1000 units; or
50gm × 20cm = 1000 units.

Therefore, 1000 units is the effective turning force which exists either side of the fulcrum and this is known as a *moment of force*. To define this expression more clearly, the moment of force about a point is equal to the product of the magnitude of the force, and the perpendicular distance between the point and the line of action of the force.

The relationships of such moments of force are very important to the designer when arranging for the stability and balance of an aircraft, because it would be rare to achieve an ideal situation where the centre of lift (known as the *centre of pressure*) is exactly aligned with the aircraft's *centre of gravity*.

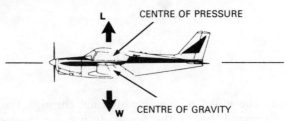

Fig. 5-14

Although, theoretically it would be possible to design an aircraft in which the weight and lift forces are arranged as shown in Fig. 5-14, it would be impractical to maintain this relationship during flight. For example, as fuel is used up, the weight will decrease and the position of the centre of gravity will usually change. Therefore to reduce the lift and so prevent the aircraft from climbing, the pilot will have to adjust the attitude of the aircraft in order to reduce the angle at which the wings meet the relative airflow. This angle is known as the *angle of attack*.

This change in the angle of attack of the wings will also move the position of the centre of pressure. From this, it can be appreciated that any change in the centre of pressure or centre of gravity will result in the two forces of weight and lift no longer acting through the same point. Therefore, a turning force (or *couple effect*) will be created between the two forces as shown in Fig. 5-15.

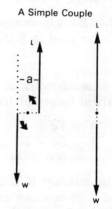

A Simple Couple

The opposing forces will tend to
pull themselves into alignment.

Fig. 5-15

The magnitude of this couple when W = L will be Wa when a is the perpendicular distance between the centres of gravity and pressure and W is the weight of the aircraft.

The designer arranges for this turning force to be controlled by placing a tailplane at the rear of the fuselage. The principles involved in the aspects of tailplane operation are covered later under the heading of 'Stability'.

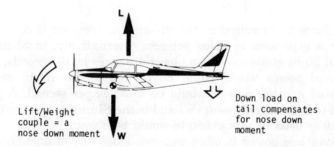

Lift/Weight
couple = a
nose down moment

Down load on
tail compensates
for nose down
moment

WORK, POWER AND ENERGY

In the mechanical sense, work is done when an applied force moves through a measurable distance. Therefore two factors are involved:

(1) Force,
(2) Movement through a distance.

For example, the action of pushing against a fixed object will produce no work although force has been used. However, if a movement occurs as a result of pushing, then work has been done, i.e.

Work = Force × Distance (moved in the direction of the force).

When force is measured in lbs and distance in feet, the work done can be expressed in ft.lbs.

Example.
How much work is done by lifting an object of 50 lbs weight to a vertical height of 10 feet?

$$W = Fd$$
$$= 50 \times 10$$
$$= 500 \text{ ft.lbs}$$

Alternatively, if SI units are used, then force is measured in *newtons* and if 20 newtons are required to lift a body through a distance of 4 metres, the work done is 80 *newton metres* (Nm). A newton metre is a unit of work called a *joule* (J).

POWER
The term power is defined as the rate of doing work. It is measured in terms of work done per unit of time. Expressed as an equation, it would be as follows:

$$\text{Power} = \frac{\text{Force} \times \text{Distance}}{\text{Time}} \text{ or, } P = \frac{Fd}{t}$$

When force is measured in lbs, distance in feet and time in seconds, power is expressed in ft.lbs per sec. Alternatively, in SI units, if a force of 20 newtons moves an object 4 metres in 10 seconds, then the measured power would equal 80 Nm (80 joules) in 10 seconds or expressed another way it would be 8 joules per second. A joule per second (J/s) is called a *watt* (W) and is the SI unit of power. Therefore the power used in this example would be 8 watts.

In aviation, power is often expressed in units of *horse power*, and one horse power is equal to 550 ft.lbs per sec, or 33000 ft.lbs per minute.

Example:
If an object weighing 3000 lbs is lifted to a vertical height of 10 feet in 4 minutes, how many ft.lbs per minute have been used?

$$\text{Power} = \frac{Fd}{t}$$
$$= \frac{3000 \times 10}{4}$$
$$= 7500 \text{ ft.lbs/min}$$

To convert this into the amount of horse power used, the equation would be as follows:

$$\text{hp} = \frac{F \times d}{t} \times \frac{1}{33000} = \frac{7500}{33000} = 0.227 \text{ (or just less than } \tfrac{1}{4} \text{ of one horse power)}$$

For those who work in SI units, it should be noted that one horse power is equal to 745.7 watts.

ENERGY

Energy is the capacity to perform work. The units used when measuring energy are the same as those used in measuring work done. Energy is obtained in various ways, for example, the winding up of a clock spring will give the spring the energy necessary to drive the moving components of the clock. A similar effect will occur if a body is raised, an action which will give it an increase of *potential energy* which can be released and utilised.

A body in motion will have what is called *kinetic energy* and can do work in coming to rest. An example of this is found in the basic principle of a pile driver.

MASS, MOMENTUM AND ACCELERATION

Newton's second law states:

> The rate of change of the momentum of a body is proportional to the applied force and takes place in the direction in which the force acts.

The momentum of a body is defined as the product of its mass and its velocity:

> Momentum = Mass × Velocity

Any body which has a large momentum has a strong tendency to maintain its motion and is therefore difficult to stop. For example, a super tanker although moving slowly will be difficult to bring to rest because of its large mass.

A force can affect the momentum of a body only by changing its velocity. This change of velocity is always proportional to the force being applied. If a force of 20 lbs gives a body an acceleration of 15 ft per second, then a force of 40 lbs applied to the same body would double the acceleration. This could be expressed as:

$$\frac{F}{W} = \frac{a}{g}$$

where,

F = force applied
W = weight of the body
a = acceleration of the body
g = acceleration of gravity.

Example:
An aircraft weighs 2000 lbs, how much force is required to give it an acceleration of 10 ft per sec?

$$F = \frac{Wa}{g} = \frac{2000 \times 10}{32} = 625 \, lbs$$

Another common method of expressing the above equation is:

$$F = ma$$

where,

F = force applied
m = mass
a = acceleration.

This is a condensed form of the previous example in which mass (m) is substituted for weight (W) and gravity (g). Therefore, using the values of W and g as given in the previous problem, the value for m can be found as follows:

$$m = \frac{W}{g} = \frac{2000}{32} = 62.5$$

By using the value of 10 ft per sec, this equation would appear as follows:

$$F = ma = 62.5 \times 10 = 625 \, lbs$$

MOTION OF A BODY MOVING ALONG A CURVED PATH

Referring to Fig. 5-16, it can be seen that if a model aircraft travels along the circumference of a circle, the pull force exerted on the string from the centre deflects the model by 'B' towards 'C'. This pull is called *centripetal force*, and its effect deflects a body from a straight path and forces it to travel along a curved path.

A further point is that for a given tangential velocity, the centripetal force is inversely proportional to the radius of the circular path, which means that if the length of the string in Fig. 5-16 is shortened and the speed of the aircraft model remains constant, the

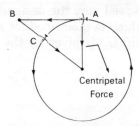

Fig. 5-16

pull on the string must be increased because the radius is decreased and the string must pull the model more rapidly from its tendency to follow a linear path.

By the same reasoning, the pull on the string will be increased if the model is made to move more rapidly in its orbit and it can be stated that centripetal force is directly proportional to the square of the velocity, and inversely proportional to the radius of orbit.

Increase in Velocity or Decrease in Radius = Increase in Centripetal Force.

Fig. 5-17

The formula used for determining centripetal force is as follows:

$$\text{Centripetal Force (CP)} = \frac{mV^2}{R}$$

where,

m = mass of the body
V = velocity
R = the radius of the body's path.

FORCE COEFFICIENTS

Because of the many variables which determine the amount of lift and drag produced from a given aerofoil, e.g. shape of section, angle of attack, air density, airspeed etc., the designer uses a measure in the form of a *coefficient* which is quantified for each type of aerofoil. For a given aerofoil, the lift (*L*) is given by the following formula:

$$L = C_L \frac{pV^2}{2} S$$

where,

C_L = coefficient of lift
p = air density
V = air velocity relative to the aerofoil
S = plan area of the aerofoil.

The drag (*D*) is given by a similar expression as:

$$D = C_D \frac{pV^2}{2} S$$

Where, C_D = drag coefficient and the other symbols are as stated above.

The magnitude of these coefficients will vary with the angle of attack and a typical example of how lift values are plotted can be seen from Fig. 5-18. It should also be appreciated that although a comparatively high lift aerofoil might have a maximum lift coefficient (C_LMax) of 1.8, an aerofoil designed for high speed flight might only have a maximum lift coefficient of 0.9.

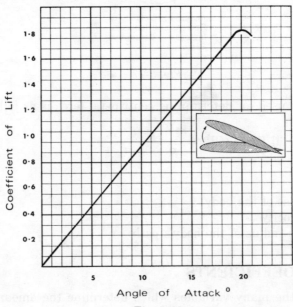

Fig. 5-18

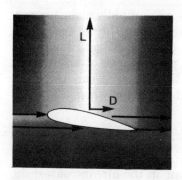

Aerofoils, Lift and Drag

An aerofoil is any surface which is constructed with such a shape that its movement through the air achieves a reaction which provides a lifting force. This movement through the air will also produce a resisting force called drag.

AIR RESISTANCE AND AIR DENSITY

Whenever an aerofoil is moved through the air, a total reaction will be produced which may be resolved into two force components, these are known as *lift* and *drag*. The greater the surface area of the aerofoil which is presented to the air at a given angle of attack and the faster it moves relative to the air, the greater these two forces will become.

It is therefore apparent that the density of the air will also play a vital part in aerodynamics, for without some density the lift and drag forces could not exist. Therefore, if all other factors were to be held constant, the value of the air density would itself control the amount of lift and drag produced from an aerofoil.

Air density is simply the mass of air per cubic foot or metre of volume, and it is a direct measure of the amount of matter in a unit volume of air. In standard atmospheric conditions, the density of air at the earth's surface is approximately 0.0765 lb per cubic foot, or, expressed in metric units 1.225 kg per cubic metre. The actual value will however be affected by the air temperature and pressure in accordance with the following rules:

● Density varies in direct proportion with the pressure;
● Density varies inversely with the absolute temperature.

That is, the greater the pressure the higher the density, and the lower the temperature the higher the density.

Aircraft fly at varying altitudes, and since both temperature and pressure decrease with altitude, it might be thought that the air density remains constant regardless of the altitude flown. However,

because pressure drops more rapidly than temperature when altitude is increased, the net result will always be a lowering of air density. Changes of density will affect the performance of an aircraft, but if the propulsive thrust value can be maintained, an aircraft will fly faster when the air is less dense.

If the humidity (amount of water vapour in the air) increases, the density will decrease since water vapour weighs approximately $\frac{5}{8}$ as much as dry air. If the temperature and pressure remain constant, the density of air will vary inversely with the humidity, therefore the lift produced from the wings will become less with increase of humidity.

AEROFOIL SHAPES AND WING PLAN FORMS

A flat plate placed at an angle to a moving airstream could be used to obtain a reaction similar to lift by creating a higher pressure below the plate, Fig. 5-19.

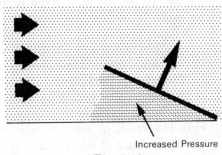

Increased Pressure

Fig. 5-19

However, the properties of reaction to movement of air can be utilised more efficiently in relation to the energy expended in moving such a plate through the air, if its shape is changed to that shown in Fig. 5-20.

In this example, the contours of the top and bottom surfaces are symmetrical and therefore air flowing below and above the wing would speed up by equal amounts (Bernoulli's principle). This would result in an equal pressure change above and below the wing with the result that no net force would be produced. If, however, the aerofoil were to be placed at an angle to the relative airflow as shown in Fig. 5-21, a pressure differential between the top and bottom surface

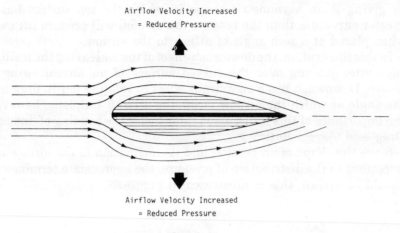

Fig. 5-20

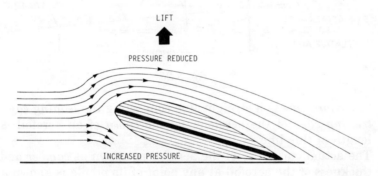

Fig. 5-21

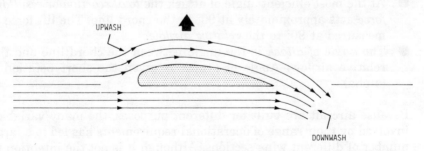

Fig. 5-22

would exist and an upward force opposing the weight would be produced.

By modifying the aerofoil section to the shape shown in Fig. 5-22 i.e.

by giving it an asymmetric shape in which the top surface has a greater curvature than the bottom, the aerofoil will produce lift even when placed at a zero angle of attack to the airflow.

In this illustration, the downwash effect of the air leaving the trailing edge after passing over the curved surface of an aircraft wing is shown. Downwash has a significant effect in relation to lift, drag and the angle at which the airflow meets the aircraft tailplane, however, the importance of this is discussed later under the heading of 'Induced Drag' and 'Aspect Ratio'.

Since the shape of an aerofoil and its inclination to the airflow are important to the distribution of pressure, the appropriate terminology should be known: this is illustrated in Fig. 5-23.

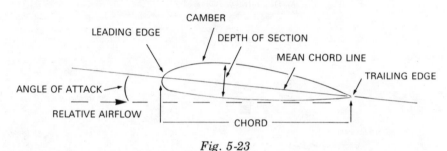

Fig. 5-23

● The *chord line* is a straight line connecting the *leading edge* and *trailing edge* of the aerofoil and the *chord* of an aerofoil is the length of this line.

● The actual curvature of the aerofoil is known as *camber* and the thickness of the aerofoil at any point of its profile is known as its *depth of section*. The greater the thickness ratio, the greater will be the displacement of air passing over it.

● At the most efficient angle of attack the *total reaction* or *resultant force* acts approximately at 90° to the chord line. The lift force is measured at 90° to the *relative airflow*.

● The *angle of attack* is the angle between the chord line and the relative airflow. Angle of attack is given the short notation α (alpha).

Because aircraft are built for different purposes, the many variables involved by their range of operational requirements has led to a large number of different wing sections. Although it is not the intention in this manual to go into a detailed explanation of the various reasons for the derivation of these wing sections, it could be stated as a general example, that thin aerofoils (low thickness ratio) are employed for high speed aircraft, and thick aerofoils are commonly used for those aircraft which operate in the lower speed range.

Low Speed Wing   High Speed Wing

Fig. 5-24

It was mentioned in the preceding Physics and Mechanics section that (ignoring design shape) the lift force over an aerofoil is achieved by two basic factors, speed of airflow and angle of attack. It can therefore be seen that high speed aircraft can utilise a relatively thin wing section whereas slow speed aircraft will require a thicker wing section to create the necessary differential pressure about the wing.

Although a non-symmetrical cambered wing i.e. one having a greater camber over the top surface, can produce a positive lift force at an angle of attack of 0°, the most efficient angle i.e. the one which gives the greatest lift for the least drag, is somewhere between 2° and 6° depending on wing plan, wing section etc. Therefore, in order to minimise fuselage drag at normal cruising speeds, the wing is attached to the fuselage at a fixed positive angle of between 2° and 6° (normally between 2° and 3° for light aircraft) this angle is known as the *angle of incidence*.

WING PLAN FORMS

Apart from the variety of aerofoil sections which can be used to form an aircraft wing, the designer also has a choice of wing plan forms which can be placed in different vertical locations relative to the fuselage. The two most common arrangements used in general aviation light aircraft are, low, or high wing as illustrated in Fig. 5-25.

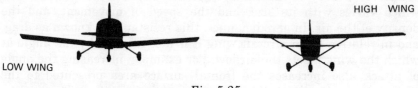

HIGH WING

LOW WING

Fig. 5-25

Other arrangements can be used where the wing is located at a more central positon, known as midwing:

MIDWING

or, the use of two sets of wings (biplane) is sometimes employed.

BIPLANE

The actual plan shape used by the designer will also vary, and will depend upon certain design requirements, some of which relate to the positioning of the centre of gravity, and centre of pressure, and the provision of stability during flight. Some of the more common plan forms are illustrated below.

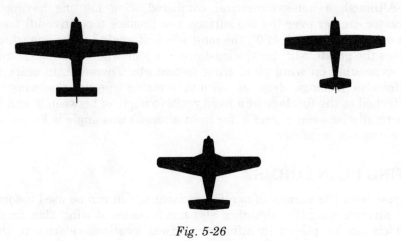

Fig. 5-26

LIFT AND DRAG

Whenever a body is moved through the air, it meets a resistance which varies with its size, and the speed of movement, and the density of the air. In aerodynamics, this resistance is known as drag, and in relation to an aircraft wing it is also affected by the angle at which the wing meets the airflow. For example, increasing the angle of attack also increases the frontal surface area presented to the airflow hence its resistance to movement is increased. This can be illustrated by constructing a parallelogram of forces showing how the total reaction from the aerofoil's movement can be resolved into vertical and horizontal forces, (Fig. 5-27).

ANGLE OF ATTACK
Figure 5-27 shows an aerofoil being passed through the air where the resultant force acts at 90° to the chord line. By resolving this total

reaction (**TR**) into perpendicular and parallel components to the airflow, the amount of the lift force (**L**), can be determined. Resolving the basic force in this manner also indicates the amount of drag, force (**D**), which is acting against the forward movement of the aerofoil.

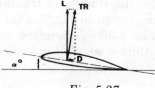

Fig. 5-27

In Fig. 5-28(a) the aerofoil is passing through the air at an angle of attack of 8°. In Fig. 5-28(b) the aerofoil is at an angle of attack of 20° and the total reaction is therefore greater. Resolving this reaction into the lift and drag components, it can be clearly seen how increasing the angle of attack will also increase the values of lift and drag.

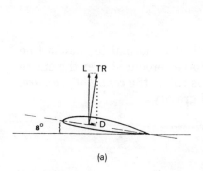
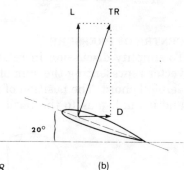

(a)   *Fig. 5-28*   (b)

AIRSPEED

The faster the aerofoil is passed through the air, the greater will be the total reaction obtained, and therefore the greater the lift and drag produced.

The value of lift increases by the square of the speed and Fig. 5-29 illustrates how the amount of lift obtained at 50 knots and 100 knots varies. It can also be seen from this illustration that the speed also affects the drag.

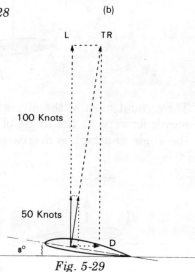

Fig. 5-29

DISTRIBUTION OF LIFT

In considering the basic shape of an aircraft, it must be appreciated that the speed of airflow passing about the wing will vary with the depth of section over which it passes. In other words, the amount of lift created will vary from the leading to trailing edge. Figure 5-30 illustrates this point. The aerofoil in Fig. 5-30(a) has a greater depth of section than that in Fig. 5-30(b), therefore, at the same airspeed and angle of attack, the thicker aerofoil wil produce more lift.

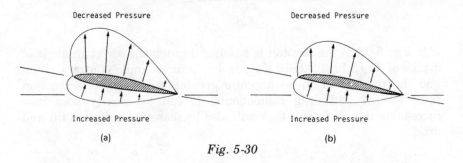

Fig. 5-30

CENTRE OF PRESSURE

To simplify discussion in relation to lift, it is normal to show a line vector representing the sum of the lift forces produced over the entire aerofoil chord. The position of this line is called the *centre of pressure*, and is analogous to the term centre of gravity.

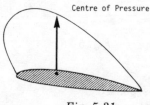

Fig. 5-31

Throughout most of the aircraft's speed range the centre of pressure moves forward as the angle of attack is increased and rearwards as the angle of attack is decreased.

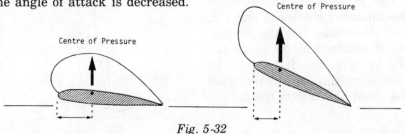

Fig. 5-32

The movement of the centre of pressure creates a turning moment leading to a pitching action which has to be taken into account by the designer when considering the aircraft's longitudinal stability.

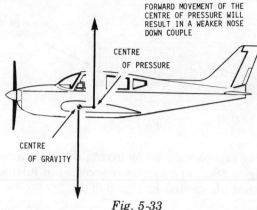

FORWARD MOVEMENT OF THE CENTRE OF PRESSURE WILL RESULT IN A WEAKER NOSE DOWN COUPLE

CENTRE OF PRESSURE

CENTRE OF GRAVITY

Fig. 5-33

DRAG — PARASITE AND INDUCED

For the purposes of aircraft performance computations, drag is divided into two classes *parasite* and *induced*. Parasite drag applies to any type of drag which is not a direct consequence of the production of lift. The three basic types of parasite drag are:

● Form drag;
● Skin friction drag;
● Interference drag.

Form and skin friction drag are often collectively referred to as 'profile drag'.

FORM DRAG
This is produced by a body in motion, and is most clearly seen as visualising the effect of moving at flat plate at right angles to the airflow as shown in Fig. 5-34.

Fig. 5-34

A high pressure is built up in front and a low pressure at the rear.

This effect can be seen in everyday life by noting the action of water spray thrown up from a wet road behind a lorry. The reduced pressure area at the rear acts as a retarding force which tends to pull against the motion of a body.

AREA OF REDUCED PRESSURE

AREA OF INCREASED PRESSURE

Fig. 5-35

This type of drag can be reduced by giving the plate a rounded shape as shown in Fig. 5-36(a) and can be reduced even further by a bullet type configuration illustrated in Fig. 5-36(b).

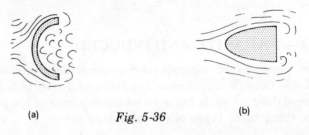

(a)   *Fig. 5-36*   (b)

By adding a tapered section at the rear, a completely streamlined shape can be constructed which will reduce the drag still further, Fig. 5-37.

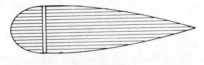

Fig. 5-37

The term *streamlined body* is used to describe the shape of a body which produces a very low coefficient of drag. Such a body will be capable of moving through the air with a minimum of resistance. Thus, it is clear that form drag is a direct consequence of the form or shape of a body.

SKIN FRICTION DRAG
When air is passed over a surface, friction between the surface and the air will always be present. For example, a wing on which a layer of dust has settled will retain this layer of dust even though it is

moved at high speed through the atmosphere. This molecular attraction between the surface of an aerofoil and the molecules of air creates a region over the wing known as a *boundary layer*.

In this layer, the laminæ of air are slowed down from the free stream velocity, until, at points of contact with the surface, the relative velocity of the air actually becomes zero. Above these points of contact with the surface, each lamina of air will travel a little faster until it reaches the free stream where the air is outside the frictional influence of the aerofoil surface (Fig. 5-38). Therefore it is important to keep the surface of an aerofoil as smooth as possible to keep the skin friction drag to a minimum.

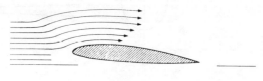

Fig. 5-38

A term often used to express the sum of form and skin friction drag is *profile drag*, and it will apply to any component or body attached to an aircraft wing or fuselage. Examples of such components would be the landing gear, struts, aerials or similar objects, and whenever possible, these items are given a streamlined shape to reduce the drag effects.

INTERFERENCE DRAG
The total drag of the wings, fuselage and other components cannot be taken as the sum of the drag of the individual components. This is because the airflow in passing over the joining points of the various aircraft components causes a mixing of the air (turbulence) and therefore creates additional drag (Fig. 5-39).

This type of drag is known as interference drag and can be kept to a minimum by the employment of fairings and fillets which are suitably shaped to minimise interference effects.

It is nevertheless of interest to note that by careful contouring of the associated surfaces, such as between a wing tip and fuel tank, a reduction in the total drag of the two components can sometimes be achieved.

The other class of drag is that which results from the production of lift about a wing of finite length. The information which has been covered so far relates specifically to the lift and drag about an aerofoil section in a two dimensional flow, i.e. tantamount to an aerofoil of infinite span in which the airflow effects about the ends are not considered. However, when an aerofoil is used to provide a wing for a

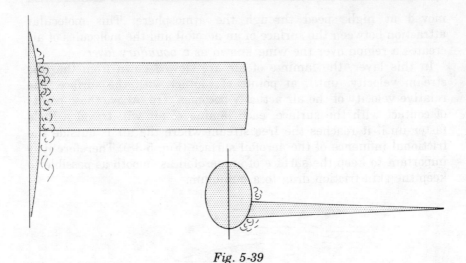

Fig. 5-39

specific aircraft, a significant difference will occur in that it will have a limited (or finite) span, and so a third dimensional aerofoil characteristic around the wing must therefore be taken into account. This is *induced drag*, sometimes referred to as *vortex drag*.

INDUCED DRAG
During flight, a reduction of pressure above the wing and an increase of pressure below the wing is produced, and the pressure differential will attempt to equalise at the tips. In consequence, there will be spanwise movement of the high pressure air below the wing, which spills out and over the tip, thus giving flow in a third dimension.

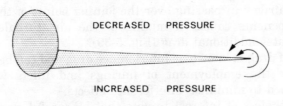

DECREASED   PRESSURE

INCREASED   PRESSURE

Fig. 5-40

The net result of this is to deflect air downwards at the wing tip and change the average direction of the relative airflow along the span. Thus the strong downwash effect at the wing tip modifies and reduces the actual angle at which the airstream passes the wing.

Referring to Fig. 5-41(b), the dotted lines represent the angle at which the wing is passing through the air and the resulting direction of the lift force (L). The unbroken lines show how the downwash

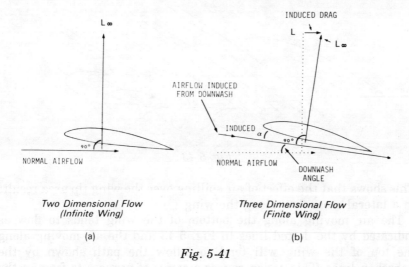

Fig. 5-41

effect alters the airflow angle in the vicinity of the wing and the resulting rearward inclination of the force **L** ∞.

Note: for reasons of clarity, the profile drag has been omitted.

It can also be seen from Fig. 5-42 that the greater the downwash angle, the greater is the induced drag and as the downwash angle is increased with increasing angle of attack, the induced drag will be greatest at high angles and least at low angles of attack.

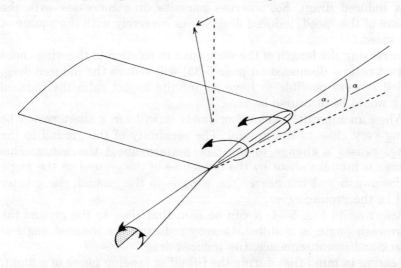

Fig. 5-42

Another way of illustrating vortex drag is presented in Fig. 5-43.

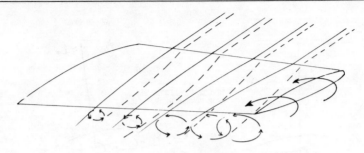

Fig. 5-43

This shows that the effect of air spilling over the wing tip area results in a lateral cross flow along the wing.

The air moving along the bottom of the wing tends to flow as indicated by the dotted lines in Fig. 5-43 and the air moving along the top of the wing will tend to follow the path shown by the unbroken lines. This action causes a series of vortices to form at the trailing edge. The strength of the vortices produced along a wing from the tip to the root will be governed by the wing section and chord, the span, and the angle of attack. Increasing the angle of attack will increase the size of the vortices and therefore the induced drag.

Bearing in mind that lift is produced by a combination of aircraft speed and angle of attack, it can be appreciated that a particular value of lift can be obtained either at a high angle of attack and low speed (high induced drag), or at a high speed and low angle of attack, (low induced drag). So, whereas parasite drag increases with the square of the speed, induced drag varies inversely with the square of the speed.

Increasing the length of the wing span in relation to the wing chord (aspect ratio – discussed on page 5-35) will reduce the induced drag, and if it were possible to have an infinite aspect ratio the induced drag would be of course be zero.

When an aircraft takes off or lands it will for a short period be flying very close to the ground. The proximity of the ground to the wings causes a change to the flow pattern about the wings. This change is brought about by the influences of the ground on the angle of downwash and the nearer the wing is to the ground, the greater will be the *ground effect*.

Referring to Fig. 5-44, it can be seen that close to the ground the downwash angle is modified, thereby reducing the induced angle of attack and in consequence, the induced drag.

Bearing in mind that during the lift off or landing phase of a flight, the induced drag may account for over 80% of the total drag, any significant decrease in induced drag at this stage could have an appreciable effect on the aircraft's acceleration immediately following

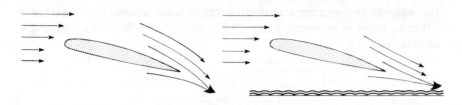

DOWNWASH PATH WHEN IN FREE AIR   DOWNWASH PATH WHEN NEAR THE SURFACE

Fig. 5-44

lift off, and on its deceleration during the float period prior to landing. The significance of ground effect in relation to operating an aircraft is covered later in more detail under the heading of 'Aircraft Performance'.

LIFT/DRAG RATIO

The lift/drag ratio is the ratio of the amount of lift to drag produced from an aerofoil and is a direct measure of aerodynamic efficiency. When the data for lift and drag for a specific aerofoil section is produced, the ratio of the lift to drag coefficient can be determined for each specific angle of attack.

Figure 5-45 shows an example of how the lift coefficient of a wing may vary for different angles of attack and Fig. 5-46 shows a similar graph relating to the change in drag coefficient.

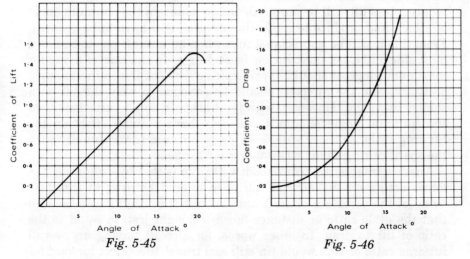

Fig. 5-45   Fig. 5-46

The information gained from these two graphs will permit the construction of a graph measuring L/D ratio as shown in Fig. 5-47. In the case of the example aerofoil section used above, the maximum lift/drag ratio is approximately 13.5, and this is achieved at an angle of attack of 6.5°.

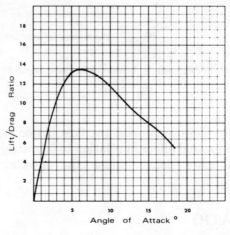

Fig. 5-47

Assuming these graphs related to an aircraft operating at a weight of 5000 kgf, at an angle of attack of 6.5° and an airspeed which produced 5000 kgf of lift, the aircraft would be in level flight and the drag would be (5000 ÷ 13.5) 370 kgf. Remembering that the total lift is related to airspeed and angle of attack, it can be seen that any change in airspeed will necessitate a change in angle of attack to maintain the lifting force at 5000kgf. If the aircraft weight is now reduced, less lift will be required, and to maintain the optimum angle of attack and produce less lift, the airspeed will have to be reduced. From this it will be appreciated that when an aircraft has to be flown most efficiently, i.e. most lift for least drag as in the case of flying for maximum range, it should in principle be flown at the optimum angle of attack, and the airspeed should be changed to vary the lift with change in weight. However, with light aircraft, small variations from the optimum angle of attack will only have a small effect on the lift/drag ratio, so there will be no practical need to continually vary the speed during flight when flying for range.

Another interesting point about L/D ratio is that by examining the forces acting on the aircraft during a glide, (the drag in this case being of the complete aircraft and not just the wing) it can be seen that the glide ratio or distance flown to height lost, is equal to the ratio of lift to drag. In other words, an aircraft having an overall lift/drag ratio of 10:1 would (in still air) travel 10000 feet forward for every 1000 feet of altitude lost.

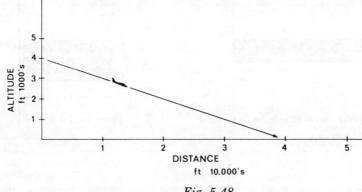

Fig. 5-48

ASPECT RATIO

This is another common term used in relation to aircraft wings. It is a measure of the proportion of wing span to mean chord, i.e. aspect ratio is equal to span ÷ mean chord, and is illustrated in the following diagram.

Aspect Ratio

$= \dfrac{36}{3} = 12$

MEAN CHORD

3′

SPAN 36′

Fig. 5-49

The span of the wing is measured from tip to tip and the mean chord is the geometric average. The product of the span and the mean chord is the total wing area, in this case 108 square feet. Since the aspect ratio is the ratio of the wing span to the mean chord, it is often more convenient to define it as span squared divided by the area, i.e.

$$\text{Aspect Ratio} = \frac{(\text{Span})^2}{\text{Area}}$$

which in this case equals

$$\frac{36^2}{36 \times 3} = 12$$

The main importance of aspect ratio is its relationship to induced drag. For example, it can be seen that the two wings in Fig. 5-50 have the same lifting area i.e.

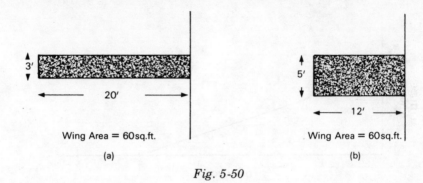

Fig. 5-50

In Fig. 5-50(b) the chord is almost twice that in (a), therefore, the effect of the spill over of pressure at the tip will be greater in (b) than in (a) and therefore the induced drag effect will be greater. To sum up, the lower the aspect ratio of the wing, the higher will be the induced drag. Bearing in mind that anything which reduces drag during flight will lead to greater efficiency, a designer will incorporate the highest aspect ratio wing which structural strength and other requirements will permit.

Flying Controls

The flying controls enable the pilot to direct the aircraft along a desired flight path. The flight path of an aircraft through the air can be resolved into three planes of movement; the up/down pitching plane about the lateral axis, the rolling plane about the longitudinal axis, and the side to side yawing plane about the vertical *normal* axis.

THE AIRCRAFT AXES

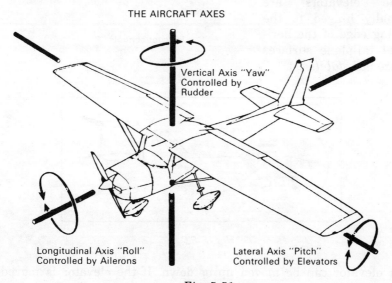

Vertical Axis "Yaw" Controlled by Rudder

Longitudinal Axis "Roll" Controlled by Ailerons

Lateral Axis "Pitch" Controlled by Elevators

Fig. 5-51

PLANES OF MOVEMENT

An aircraft is controlled in these planes of movement by means of the flying controls. Conventionally, the elevators control it in pitch, the ailerons in roll, and the rudder in yaw.

The strength of the control force will depend on the airspeed, the area of the control surface, and the amount of its deflection. To produce a given effect the control surface will have to be deflected further at low airspeed than at high airspeed. The moment produced for any degree of control deflection is dependent on the strength of the force produced and the length of its moment arm.

OPERATION OF THE ELEVATORS, AILERONS AND RUDDER

The elevators and ailerons are operated from the cockpit by a control column or a wheel and yoke assembly and the rudder is operated by foot pedals.

ELEVATORS

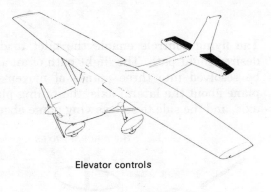

When the nose of the aircraft is raised or lowered, it is rotated about the lateral axis and this is the function of the elevators.

The elevators are normally hinged to the trailing edge of the horizontal tailplane surfaces (*horizontal stabiliser*).

Elevator controls

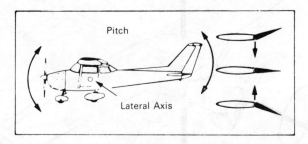

Fig. 5-52

An elevator can be moved up or down. If the elevator is moved downwards, it increases both the camber and mean angle of attack of the horizontal stabiliser. This action creates more lift at the tail section causing it to rise and the aircraft's nose to lower, and the airspeed to increase. Raising the elevators will have the opposite effect causing the nose to rise and the airspeed to reduce.

In some aircraft, an all moving surface is used in place of a fixed horizontal tailplane. This control is known as a stabilator and serves as the horizontal stabiliser and elevators combined. When the control column or yoke is moved, the complete stabilator is moved to alter its angle relative to the airflow, thus varying the lift force acting from its surface. Figure 5-53 illustrates this action.

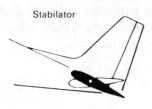

Stabilator

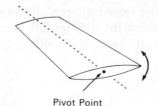

Pivot Point

Fig. 5-53

AILERONS

Movement about the longitudinal axis is called rolling or banking and the ailerons are used to control this.

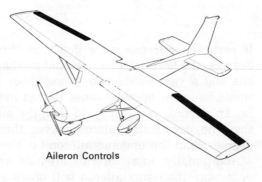

Aileron Controls

The ailerons form part of the aircraft wing and are deflected up or down by a left or right sideways movement of the control column, or where a wheel is fitted, by rotating this. Ailerons are linked together by a control system so that when one aileron is moved down, the opposite aileron moves upwards.

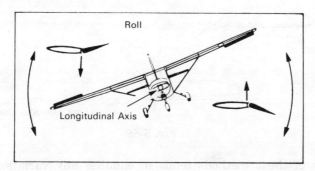

Roll

Longitudinal Axis

Fig. 5-54

Rotating the wheel on the control column to the left causes the left aileron to rise and the right aileron to lower. This action makes the left wing drop and the right wing rise and induces the aircraft to bank to the left. The control wheel works in this manner regardless of the fore or aft position of the control column.

The function of the lowered aileron is to increase the lift by increasing the wing camber and mean angle of attack. At the same time, the raised aileron on the opposite wing will reduce the lift and so create a lift differential between the left and right wings, which results in the aircraft rolling about the longitudinal axis.

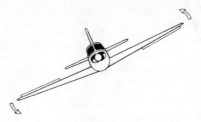

Fig. 5-55

If both the ailerons were deflected through the same number of degrees, the lowered aileron would produce more drag than the raised one and a yaw would take place about the vertical axis. This yaw would be in the opposite sense to that in which the aircraft is rolling i.e. an adverse yaw. To avoid this, the aileron system is arranged so that the downgoing aileron moves through a smaller number of degrees than the upgoing aileron i.e. there is a differential travel.

Additionally, most aircraft ailerons are designed so that, during deflection, the rising aileron will produce a little more parasite drag as shown in Fig. 5-56. When this method is employed, they are known as 'Frise' ailerons.

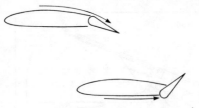

Leading Edge protrudes into Airstream

Fig. 5-56

The use of these methods tends to equalise any variation of drag between the two ailerons as they are operated.

RUDDER

Movement of the aircraft about its vertical axis is known as yawing. Yaw is controlled by the use of a rudder hinged to the vertical stabiliser (or fin). The main purpose of the rudder is to prevent or control any yaw which might occur during flight.

The rudder pedals are situated forward on the cockpit floor and

depressing (moving for-
ward) the left pedal
moves the rudder to the
left and causes the air-
craft to yaw to the left.

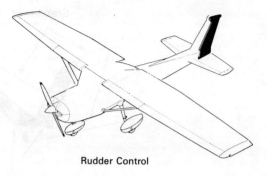

Rudder Control

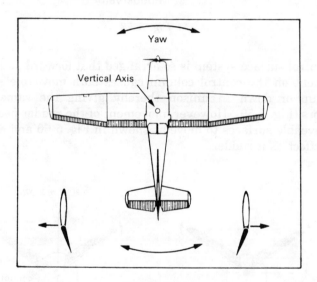

Fig. 5-57

On many aircraft, the rudder pedals are hinged so that they can be
tilted forward by toe pressure applied to the top of the pedal and this
action operates the wheel brakes. (The braking system is covered
later in Section 6.) One method of obtaining directional control on the
ground is to connect the rudder system through to the nosewheel so
that forward pressure on the left rudder pedal causes the nosewheel
to turn left and vice versa. This arrangement gives much easier
directional control during taxying and, in conjunction with appropriate brake co-ordination, facilitates manoeuvring in confined spaces
on the ground.

A few light aircraft are equipped with a tailplane design known as
a butterfly or Vee tail in which the fixed stabiliser portion is set at an
angle as shown in Fig. 5-58. The moveable control surfaces in this
case are known as *ruddervators* since they perform a dual role.

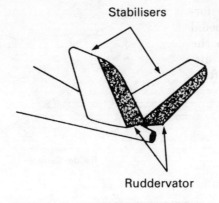

Stabilisers

Ruddervator

Fig. 5-58

The control surface system is so arranged that forward and backward movement on the control column causes both moveable surfaces to move up or down in unison thereby giving the same effect as elevators (Fig. 5-59). However, movement of the rudder pedals causes the moveable surfaces to move as shown in Fig. 5-60 and achieve the same effect as a rudder.

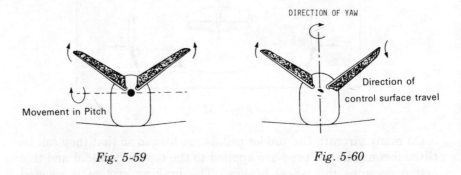

DIRECTION OF YAW

Movement in Pitch

Direction of control surface travel

Fig. 5-59   *Fig. 5-60*

MASS BALANCE

It has already been explained that for an aircraft to remain in steady flight, the forces acting on it must be in a state of balance. A similar requirement applies to the flying controls, in that without some form of balance, they will tend to oscillate about their pivot points. When the amplitude of these oscillations continues to get larger, this is then known as flutter. For example, it can be seen from Fig. 5-61 that the pivot point of the control surface is well forward of its centre of gravity, therefore a condition of static unbalance exists.

The consequence of this during flight can be seen by taking as an

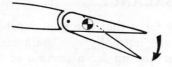

Fig. 5-61

example the effect that this unbalance has with respect to the ailerons. An aircraft wing cannot be made completely rigid and during flight it will flex as a result of changing air loads as shown in Fig. 5-62.

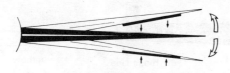

Fig. 5-62

The effect of this upward and downward movement of the outboard wing sections will cause the ailerons to float up and down, i.e. as the wing flexes upwards, the aileron tends to lag behind. This out of balance condition can cause the control surface to flutter during flight and create difficulties for the pilot in controlling the aircraft.

To reduce this effect, it is normal in light aircraft to add weights inside or along the leading edge of the particular control surface to bring its centre of gravity forward of the hinge line and thereby achieve a state of balance for the control itself (Fig. 5-63).

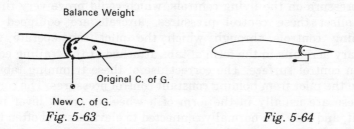

Balance Weight

Original C. of G.

New C. of G.

Fig. 5-63   *Fig. 5-64*

Another method is to mount a weight further ahead of the leading edge as shown in Fig. 5-64. The length of the resulting arm so produced means that the balance weight can be smaller and lighter, yet produce the same effect. Either method will assist in reducing the moments of inertia, lessen the stresses on the aircraft structure, and make control easier for the pilot.

AERODYNAMIC BALANCE

In order to reduce the force that the pilot must apply to move the flying controls, they are normally also balanced aerodynamically. This is achieved by arranging for a portion of the control surface ahead of the hinge line to protrude into the path of the airflow. A common example of this is given in Fig. 5-65. From the plan view, it can be seen that a portion of the wing is ahead of the hinge line and this area is increased towards the tip so producing a horn shape.

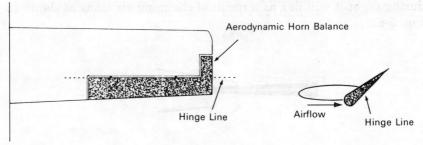

Aerodynamic Horn Balance

Hinge Line   Airflow

Hinge Line

Fig. 5-65

When the control surface is raised or lowered, the forward portion protrudes into the oncoming air and a force will be present, which in the example shown above, can be seen to assist in raising the control surface and so reduce the force required from the pilot.

TRIMMING CONTROLS

When an aircraft is placed in a different flight attitude, e.g. a climb, descent or level flight, or when control loads vary due to loss of weight (fuel), changes of power etc., the pilot will need to apply and hold pressure on the flying controls, which could prove very tiring.

To offset these control pressures, aircraft are equipped with trimming controls through which the pilot can operate small auxiliary aerofoils in the form of tabs attached at the trailing edge of a main control surface. The correct use of these trimming tabs will relieve the pilot from holding constant control pressures. The controls for these are usually in the form of a wheel or crank lever in the cockpit, and they are normally connected to elevators and often to the rudder and the ailerons. The principle of trim control operations is as follows.

Consider the situation after the elevators have been raised to hold the aircraft in a new attitude, (Fig. 5-66), the trim tab must be adjusted downward so that the elevators are held in the new attitude without the continued application of a force by the pilot.

The correct sequence of actions is to select the required aircraft

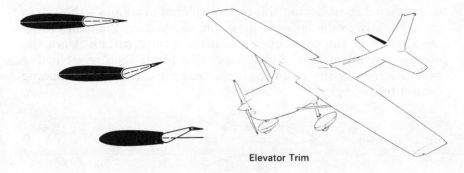

Elevator Trim

Fig. 5-66

attitude by the use of the primary flying controls, and then to adjust the appropriate trimmer until no pressure is needed on the control column or rudder pedals.

Trimming controls are a great help to the pilot, but as they are powerful and sensitive, they should be used carefully. Mishandling can lead to reduced aircraft performance, and may also cause undue stress of the airframe. Trimming controls should not be used to relieve control loads of a transient nature.

There are several types of trim tabs and the three types considered in the following paragraphs are:

● Fixed tab;
● Basic trim tab;
● Balance tab.

The fixed tab usually consists of a metal strip attached at the trailing edge of the particular control surface. It can only be adjusted on the ground and is mainly used to correct any permanent out of trim effects during straight and level flight at cruising power. Fixed tabs are normally only used on the rudder or ailerons.

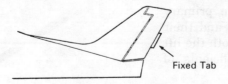

Fixed Tab

Fig. 5-67

The two most common types of tab fitted to light aircraft are the basic trim tab and the balance tab.

The principle of the basic tab has already been described in Fig. 5-66 and the balance tab is a variation of this type in that the tab is so connected that moving the control column also causes the tab to move slightly in the opposite direction, so assisting the pilot during the change in the position of the main control surface. Once the desired aircraft attitude is achieved, this tab is then re-set in the same manner as the basic trim tab, i.e. by means of the trimming control in the cockpit.

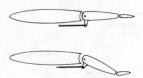

When a stabilator is fitted instead of elevators, it is common practice to incorporate a balance tab which moves in the same direction as the stabilator, thus damping its movement. This arrangement is called an *anti balance tab*, and is fitted because a stabilator requires very small movements to produce changes in the aircraft attitude when the aircraft is flown at cruising or higher airspeeds.

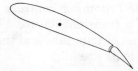

The action of an anti-balance tab assists in reducing any large movements which the pilot may inadvertently make at other than a low airspeed, i.e. it makes the stabilator control less sensitive and easier to use.

FLAPS

These are auxiliary wing surfaces which are integrated into the primary wing structure and their use increases both the lift and drag coefficients of the wing.

In light aircraft, their primary function is to allow the approach to landing to be made more slowly (by reducing the stalling speed) or more steeply at a given speed

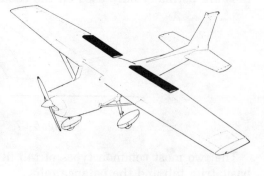

Fig. 5-68

(by increasing the drag). This latter effect has the particular advantage of permitting the pilot a better view of the landing area while on the approach path. Fig. 5-69 illustrates advantages of using flaps during the approach phase.

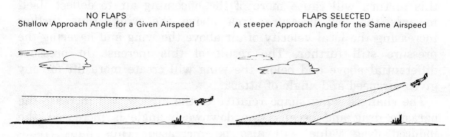

NO FLAPS
Shallow Approach Angle for a Given Airspeed

FLAPS SELECTED
A steeper Approach Angle for the Same Airspeed

Fig. 5-69

The use of flaps can also affect the take-off run of an aircraft in that they lower the stalling speed which enables the pilot to lift off at a lower airspeed. This has a particular advantage when taking off from rough or soft ground.

There are several different designs of flap, all of which have their own advantages. However, the many variations of wing design have different effects on the particular values of any specific type of flap, and a detailed discussion of these factors is outside the scope of this manual.

The most common types of flaps used on aircraft are as follows:

- Simple (plain);
- Split;
- Slotted;
- Fowler.

The Fowler type is most commonly used with heavy aircraft but because they are sometimes fitted to light aircraft, a description is included at the end of this section.

SIMPLE (PLAIN) FLAP

The basic principles involved when flaps are extended are related to the change in wing shape. Reference to Fig. 5-70 will enable the reader to visualize in simple terms the effect upon the airflow passing above and below a wing section whenever they are deployed.

(a) (b)

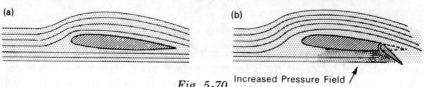

Fig. 5-70 Increased Pressure Field ⁄

In Fig. 5-70(a), the normal pattern of flow above and below an aerofoil is depicted. In Fig. 5-70(b), the simple flap has been lowered and this will create an obstruction to the air passing immediately below the wing. An increased pressure field will be created below the wing and this in turn will cause more of the oncoming air to deflect itself towards the low pressure area above the wing, thus further increasing the local velocity of air above the wing and lowering the pressure still further. The result of this increase in pressure differential above and below the wing will create more lift for any given airspeed and angle of attack.

The changed wing shape relative to the airflow will increase the parasite drag and because the downwash angle is increased, the induced drag value will also be increased. Thus flaps create additional lift and additional drag.

SPLIT FLAP

A split flap essentially consists of a flat plate section deflected from the lower surface of the wing. This type of flap produces a larger amount of drag than a simple flap due to the turbulent wake at the trailing edge.

Fig. 5-71

SLOTTED FLAP

This type is similar to the simple flap, but when lowered, it forms a slot between the trailing edge of the wing section and the leading edge of the flap. This permits higher pressure air from underneath the wing to flow up and into the lower pressure area above the wing. The air accelerating up through this gap also speeds up the upper surface boundary layer (the layer of air immediately above the wing) thereby delaying flow separation and achieving a higher lift coefficient. Slotted flaps therefore give a greater increase in lift and less drag than simple and split flaps of comparable size.

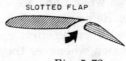

Fig. 5-72

FOWLER FLAP

This type of flap was designed to increase the chord of the wing when required, and by creating a larger surface area, it reduces the wing loading and stalling speed, thereby permitting a lower lift-off speed during take off. It operates along specially designed tracks or rails which protrude from the trailing edge of the wing. When retracted, it is hidden within the contours of the main wing leaving its tracking mechanism (or rails) protruding from the wing trailing edge.

Fowler flaps may also incorporate the principle of the slotted flap by contouring the trailing edge recess of the wing in a manner which forms a slot along the flap leading edge when in the extended position.

FOWLER FLAP

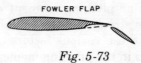

Fig. 5-73

It has already been stated that the exact change in lift coefficient when flaps are lowered will depend on the combination of flap type, wing section and wing plan form. The degree of change in the lift coefficient will also be related to the degree of flap selected.

The largest increases of lift for relatively small increases of drag will be attained at small flap settings whereas the greatest increase of drag is achieved at large flap settings. An approximation of the difference in maximum lift coefficient with angle of attack is illustrated in Fig. 5-74.

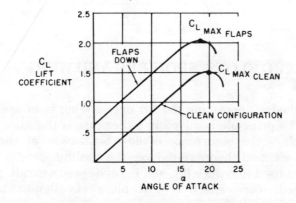

Fig. 5-74

Although the use of flap increases the lift coefficient for any given angle of attack, it will also increase the drag. The proportionate increases of lift and drag usually result in a reduction of the lift/drag ratio, although, depending on the type of flap and wing configuration concerned, it may be possible to achieve a slightly higher lift/drag ratio at very low speeds where the reduction in parasite drag more than offsets the normal increase in induced drag.

The lowering or raising of flaps will usually cause a pitching moment. This is due to the following:

- Changes in the position of the centre of pressure;
- Changes to the angle of downwash over the tailplane (Fig. 5-75);
- The increase of drag;
- The lowering of the aircraft's mean drag line.

The interaction of these various factors and the strength and direction of their particular pitching moment effect will determine the ultimate direction and strength of the actual pitching moment. In some cases the effects of these various factors can cancel each other out and little or no change in the pitching moment on the aircraft will result.

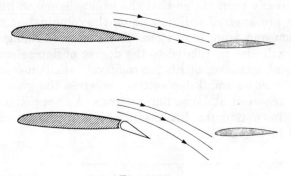

Fig. 5-75

SLATS, FIXED SLOTS, SPOILERS AND WING WASHOUT

Another method of increasing the lift over a wing is to use slats or fixed slots. The principle involved in either case is the same, in that their use delays the occurrence of flow breakaway at the higher angles of attack, and therefore reduces the stalling speed.

Spoilers are used to reduce lift, and in high speed aircraft, they can often be used more effectively in place of ailerons to cause asymmetric lift along the wing span.

SLATS

Slats are moveable control surfaces fitted to the leading edge of the wing. When in the closed position, the slat forms the leading edge of the wing. When the slat is moved forward, a slot is created between the slat and the wing's actual leading edge (Fig. 5-76).

This effectively introduces high energy air into the boundary layer over the top of the wing with the result that lift increases and the stalling speed decreases.

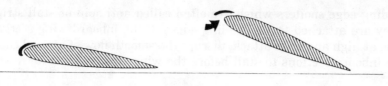

Fig. 5-76

FIXED SLOTS

Another method of achieving the same results is to integrate fixed slots into the wing structure as shown in Fig. 5-77.

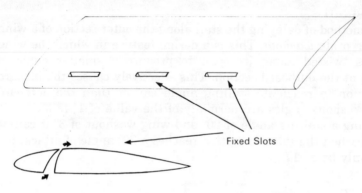

Fixed Slots

Fig. 5-77

When fixed slots are used they are normally integrated in the leading edge section of the main wing, but sometimes they are incorporated in stabilators in order to maintain a smooth flow of air around this type of control surface at the higher deflections necessary during low airspeed operation.

SPOILERS

The fitting of spoilers to create drag is no longer common practice on light aircraft. However, an important design consideration is the need to prevent the outer section of the wing from stalling first when the aircraft is flown at high angles of attack, e.g. low airspeed. If the outer section is first to stall, then a sharp wing drop can occur perhaps leading to a spin.

Various design features can be used to reduce this tendency, among which are the use of slats, fixed slots or spoilers. The method of using slats or fixed slots in this case is to place them at the leading edge along the outer sections of the wings, thereby delaying the onset of the stall in the vicinity of the wing tips.

On some aircraft, however, it is sometimes more practical to use leading edge spoilers which are often called anti spin or stall strips. They are attached to the leading edges of the inboard wing sections and, at high angles of attack, disrupt the smooth flow of air and cause the inboard sections to stall before the wing tips.

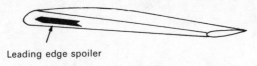

Leading edge spoiler

Fig. 5-78

WING WASHOUT

Another method of delaying the stall along the outer section of a wing is to incorporate *washout*. This is a design feature in which the wing section is twisted along its span to produce a smaller angle of incidence at the outboard section. This effectively causes the inboard wing section to reach its stalling angle earlier than the outboard section. Washout angles are normally of the value of 1° to 3°.

Assuming a stalling angle of 20° and wing washout of 3° it can be seen that when the inboard section reaches a 20° angle of attack, the tip will only be at 17°.

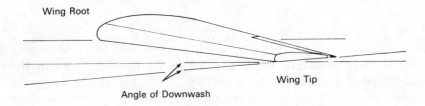

Wing Root

Angle of Downwash

Wing Tip

Fig. 5-79

Equilibrium

During flight, an aircraft is subject to the effects of the forces of lift, weight, thrust and drag. In level flight at a steady airspeed, the aircraft will be in *equilibrium*, i.e. the lift will equal the aircraft weight, and thrust will equal the drag.

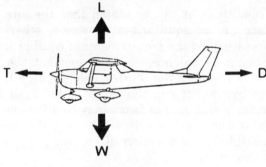

Fig. 5-80

RELATIONSHIP OF THE FOUR FORCES

The aircraft will have to be flown at a particular combination of airspeed and angle of attack to produce the required lift force. In order to obtain the necessary airspeed, a particular value of thrust must be used, which will be equal to the amount of drag produced as the aircraft moves through the air.

Bearing in mind that the aircraft wings will produce a large amount of lift relative to drag, the thrust force in level flight will be relatively small in relation to the lift force. It has already been mentioned that an efficient wing for a light aircraft could produce about fifteen times more lift than drag, but after the addition of the fuselage, this could be reduced to about ten. Therefore it can be seen that if 2000 units of lift are required, the drag force could be in the region of 200 units.

Assuming an aircraft weight of 2000 lbs and a lift/drag ratio for the total aircraft of 10:1, the figures shown in Fig. 5-81 would apply.

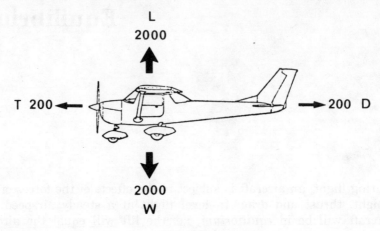

Fig. 5-81

In these conditions, it can be stated that the aircraft will be in a steady state i.e. in equilibrium. However, other factors are also involved in satisfying the requirements of equilibrium i.e. in addition to forces being in balance, so must moments be in balance. For example, it can be seen that during level flight, although the weight is balanced by the lift and the thrust is balanced by the drag, the lines of action of each pair of forces may be different. This leads to the production of a moment which will have a significant effect on the moment equilibrium of the aircraft i.e. as shown in Fig. 5-82.

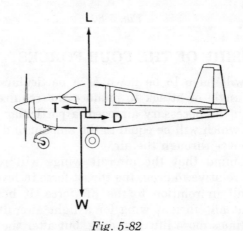

Fig. 5-82

Ideally, the designer would arrange the 4 forces to act through a common point, but in practice this would be extremely difficult because the points through which these forces act change position during flight. To consider this statement a little further it is fairly simple to appreciate that during flight, an aircraft will have an ever decreasing fuel weight and this can, and usually will, cause a change in the position of the aircraft's centre of gravity.

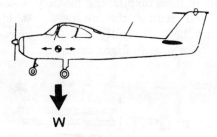

Fig. 5-83

Apart from this, there is the linear movement of the centre of pressure when the airspeed or angle of attack change, and the mean drag will change when flaps or landing gear are lowered.

Normal Drag line
Flaps Down Drag line

Fig. 5-84

Although the four forces are subject to change, the designer must ensure that a stable condition in pitch will remain regardless of their movement or change in strength. To satisfy this requirement, he arranges for the aircraft's centre of gravity to be ahead of the wing's centre of pressure so that a nose down moment predominates. This nose down pitching moment is then balanced by the forces which can be produced from the horizontal tailplane at the rear of the fuselage.

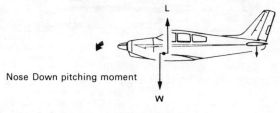

L

Nose Down pitching moment

W

Fig. 5-85

This arrangement of the lift and weight forces now produces stable moment equilibrium i.e. whenever the power is reduced, there is a sufficient nose down moment to ensure that the airspeed will tend to remain adequate, and thereby enable the pilot to retain control by producing the requisite stabilising moment from the tailplane.

If the forces were arranged the other way round, with lift ahead of weight, a permanent nose up pitching moment would exist, tending to raise the nose and reduce the airspeed. At low airspeeds, the elevators may not be sufficiently effective to correct this action, thereby leading to an unsafe flight condition.

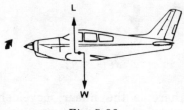

Fig. 5-86

When considering the disposition of the thrust and drag forces, it will be appreciated that these are not so easy to vary, as they will be fixed depending on the vertical position of the aircraft engine and the mean drag line. The latter is affected primarily by whether a high, low or centrally placed wing is used.

The general location of the four forces is shown in Fig. 5-87 and it can be seen that a nose down couple will normally pertain. To enable this situation to be controlled, a small horizontal wing surface is positioned at the rear of the aircraft. This tailplane is usually set at a negative angle of attack, so that a download moment is present, but because of the length of its lever, i.e. the fuselage, the actual forces it produces during flight are fairly small.

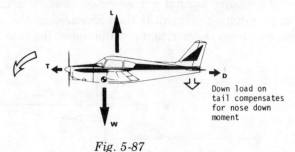

Down load on
tail compensates
for nose down
moment

Fig. 5-87

The pilot can control the amount and direction of the force produced from the tailplane either through the use of elevators situated at the rear of the horizontal tail surface, or by a moveable horizontal stabilator.

THE FORCES IN THE CLIMB

The balance of the four forces, Fig. 5-87, shows how the forces acting on the aircraft during level flight are balanced. If now the aircraft's path is altered from level to climbing flight, the situation will be changed.

Once the aircraft is placed in correct climbing flight, three of the forces, (lift, thrust and drag), will have a similar relationship to the flight path as they had in level flight. However, since the weight will remain acting vertically downwards, there will be a component of the weight acting backwards relative to the aircraft's flight path thus augmenting the drag force.

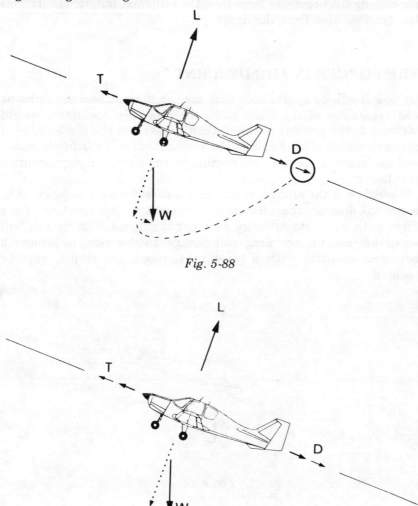

Fig. 5-88

Fig. 5-89

This effect will cause the airspeed to decrease so that both lift and aerodynamic drag are reduced. However, the addition of the weight component along the line of remaining aerodynamic drag causes the total retarding effect to become greater, and to keep the forces in balance at a steady airspeed, the thrust must be increased.

When this additional thrust is applied it will balance the aerodynamic drag plus the component of the weight. Therefore, climbing flight is a steady state process during which additional thrust is used. If a constant airspeed is maintained, a steady gain in height is achieved, and the aircraft will be in equilibrium. It will of course also be necessary to maintain moment equilibrium by generating the necessary force from the tailplane, but, for clarity, this has been omitted from the figure.

THE FORCES IN THE DESCENT

By now it will be appreciated that once an aircraft becomes airborne and regardless of its flight path, there is only one force, weight (defined as the product of the aircraft's mass and the acceleration of gravity), which always acts in the same direction, i.e. straight down, and the geometry of the forces acting on the aircraft is dependent on this factor.

Therefore, if the aircraft is placed in a nose down attitude, i.e. as in a normal descent, the component of weight in the direction of the flight path will automatically augment the thrust. The aircraft will accelerate and lift and drag will change. In this case, to achieve a balanced condition with a constant airspeed, the thrust must be reduced.

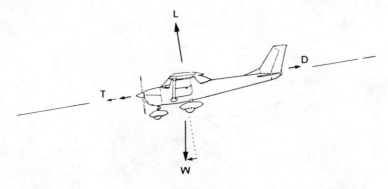

Fig. 5-90

Once the thrust is reduced to the correct value and the angle of the descent path established, the aircraft's speed and rate of descent will be constant and a condition of equilibrium will have been achieved.

If the aircraft is placed in a glide (a condition of no engine thrust) at a constant airspeed, the aircraft's descent path will become steeper until the component of weight acting forwards along the flight path totally substitutes for the engine thrust.

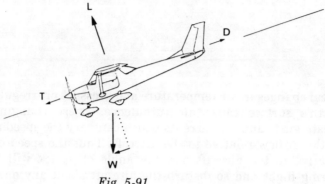

Fig. 5-91

The steeper the angle of glide, the greater will be the forward component of weight and therefore the greater the airspeed. The forces will still remain in balance, with lift balancing the component of weight perpendicular to the flight path, and the forward component of the weight parallel to the flight path acting as 'thrust', balancing the drag.

Stability

Local changes in air temperature and pressure or irregularities in the earth's surface cause air turbulence. These changing conditions create gusts and air currents which can vary the speed and direction of the airflow relative to the aircraft. Thus the speed of the airflow relative to the aircraft and the angle of attack will tend to vary during flight and so disturb the aircraft about any one or all of its axes.

Although the pilot can overcome the effects of gusts etc. by use of the flying controls, this could become a very tiring business if the aircraft was not designed with some inherent stability causing it to tend to return to its original condition if displaced during flight.

Before going into the subject in more depth, it can be stated that an aircraft is designed to have a certain degree of the following three qualities:

● Stability;
● Manoeuvrability;
● Controllability.

In relation to an aeroplane, the term stability can be summarised as that characteristic which tends to cause the aircraft to fly (hands off) in a steady attitude along a constant path. A body is defined as stable if, after disturbance, it has a natural tendency to return to its original state of equilibrium. Manoeuvrability is the measure of an aircraft's ability to be directed along a certain flight path, and to withstand the stresses imposed upon it by the manoeuvre. Controllability is the quality of the aircraft's response to the pilot's operation of the controls.

From these statements, it can be seen that the degree of stability of an aircraft has an important bearing on its operation. For example, an unstable aircraft would be difficult to control, whereas too much stability would make it difficult to manoeuvre.

Aircraft stability in any form applies to the state or quality of equilibrium which the aircraft can achieve during flight, and therefore relates to the aircraft's horizontal, lateral and vertical axes.

It is, however, necessary to appreciate that there are two basic forms of stability, these are *static* and *dynamic*.

STATIC STABILITY

When an aircraft is in a state of equilibrium, the sum of all the forces acting upon it is equal to zero. Therefore an aircraft in equilibrium is experiencing no accelerations other than that of gravity and will thus continue its movement through the air in a state of steady flight. Any gust, or turbulence or deflection of the flying controls will disturb this state of equilibrium and the associated force or acceleration will unbalance the steady state moments and forces.

Three types of static stability apply and are separately defined as, static stability, neutral static stability or static instability. An explanation of these terms can be given as follows.

If an object is disturbed and then returns to a state of equilibrium, a condition of positive stability is said to exist. For example, if a ball bearing is placed in a concave receptacle, it will, if disturbed, return to its original position without any external influences. (Fig. 5-92.)

Fig. 5-92

Fig. 5-93

When an object is disturbed and has neither the tendency to return to its original position nor to continue its displacement, it is said to have neutral static stability. An example of this would be a ball placed on a level surface as shown in Fig. 5-93. Having once been disturbed, it would come to rest but in a different place to its original position.

If, however, an object is disturbed and continues in the direction of the disturbance, it will have a negative static stability. This characteristic can be seen by referring to Fig. 5-94. In this diagram, the ball bearing has been placed on the top of a convex surface and it can be seen that any disturbance will therefore cause the ball to continue its movement.

Fig. 5-94

DYNAMIC STABILITY

Although an aircraft may be statically stable in that it has the tendency to return to its original position of equilibrium, it may also have a tendency to overshoot the original position during its return movement and a series of oscillations may occur before the original state of equilibrium is once again achieved. In the terminology of aerodynamics, this type of oscillation is known as a *phugoid*.

Providing the phugoid motion damps out, the aircraft will have a degree of dynamic stability. If the movement persists without any increase or decrease in its rate of movement, a condition of neutral dynamic stability will exist, but if the amount of its original oscillation increases, the aircraft will be dynamically unstable. Figure 5-95 illustrates the difference between these three types of dynamic stability.

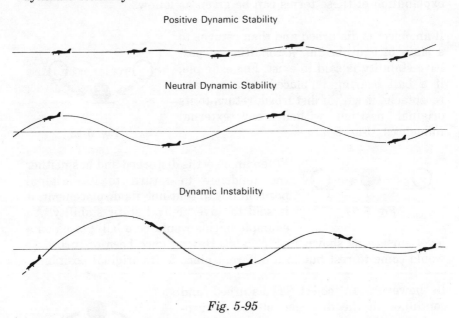

Positive Dynamic Stability

Neutral Dynamic Stability

Dynamic Instability

Fig. 5-95

LONGITUDINAL STABILITY

In order to foster an understanding of how the weight and lift forces act relative to one another, the considerations in respect of these two forces have so far been simplified. This has been done to ensure that the effect of the couple action between the lift acting through the centre of pressure, and the weight acting through the centre of gravity, can more easily be appreciated. In fact, the designer is less interested in the position of the centre of pressure, than in the strength of the moment arm which it produces. This is measured through what is known as the *aerodynamic centre* which is a point on the wing chord where the moment coefficient remains constant regardless of changes in angle of attack. In general, this point is about 25% of the chord measured from the leading edge.

However, a detailed understanding of the principles involved with the measurement and effect of the position of the aerodynamic centre is not essential in order to understand the basic principles of longitudinal stability. Therefore, the movement of the centre of pressure and the centre of gravity will be referred to in the following text, rather than involving pitching moments which relate to the aerodynamic centre of the wing.

When an aircraft has a tendency to maintain its flight path at a constant angle of attack, that is to say, it does not tend to raise or lower its nose when in a trimmed condition, it possesses longitudinal stability. Longitudinal stability therefore refers to motion in pitch and so the horizontal tailplane (or stabilator) is the primary surface which controls this stability.

It has already been pointed out that the forces of lift, weight, thrust and drag seldom act from the same point on the aeroplane, and also that the exact point from which the forces of lift, weight and drag act will change during flight. Added to this is the fact that the strength of each force will vary depending on the aircraft's attitude, configuration and the power being used. Although the pilot can control the pitching effects which result from changes in these forces by use of the flying controls, the designer also arranges for a degree of inherent stability to be present by arranging for the horizontal tailplane to be set at a smaller angle of incidence than the mainplanes. This difference between the angle of the mainplanes and the tailplane is often referred to as *longitudinal dihedral*. The effect of this arrangement can be explained as follows:

> When an aircraft is disturbed by a gust, it will take up a different attitude but, due to inertia, it will remain temporarily on its original flight path. The result of this is that both the mainplanes and tailplane will undergo the same change in angle of attack.

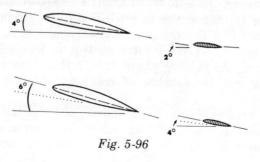

Fig. 5-96

Referring to Fig. 5-96, it can be seen that the mainplane angle of incidence is +4° and the tailplane angle of incidence is +2°. Assuming the effect of a gust increases the angle of attack by 2°, this will cause a 50% increase of the mainplane angle of attack and a 100% increase in the tailplane's angle of attack. Therefore, due to the different angles of incidence, a greater proportional increase of lift will occur on the tail. The tail will therefore rise and this will result in a lowering of the aircraft nose. In other words, the aircraft will tend to return to its original trimmed position. Although other factors affect it, the above explanation illustrates the simple principle involved.

Note 1: Tailplane incidence is normally negative due to the need to maintain a small tail down force and balance the nose down moment produced from the c.g. being ahead of the c.p., but for simplicity, +2° is used for this example.

Note 2: Any large chordwise movement of the centre of pressure resulting from a change in angle of attack, which would occur with an asymmetrical tailplane section, could produce aerodynamic problems relating to longitudinal stability. For this reason, a symmetrical aerofoil section is normally used for the horizontal tailplane or stabilator.

RELATIONSHIP OF CENTRE OF GRAVITY TO CONTROL IN PITCH

All aircraft are designed to be longitudinally stable over a limited centre of gravity range. If the centre of gravity moves outside these limits, the performance of the aircraft and the pilot's control over it will be affected, in serious cases to the point where the aircraft's attitude could become uncontrollable.

If the aircraft is loaded so that the centre of gravity is at its forward limit, a relatively long lever arm between the centre of gravity and the tailplane will exist, and the aircraft will be at its most stable so that, if disturbed in flight, it will quickly return to its original attitude. However, if the forward limit is exceeded, the aircraft will become tiring to manoeuvre in pitch due to its strong longitudinal stability. It can also become uncontrollably nose heavy, particularly at lower airspeeds when elevator control is less effective, as for example, during the landing phase. It is in this situation that full up elevator may not be capable of creating a round out prior to touchdown.

When the centre of gravity is moved aft, the tail lever arm is decreased and the degree of longitudinal stability decreases, which means the aircraft will take longer to resume its original attitude

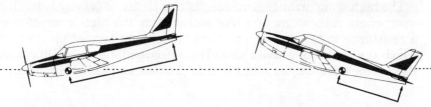

Action of Forward Centre of Gravity   Action of Aft Centre of Gravity

Fig. 5-97

when disturbed. If the centre of gravity position moves aft beyond a certain point, the aircraft will become uncontrollably tail heavy, the nose will rise and the aircraft will eventually stall. The permitted range of movement, and forward and rear limits of the centre of gravity position, are primarily based on the effectiveness of the elevators or stabilator to control the aircraft in pitch at the point of stall, (i.e. at the lowest possible flight speed). It can be seen from these considerations that when operating an aircraft, the pilot must ensure the correct procedure for determining the weight and position of the centre of gravity is complied with.

LATERAL AND DIRECTIONAL STABILITY

As with longitudinal stability, the gusts and irregularities which occur in the atmosphere also affect the attitude of an aircraft both in the lateral and directional sense.

Here, an added complication arises, because any movement about the horizontal plane (rolling) also affects the aircraft in the vertical plane and produces a yawing action. Similarly, any movement about the vertical plane (yawing), will also cause a rolling action. Hence, lateral and directional stability are inter-related. However, for simplicity in the explanations which follow, the two types of stability are initially discussed separately following which, their inter-related effects are considered.

LATERAL STABILITY

The lateral stability of an aircraft involves the rolling moments which result from sideslip. A sideslip tends to produce both a rolling and yawing motion, but if a favourable rolling moment can be built into the design, a sideslip will tend to return the aircraft to a laterally level attitude.

The design features which are normally employed in light aircraft design to achieve a favourable rolling moment are, a high wing in relationship to the centre of gravity, geometric dihedral or a combination of these features.

The high wing arrangement results in a centre of gravity below the wing where it therefore acts like a pendulum, the high wing offering a resistance to the airflow and thus becoming a type of pivot about which the centre of gravity acts. This effect on lateral stability is by itself somewhat limited and tends to produce an oscillating motion.

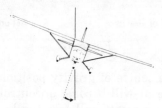

Fig. 5-98

Geometric dihedral however, offers a more positive action, and is accomplished in the following manner. The wings are arranged to produce an angle to the plane of symmetry as shown in Fig. 5-99.

Dihedral Angle

Plane of Symmetry

Fig. 5-99

Whenever a wing drops, the aircraft will sideslip in that direction due to the tilt of the lift line in relation to the weight, (Fig. 5-100).

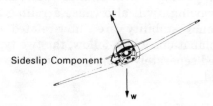

Sideslip Component

Fig. 5-100

A sideways component is produced and lift being inclined, has a shorter vertical component and is no longer sufficient to balance the weight. The result of this is to cause the aircraft to sideslip in the direction of the lower wing. The effect of sideslip is to change the direction of the relative airflow which now comes from ahead and slightly from one side, (Fig. 5-101).

This produces a greater angle of attack to the lower wing and a

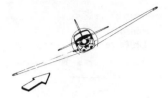

Fig. 5-101

smaller angle of attack to the raised wing. The lower wing therefore obtains more lift than the higher wing and a tendency to restore the aircraft back to a laterally level position occurs. In this situation, a very minor masking of the airflow occurs on the higher wing due to fuselage interference, but at the small sideslip angles incurred, the effect of such masking can be virtually ignored, unless of course, the aircraft is placed into a positive sideslip by the pilot.

It can be seen from the foregoing, that geometric dihedral has a beneficial effect on lateral stability, but its actual restoring action is limited due to the fact that if the wing was returned to the laterally level position by the dihedral effect, inertia would cause the rising wing to continue beyond the laterally level position and the opposite wing would drop. This would produce a cycle known as oscillatory instability (commonly called *Dutch roll*). This is a condition which would make it more difficult for the pilot to maintain a laterally level position. An aircraft with strong lateral stability would also be more difficult to manoeuvre in roll. The designer will therefore normally limit the dihedral angle to one which will give an aircraft a tendency to resist a rolling motion set up by disturbances of the air.

To sum up, it can be stated that the amount of effective dihedral will vary with the type and purpose of the aircraft. Normally the effective dihedral is kept low since a strong rolling tendency due to sideslip can lead to a Dutch roll, difficult rudder co-ordination in rolling manoeuvres, and excessive demands on lateral stability during crosswind take-offs and landings.

DIRECTIONAL STABILITY

The directional stability of an aircraft is essentially *weathercock stability* and concerns movement about the vertical axis and its relationship to yaw and sideslip angle.

An aircraft which possesses directional stability will tend to maintain its heading or damp out any tendency to diverge from its heading should it be disturbed. The vertical tailplane (fin) and that area of the fuselage behind the centre of gravity are the primary surfaces which control the degree of directional stability. Whenever an aircraft is sideslipping or yawing, the vertical tailplane will experience an angle of attack as shown in Fig. 5-102.

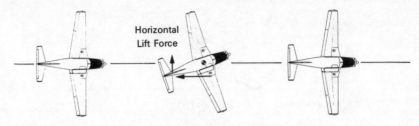

Fig. 5-102

Due to inertia, an aircraft will continue for a short while along the original flight path after its heading is disturbed, this will produce a relative airflow which results in a horizontal lift force setting up a restoring moment about the centre of gravity. This tends to return the aircraft to its original flight path. This corrective action will be increased by the effect of airflow direction on the side surface of the fuselage behind the centre of gravity and the greater this area, the stronger the restoring effect.

INTER-RELATIONSHIP OF LATERAL AND DIRECTIONAL STABILITY

As stated at the beginning of this section on stability, there are many inter-related factors affecting the adequate provision of both lateral and directional stability. Due to the conflicting aerodynamic needs of these two stabilities in relation to sideslip and yaw, most aircraft are designed to have a lateral stability which will not overcome the properties of directional stability. This results in the aircraft having a weak spiral divergence, i.e. if a wing should drop, the aircraft will eventually go into a gentle spiral descent unless checked by the pilot. This action is known as *spiral instability*.

The Stall

A feature of any aircraft wing is that as the angle of attack is increased a point is eventually reached where the airstream is unable to maintain a smooth flow over the wing and at this point the streamline flow breaks down and turbulence occurs. This is known as wing stall and the angle at which the stall (flow breakaway) occurs varies with the wing section and the aspect ratio. The general rule is that as the aspect ratio is increased, the stalling angle is reduced. Therefore, a wing with a low aspect ratio will have a relatively high stalling angle. Most light aircraft have stalling angles ranging from 18° to 20°, whereas high speed aircraft with swept or delta shaped wings and corresponding low aspect ratios, have stalling angles which are considerably higher.

The basic reason for the occurrence of flow breakaway lies in the fact that the layer of air which is in immediate contact with the skin of the wing is appreciably slowed down due to surface friction, whereas the layers of air further away from the wing surfaces are less affected. This produces a velocity profile or shear gradient similar to that shown in Fig. 5-103.

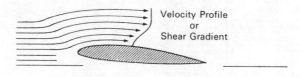

Velocity Profile
or
Shear Gradient

Fig. 5-103

The thickness of this shear or boundary for streamline flow is commonly a few millimetres, but for purposes of illustration, this is somewhat magnified in Fig. 5-103.

As the airflow proceeds across the wing towards the trailing edge, the speed differential between the layer of air in contact with the wing and the layer of air further from the wing increases, until eventually the airflow within the boundary layer becomes turbulent and the boundary layer thickens considerably.

STALLING ANGLE

The point on the wing where smooth flow changes to turbulent flow is known as the separation point. The further back along a wing that separation occurs the more lift and the less drag is produced. Although separation always occurs at some stage through a wide range of angles and airspeeds, it is at one particular angle known as the stalling angle, (for a particular wing section and aspect ratio), that the flow breakaway produces a sharp and positive loss of lift. It should be noted that whereas lift is still being produced ahead of the separation area, behind it the drag predominates, (Fig. 5-104).

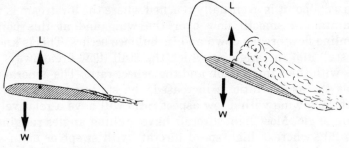

Fig. 5-104

The variation of lift coefficient with angle of attack up to the stall and beyond is shown in Fig. 5-105.

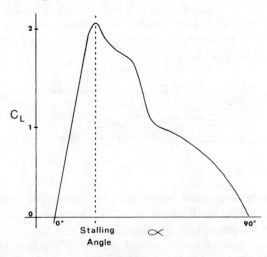

Fig. 5-105

It has been stated earlier that the centre of pressure moves forward as the angle of attack is increased, thereby reducing the strength of the couple between lift and weight. However, at the stall, the disruption to the total lift force is such that the aircraft will normally pitch nose down unless the elevators remain sufficiently effective to allow the pilot to prevent this.

WING LOADING

This is the weight of the aircraft divided by the wing area and is usually defined in pounds per square foot and occasionally in kilograms per square metre. For example, an aircraft which weighs 2000 lbs (906 kg) and has a wing area of 200 square feet (18.58 m²) would have a wing loading of 10 lbs per square foot (48.76 kg/m²).

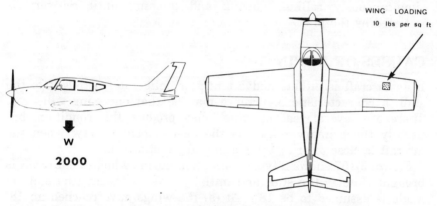

Fig. 5-106

A point of operational importance is that the higher the wing loading the higher will be the speed at which the aircraft stalls. A rule of thumb which can be used for light aircraft is 'a 2% change in weight for a given aeroplane will cause a 1% change in stalling speed' i.e.

> assuming an aircraft weight of 2000 lbs with a basic stalling speed of 50 knots, a 20% increase in weight (400 lbs) will increase the stalling speed to about 55 knots.

The practical aspects of stalling and the factors which affect the behaviour of aircraft at the stall are covered in *Student Manual Part 2* under the 'Long Briefing' section on 'Stalling'.

The Spin

A spin is a condition of stalled flight in which the aircraft also describes a spiral descent. During a spin, the aircraft will be simultaneously rolling, yawing and pitching until recovery is initiated by the pilot.

CAUSES OF A SPIN

If an aircraft is either inadvertently or deliberately brought to the stall, a characteristic occurrence may be that one wing will drop. There are several reasons which may produce this condition, but usually the primary reason is the development of yaw when the aircraft is close to or at the stalling angle of attack.

Figure 5-107 shows a typical situation during which the aircraft is brought close to the stall and initially, yaw is absent (the stalling angle is assumed to be 18°). At (a) the wings have reached an 18° angle of attack. At (b) a yaw to the left has occurred which will temporarily change the airflow speed about each wing and the slight differential of lift between the two wings causes the right wing to rise and the left wing to drop. This small rolling action leads to a change in the angle of attack affecting each wing. The lowering wing obtains a higher angle of attack while that of the rising wing decreases. The lowering wing now reaches the stalling angle and drops more quickly, which will, in turn, lead to a higher angle of attack and a more stalled condition.

For a spin to develop, an excessive angle of attack and a positive yawing action are usually required. Generally, the conventional aeroplane must be stalled before autorotation takes place.

AUTOROTATION

Figure 5-108 illustrates the aerodynamic characteristics in relation to the C_L and C_D curves versus the angle of attack for a typical light aircraft during the fully developed autorotative stage.

The downgoing wing being more stalled will produce more drag

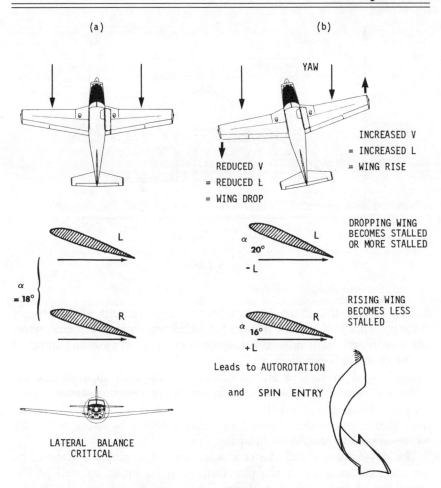

(a)   (b)

INCREASED V
= INCREASED L
= WING RISE

YAW

REDUCED V
= REDUCED L
= WING DROP

DROPPING WING
BECOMES STALLED
OR MORE STALLED

α
20°
-L

RISING WING
BECOMES LESS
STALLED

α
= 18°

α
16°
+L

Leads to AUTOROTATION

and   SPIN   ENTRY

LATERAL   BALANCE
CRITICAL

Fig. 5-107

causing the aircraft to yaw in the direction of the downgoing wing.
Due to the upgoing wing being less stalled, it will always have more
lift than the downgoing wing and this action will be self perpetuat-
ing, hence the term *autorotation*.

SPIN CHARACTERISTICS

During a spin, the aircraft will lose altitude rapidly and descend
along a vertical path about the spin axis, the helix of which is fairly
small and can be less than the span of the wings. An important
characteristic is that during a spin, the predominant tendency is to
continue the autorotation and the aircraft generally has a spinning
motion which is primarily rolling, but with moderate yaw and a

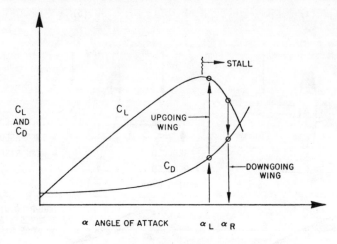

Fig. 5-108

degree of sideslip. If an aircraft has a large amount of directional stability, this will have a favourable influence on the spin characteristics as it will minimise the displacement due to yaw and make it easier to effect a recovery.

The actual motion of an aeroplane and its path through the air during a spin manoeuvre depends on many complex aerodynamic considerations which involve inertia forces and moments. Nevertheless, there are certain basic facts which relate to spins and with which all pilots should be familiar.

The development and the characteristics of a spin will depend on the aircraft design and the distribution of its mass, as well as the operation of the control surfaces. The aircraft will usually rotate several times before it settles down into the state of spinning steadily and the pitch angle it takes up may be steep or flat, the latter characteristic being significantly affected by the position of the centre of gravity.

The actual motions of the aircraft throughout the entry to, and during a spin, are of a complex nature. Once the aircraft has settled into a spin, the forces and moments acting upon it will be in equilibrium, and this balance of forces and moments will determine the values of angle of attack, sideslip, turn radius, rate of descent and other factors.

During the steady spin, the aircraft will be in a condition where the rate of yaw and roll will settle down to a constant value and the rate of descent will also stabilise. Some aircraft through design features, or the position of the centre of gravity, may be unable to achieve a true spin, and as a result, the forces and moment will not balance out.

In this case, an oscillatory spin motion will occur which could more accurately be described as an autorotative spiral.

During a settled spin, it is the balance of the moments which will determine the final state of equilibrium and which will have a large influence upon the recovery characteristics. The actual balance of the forces is of less importance, but in view of their effect on the rate of descent and the considerations relating to the position of the centre of gravity, they must be discussed here. The three primary forces are the resultant of the aerodynamic forces, the inertia forces (considered as centrifugal forces) and the weight, and these forces interact approximately as shown in Fig. 5-109.

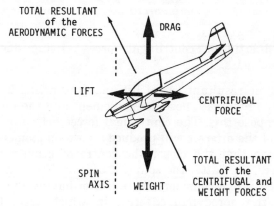

Fig. 5-109

The position and direction of weight is easily established as acting directly downward through the centre of gravity and as throughout the spin, the aircraft will be descending, the overall relative airflow will therefore be coming from below. In consequence, the vertical component of the resultant of the aerodynamic forces labelled drag in the diagram, will be acting against the weight and at a certain rate of descent will balance the weight, i.e. in a steady spin the rate of descent will settle to a constant value.

Lift acting at 90° to the overall relative airflow will now be approximately horizontal, and the centrifugal force brought about by the aircraft rotation in the spin will oppose the lift. The conditions for equilibrium will be met when drag = weight and lift = centrifugal force.

Figure 5-110 shows the resultant of the aerodynamic forces, the effect of up elevator and the direction of the centrifugal forces in relation to the centre of gravity.

A = aerodynamic force (resultant of lift and drag)
B = aerodynamic effect of 'up elevator'

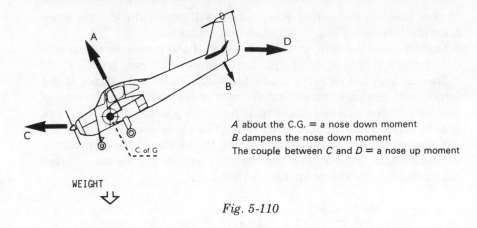

A about the C.G. = a nose down moment
B dampens the nose down moment
The couple between *C* and *D* = a nose up moment

WEIGHT

Fig. 5-110

C, *D* are inertia or centrifugal forces arising due to the ditribution of mass.

The aerodynamic resultant (*A*) of lift and drag acting behind the centre of gravity produces a nose down moment and the up elevator force tends to oppose this. The centrifugal forces acting on the fore and aft masses of the aircraft will produce a nose up moment. It can, therefore, be seen that the closer the centre of gravity is to the aerodynamic force, the flatter the spin will become. This may be more clearly visualised if one considers the effect of having the centre of gravity aft of the aerodynamic force, in which case, both the aerodynamic force and the centrifugal forces will be acting together to flatten the spin. If the spin flattens, the angle of attack increases and the resulting increase of drag will decrease the rate of descent. The moment due to the centrifugal forces will have a stronger effect in the horizontal plane, which will lead to a decrease in the spin radius and an increase in the rate of rotation.

EFFECT OF THE CENTRE OF GRAVITY ON SPINNING CHARACTERISTICS

The spinning characteristics of any particular aircraft will vary with the position of the centre of gravity, even though its position is within the permitted limits for the aircraft concerned. The effect of a forward position of the centre of gravity is to cause a steeper spin with a faster rate of descent. However, recovery action is easier as the spin is far less stable. An extreme forward position of the centre of gravity may in some cases prevent a spin being achieved altogether, in which case, the aircraft will remain in a steep, and usually tight, spiral descent during which the airspeed increases.

The effect of an aft centre of gravity is to make the spin flatter, in which case, the rate of descent is less, the spin is more stable, and recovery is more difficult. If the centre of gravity is aft of the permitted limits, a serious situation can occur where the aircraft may not be capable of recovering from a settled spin condition.

EFFECT OF AIRCRAFT INERTIA ON SPIN RECOVERY CHARACTERISTICS

The ratio of pitching, rolling and yawing inertia may vary in different aircraft and will affect the spin recovery characteristics and the part that using ailerons will play in spin recovery. Therefore, reference to the particular aircraft manual *must* be made to ascertain the correct use of the controls during spin recovery.

Turning Flight

In turning flight, an aircraft is no longer in a condition of static equilibrium, because an unbalanced force has to be present to produce the centripetal acceleration required during a turning manoeuvre.

Although the horizontal flight path of an aircraft can be changed by simple application of rudder, this will produce an action similar to that applied to a car when taking a corner at speed. It will, therefore, be uncomfortable and due to the aircraft's inherent stability, it would result in an extremely inefficient flight condition and one with a limited practical application.

THE FORCES IN THE TURN

During steady straight and level flight, the total lift produced equals the aircraft weight and a state of balance exists between the lift and weight forces. However, in order to produce a steady co-ordinated turn at constant altitude, a force must be present which acts towards the centre of the turn. This force is produced by banking the aircraft and tilting the lift force. This effectively produces two components of lift at right angles to each other. One acting into the direction of turn and supplying a turning force, and the other acting upwards to support the aircraft weight.

Figure 5-111(a) shows the relationship of the forces acting on an aircraft during normal banked turning flight. It can be seen that the lift which acts at 90° to the wing is inclined at an angle to the vertical, and by resolving this into a parallelogram of forces, a horizontal component of the total lift produces the sideways, i.e. the centripetal, force which causes the aircraft to turn.

It is often convenient to refer to a centrifugal force rather than speak of the centripetal acceleration associated with curved motion. This is an apparent force, directed outward from the centre, and which the curved motion appears to exert in order to balance the forces producing the centripetal acceleration. Employing the concept of centrifugal force, the force diagram becomes that shown in Fig. 5-111(b). However, by banking the aircraft, and tilting the lift line,

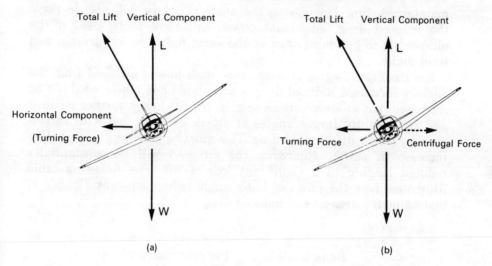

Fig. 5-111

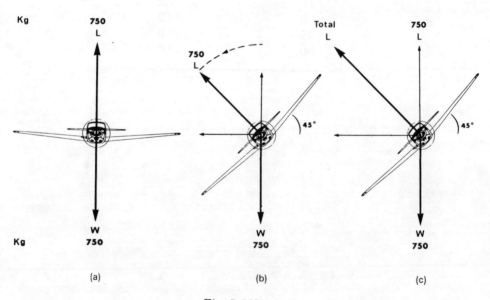

Fig. 5-112

the amount of lift which was balancing the weight is decreased as shown in Fig. 5-112(b). Therefore, either the angle of attack or airspeed will have to be increased to extend the lift line as shown in Fig. 5-112(c).

In practice, the simplest method is to increase the angle of attack to achieve the required increase of lift so that constant altitude is maintained. Since increasing the angle of attack will also increase the induced drag, additional power will have to be used if the airspeed is to be maintained at the same figure as for straight and level flight.

For moderate angles of bank, the small loss of airspeed from the slightly increased induced drag is acceptable and power need not be increased, but at steeper bank angles, the lift line is further inclined and significantly larger angles of attack are required with corresponding larger increases in drag. This must be overcome by a positive increase in power, otherwise, the airspeed will be substantially reduced leading to a significant loss of lift. The following table illustrates how the effect of bank angle (when constant altitude is maintained) increases the induced drag.

Bank angle (degrees)	Per cent increase in induced drag
15	7.2
30	33.3
45	100.0
60	300.0

Load Factor and Manoeuvres

An aircraft in turning flight will clearly have greater loads imposed upon it which will increase the structural stresses and also the stalling speed. In a steady co-ordinated turn during level flight, the vertical component of lift must be equal to the weight of the aircraft so that there will be no acceleration in a vertical direction. This introduces an important term in relation to manoeuvring flight, i.e. *load factor*. The load factor is the ratio between lift and weight and is determined by:

$$n = \frac{L}{W}$$

where

n = load factor
L = lift
W = weight.

Referring to Fig. 5-113, it can be seen that the more the lift force is tilted, the more total lift will have to be produced to bring its vertical component back to the original value. It will also be seen that a 60° angle of bank will necessitate a doubling of the total lift to achieve the original vertical lift force.

Therefore, for a steady co-ordinated turn at a constant height, a specific load factor will be incurred, the value of which will depend on the angle of bank, e.g. a bank angle of 60° will result in a load factor of 2.

EFFECT ON STALLING SPEED

Apart from the significance of the wing having to supply more lift than the weight to maintain the aircraft at a constant altitude, the resulting increase in load factor will cause an increase in the stalling speed.

During turning flight and manoeuvres, the effect on stall speed is

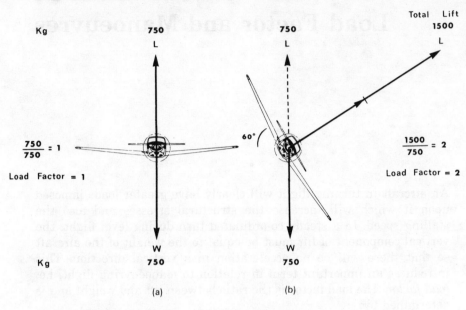

Fig. 5-113

similar to the effect of weight. A steady level turn requires the vertical component of lift to be equal to the weight of the aircraft and the horizontal component of lift to be equal to the centripetal force. Therefore, in a steady turn, the aircraft has to develop more lift than its weight.

During the turn at constant speed and altitude, the angle of attack will have to be increased to produce the extra lift required to support the aircraft. This causes an increase in the stalling speed which is related to the bank angle. Figure 5-114 illustrates the percentage variation of stall speed with angle of bank.

Therefore, as the bank angle is increased, three important things happen – the load factor, stalling speed, and drag, all increase. This increase in drag will cause the airspeed to decrease unless sufficient power is available to combat the added drag and keep the airspeed constant. It can therefore be seen that if insufficient power is available to overcome the additional drag, the flying speed will decrease and approach the already increasing stalling speed as the angle of bank increases. A condition of stall will then occur at a substantially higher speed than would normally be expected.

It can also be seen from this illustration that whereas no significant change occurs to the stalling speed at moderate angles of bank up to 30°, the increase of load factor at greater angles than this has a startling effect on stall speeds, i.e., at approximately 75% of bank the stalling speed is increased by 100%.

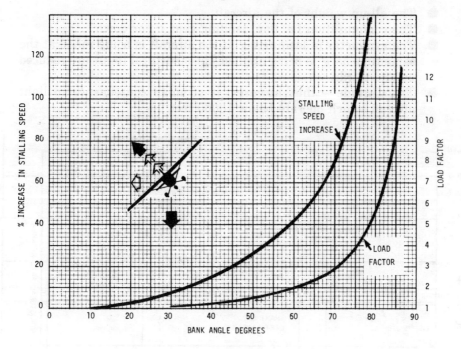

Fig. 5-114

STRUCTURAL CONSIDERATIONS

All aircraft are constructed to withstand any reasonable load factors which may be imposed upon them during flight, but the load factor limitation varies with different types of aircraft. The operation of any aircraft is subject to specific strength limitations, and overstressing can at best reduce the aircraft life and at worst can lead to catastrophic failure in flight.

The differences between the structural strength limitations of different aircraft types has a significant bearing when carrying out advanced turning or similar manoeuvres which impose high load factors on the airframe. The importance of understanding this can be seen by referring to Fig. 5-115 which illustrates a basic V_n envelope, i.e., airspeed versus load factor for a representative modern training aircraft.

The V_n (or V_g) diagram is used to illustrate the operating strength of the aircraft and is in a form where the horizontal scale represents airspeed (V) and the vertical scale represents the load factor (n). The presentation of the aircraft strength is based on four factors being known:

- The all-up weight of the aircraft;
- The configuration i.e. flap, landing gear up or down;
- The symmetry of loading e.g. if the aircraft is being rolled at the same time as 'g' is being applied, the structural limits are reduced by one third;
- The altitude – this, however, is of small consequence to light aircraft which operate below 10000 feet.

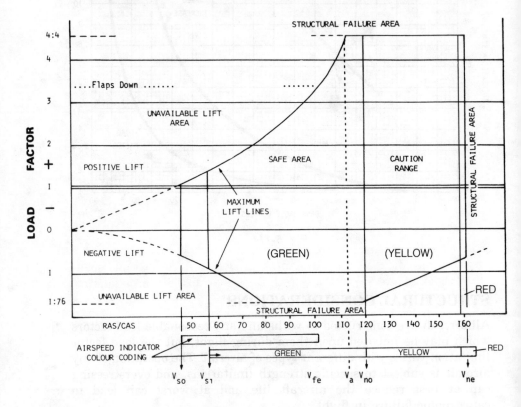

Fig. 5-115

During the construction of a particular V_n envelope, the designer establishes certain airspeeds which are important to the operation of the specific aircraft. These speeds have official abbreviations and those which are of special significance to the pilot are defined below:

V_{SO} The stalling speed, no power, flaps down and a load factor of 1.

V_{S1} The stalling speed, no power, flaps retracted and a load factor of 1.

V_{fe} Maximum speed permitted with wing flaps extended.

V_a The design manoeuvring speed.

V_{no} Normal operating speed. (Maximum speed in turbulent air.)
V_{ne} The never exceed speed.
V_{ra} A specifically recommended speed for flight in turbulent air.

Note: These abbreviations are applicable to light aircraft. In the case of those aircraft which operate at higher airspeeds, several different abbreviations appropriate to Mach number terminology are used.

Load factors are positive (+) when a positive g is being pulled, as for example, in a steep turn or 'pull up' manoeuvre, and negative (−) in the case of pushing the control column forward. High negative loadings are rare due to resultant pilot discomfort and the abnormal attitudes required to achieve them, and because of this, aircraft need not be designed to withstand negative load factors to the same extent as is necessary with positive load factors.

The aircraft to which Fig. 5-115 relates has a limiting positive load factor of $4.4g$ (flaps down $3.4g$) and a limiting negative load factor of $1.76g$. The limiting airspeed is just over 160 mph and the basic stalling speed V_{S1} is 57 mph.

IN-FLIGHT PRECAUTIONS

The maximum lift line (stall line) in the V_n diagram represents the maximum load factor which can be produced at the various speeds between V_{S0} and V_a without stalling. For example, the maximum g which can be pulled at 70 mph is just under 2, and at this point, the maximum lift line will be exceeded i.e. the aircraft will stall, thus preventing the pilot from increasing the load factor any further regardless of how abruptly or with what force the pull is applied. From this it can be seen that in Fig. 5-115, the flaps up limiting load factor cannot be reached until the airspeed is over 110 mph

This last statement leads to consideration of an important speed which is normally defined for all modern general aviation aircraft as the *manoeuvring speed* (V_a). This speed is the maximum speed at which the pilot can make abrupt and extreme control movements involving their full deflection without causing structural overloading. Above this speed, it is possible to overload the structure, and for this reason, abrupt and maximum deflection of the controls should not be used when operating above the manoeuvre speed, as for example, the application of full rudder during the recovery from an autorotative spiral.

The colour coded dials of airspeed indicators are directly related to the V_n envelope for the particular type of aircraft. The bottom of the white band shows the stalling speed with flap down, no power and a load factor of 1. The bottom of the green band indicates the stalling speed under the same conditions but with the flap up.

The top of the white band indicates the limiting speed with flap lowered (V_{fe}) and it can be seen that this also coincides with the maximum g which can be pulled without exceeding the maximum lift line, or in other words, the example shows that the maximum load factor permitted is $3.4g$ which in the illustration is directly in line with the flap limiting speed.

Once the speed exceeds the V_a, the pilot will be able to pull g forces in excess of the structural limitations, and this has to be borne in mind, particularly if the nose is allowed to drop during turns at steep angles of bank, a situation in which the pilot will have a natural tendency to apply greater load factors to the aircraft by applying further back pressure on the control column in an attempt to raise the nose. This can, however, be avoided by reducing the bank before applying this further back pressure.

The top of the green band (V_{no}) relates to load factors produced by gusts during turbulent conditions. Gusts are associated with both vertical and horizontal velocity gradients in the atmosphere. The effect of vertical gusts is an important factor in relation to structural considerations, in that they cause rapid changes to the angle of attack in the same way that a pilot does when applying a sudden extreme back pressure to the control column. When a sudden backward pressure is applied to the control column, the aircraft will respond by a change in its attitude, but inertia will delay it from altering its flight path until a short time has elapsed. During this time, the angle of attack will have increased and with it the load factor. Figure 5-116 shows how a vertical gust changes the relative angle of attack.

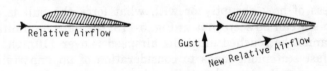

Fig. 5-116

The higher the airspeed, the greater will be the increase of load factor due to gusts. Small training aircraft are usually designed to safely encounter gust velocities of 30 feet per second (20 mph) which is greater than those likely to be experienced during normal flight operations. However, airspeed will still be a significant factor regardless of the gust intensity, and because of this, the V_{no} is designed to ensure that pilots do not operate the aircraft during turbulent conditions at speeds which in the event of meeting a 30 fps gust will overstress the airframe.

Figure 5-117 shows the load factor related to bank angle for a constant altitude turn at any speed. It can be seen that the load factor increases very slowly in the moderate bank range, and even at 45° of bank, it has only increased to 1.4, however, at 60° it has increased to 2 and thereafter rises extremely rapidly for only small increases of bank.

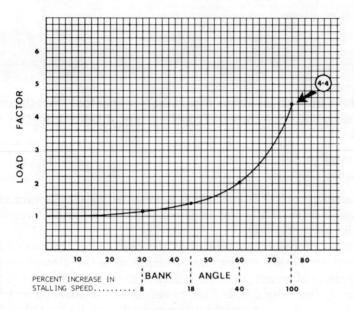

Fig. 5-117

The Propeller

This is the unit which has to absorb the power output from the engine and convert it into thrust. Propellers are divided into two basic classes:

● Tractor propeller;
● Pusher propeller.

A tractor propeller is one which is mounted on the forward end of the engine drive shaft, and in effect produces a thrust force which pulls the aircraft along.

A pusher propeller is mounted at the rear end of the engine drive shaft and produces a thrust force which pushes the aircraft along.

Regardless of which propeller is fitted, there are a variety of types which vary from the simple fixed blade design, to those on which the blade angle can be adjusted by the pilot during flight. Other types have an additional unit which is used to automatically maintain a constant RPM once the value has been set by the pilot. In multi-engine aircraft, a further facility is included in the form of a mechanism to change the angle of the blades so that they can be presented to the airflow at a minimum drag angle should an engine fail.

Yet another type of propeller incorporates a reversing mechanism which changes the angle of the blades such that forward thrust can be changed to rearward thrust and thereby create a braking action which may be utilized to shorten the landing run.

The propellers fitted to small training aircraft are normally of the fixed blade type, but higher performance light aircraft utilise the principle whereby the angle of the blade can be varied by the pilot during flight.

CONSTRUCTION AND SHAPE

Basically, a propeller consists of two or more blades which are attached to a central hub which in low power engines is simply an extension of the engine crankshaft. In effect, each blade is a rotating aerofoil which produces forces similar to those of an aircraft wing, but in so doing, transforms rotary power into axial thrust.

The typical propeller blade is an aerofoil which is twisted along its length and has a decreasing chord and depth of section from the root to the tip. Figure 5-118 illustrates the sort of shape and cross section of a typical blade.

Fig. 5-118

The blade angle (which is akin to the angle of incidence of an aircraft wing) varies along the blade length so that the tip section which travels fastest is set at a low angle of attack to the airflow, and the section near the root has a high angle of attack. This variation in blade angle is designed so that each section of the blade from root to tip operates at an efficient angle to the relative airflow. It also produces a more uniform thrust load over the propeller as a whole so reducing the high thrust stresses which would otherwise be produced towards the tip of the blades.

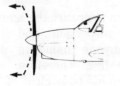

Fig. 5-119

Propeller blades undergo very high centrifugal, twisting and bending forces. The twisting forces come from the aerodynamic and centrifugal moments:

The *aerodynamic twisting moment* is a consequence of the centre of pressure of the blade acting ahead of the centre of twist of the blade section. Thus during its rotation, there is a tendency for the blade to twist about the hub axis, thereby exerting a force which tries to turn the blade to a higher angle, (Fig. 5-120).

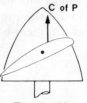
Fig. 5-120

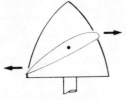
Fig. 5-121

The *centrifugal twisting moment* is a consequence of the centrifugal force tending to untwist the blades i.e. twisting the blades towards a lower blade angle, (Fig. 5-121).

The consequence of these twisting moments and centrifugal force is to induce fairly high stresses within the material of the propeller blade. Because these stresses will multiply if there is any propeller imbalance or surface defects, it is important to inspect the propeller carefully before flight.

Although modern metal propellers are generally considered to be very durable and relatively maintenance free, in-flight breakage can occur when minor damage in the form of nicks, dents, scratches etc., which have been incurred by the propeller vortex picking up stones and other debris from the ground, is present.

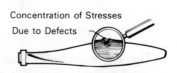
Fig. 5-122

To guard against this type of incident, pilots should examine the condition of the propeller during pre-flight inspections. It is also advisable to lightly run one hand along the whole of the blades, as nicks and cuts can often be more easily felt than seen. Any damage should then be reported to an engineer.

Note: Added care must be taken to ensure the ignition switches are in the off position during this inspection, and in any case, safety precautions demand that anyone handling a propeller should automatically consider it as *live*. Therefore, when examining a propeller, the pilot should keep his body clear of the areas traversed by the propeller arc. Finally, pilots should ensure that all engine run-ups take place in areas which are free from stones, gravel, and similar material.

PRINCIPLES OF PROPELLER THRUST

When an aircraft is stationary on the ground (in zero wind), the direction of the airflow passing over the propeller blades is directly induced by the propeller's rotation, and the angle of attack in this case is the same as the blade angle, (Fig. 5-123).

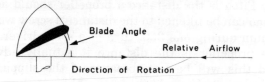

Stationary Aircraft

Fig. 5-123

The air deflection caused by this angle increases the atmospheric pressure behind the propeller blade and produces a thrust force, (Fig. 5-124).

Fig. 5-124

At the same time, and because the blade is essentially a rotating aerofoil, a decrease of pressure will occur ahead of the blade surface in the same manner as over the top of an aircraft wing. In the case of the wing, a net force called lift which acts upwards is produced, whereas in the case of the propeller, this force acts in a forward direction (thrust). Therefore, the thrust from a propeller is the result of its aerodynamic shape and the angle at which the blades meet the air. Alternatively, one may consider that the propeller bites into the air and moves a large mass of air backwards, thereby generating thrust. The magnitude of the thrust created is equal to the:

> Mass of air moved per unit time, multiplied by the slipstream velocity, minus the speed of the aircraft.

The power absorbed by an aircraft in a steady flight is directly proportional to the product of the propeller thrust and the speed of the aircraft. Thus, the amount of power required to create this thrust is therefore dependent on the mass of air moved per second, and its increase in velocity. For example, a given thrust may be generated by moving a small mass of air and giving it a large increase in velocity, or by moving a large mass of air and giving it a small increase in velocity. The latter case will require the least power.

When converting engine power into thrust, certain horsepower losses are inevitable due to friction and propeller slip. Propeller slip is the difference between the geometric pitch of the propeller blade, and its effective pitch.

Geometric Pitch is the distance a propeller should advance in one revolution and can be likened to the distance a screw would move into a solid medium during one 360° turn of a screwdriver. The effective pitch of the propeller is the distance it actually advances in one rotation and this will be less, because of the slippage which will inevitably occur when working in the thin medium of air, (Fig. 5-125).

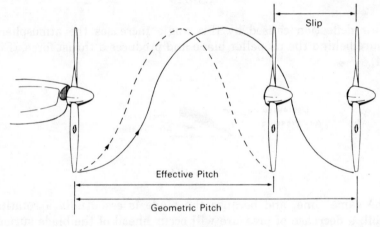

Fig. 5-125

Because of slippage and friction, the thrust horse power produced from the propeller is on average, only 80% of the total horsepower absorbed by the propeller.

LIFT, DRAG, THRUST AND TORQUE

The aerodynamic principles which govern the design of a propeller are similar to those which apply to an aircraft wing. Certain additional factors occur in that the length, shape, chord and number of blades used for any particular propeller, will depend on the amount of engine power that it has to absorb.

The blade length is largely determined by the ground clearance necessary when the aircraft is on the ground and an acceptable tip speed at high RPM during flight. In relation to this second factor, it should be appreciated that a single propeller blade having a length of 3 feet and rotating at 2700 RPM will have a tip speed of roughly 850 f.p.s. The speed of sound is approximately 1100 f.p.s. under standard atmospheric conditions, so when the blade section towards the tip approaches this speed, the effect of compressibility will markedly reduce the propeller efficiency.

The efficiency of a propeller in converting engine power to thrust is of great importance to an aircraft's performance in terms of airspeed, range and take-off distance. Propeller efficiency is expressed as the ratio of thrust horse power delivered, to engine power required to turn the propeller at a given RPM, or expressed another way, it is the ratio of useful work done by the propeller in moving the aircraft, to the work supplied by the engine (brake horse power – BHP). The work which is done in moving the aircraft is equal to the thrust multiplied by the velocity of the aircraft therefore:

$$\text{Propeller Efficiency} = \frac{\text{Thrust (lbs)} \times \text{Velocity (ft. per sec)}}{550 \times \text{BHP}}$$

In relation to its shape, the propellor is constructed with a similar profile and cross section to an aircraft wing, and as the blade moves through the air, the forces of thrust (T) and torque (TQ) are produced, these forces being roughly equivalent to the forces of lift and drag produced from an aircraft wing. Thrust is the propulsive force, and torque is the resistance to rotation of the propeller. The magnitude of thrust and torque forces will depend on the size, shape, number of blades, the blade angle, the speed of rotation, the forward speed and the air density.

Figure 5-127 shows the propeller blade in section, and it can be seen from this that the component of the lift line which acts directly forward is the measure of the thrust being produced. The fact that the propeller is rotating and moving forward through the air at the same time results in a different relative airflow to that experienced when the aircraft is stationary with the propeller rotating.

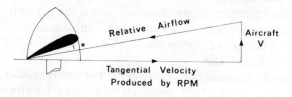

Fig. 5-126

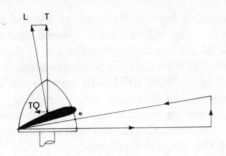

Fig. 5-127

FIXED PITCH PROPELLER

A fixed pitch propeller is of one piece construction and made of wood or metal. The blade pitch (or blade angle) is built into the shape of the propeller during construction and therefore cannot be changed.

As a result of this, there is a change in angle of attack as the airspeed varies, but since the propeller blade is just like a wing it has an optimum angle of attack (most lift for least drag), which is usually between 2° and 4°. Therefore in the case of the fixed pitch propeller, when the aircraft is stationary, a high angle of attack will occur which reduces the propeller efficiency.

Because of this, the designer's choice is limited when determining the blade angle: i.e. he can either have one which gives the most efficient angle of attack at cruising speed, or, if he wishes the aircraft to have improved performance on take-off, he can arrange for the propeller to have a small blade angle, which will lead to less efficiency at cruising or higher airspeeds.

If on the other hand he wishes to obtain a better performance at high speed as in the case of a racing aircraft, he can arrange for a large blade angle so that at the higher speeds, the angle of attack will be at its optimum.

Normally in the case of a general purpose light aircraft used for training or touring, the blade angle is arranged so that the propeller blade is at its optimum angle of attack when the aircraft is flying in the cruising speed range. An example of the variation in angle of attack with change of airspeed (V) at constant RPM is shown graphically in Fig. 5-128.

When using engines of relatively low horsepower, the dis-advantages of a fixed blade propeller are operationally acceptable. However, when more powerful engines are employed, the disadvant-

FIXED PITCH (BLADE ANGLE) PROPELLER.

Relative angles of attack at different airspeeds

Fig. 5-128

ages are magnified to an unacceptable degree, and to overcome this problem, the variable pitch propeller was developed.

VARIABLE (CONTROLLABLE) PITCH PROPELLER

This type of propeller is used on higher performance aircraft, many of which come into the category of general aviation aircraft. It is designed so that the blade angle can be changed by the pilot using a lever on the throttle quadrant, and so reduce the deficiencies inherent in the fixed pitch propeller.

This feature allows the pilot to alter the pitch of the propeller blades in accordance with the aircraft operating requirements at any one time. The number of pitch positions may be limited in the older variants of this type, but most modern controllable pitch propeller blades may be adjusted over a wide range within the angles of the minimum and maximum pitch settings of the particular propeller.

Propellers of this type consist of a number of separate blades mounted in a central hub, in ball or tapered roller bearings. A suitable pitch change mechanism is attached to the hub and connected to each blade by rods, yokes, or bevel gears. Operation and control of the pitch change mechanism varies considerably between types of propellers, and Fig. 5-129 shows a typical variable pitch propeller mechanism fitted to many light single and multi engine aircraft.

A cylinder bolted to the front of the hub contains a piston and piston rod which move axially to alter blade angle. On some propellers, oil is fed under pressure through the hollow piston rod to the front of the piston. This moves the piston rearwards and so turns the blades to a finer pitch. When oil pressure is reduced, the counterweights and feathering spring move the piston forward to turn the blades to a coarser pitch.

Note: Counterweights attached to the blades produce a centrifugal twisting moment as described on page 5-90 but, because they are positioned at 90° to the chord line, they tend to move the blades to a coarser pitch.

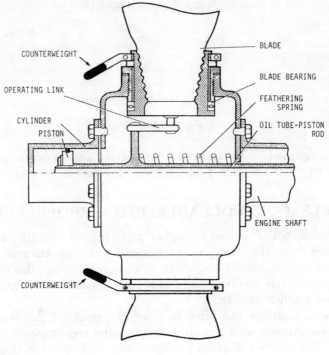

Fig. 5-129

During take-off when the aircraft is travelling at a low speed, the pilot will select the fine pitch position to allow the most efficient use of the propeller, Fig. 5-130(a). During operation at higher airspeeds, the pilot can change the pitch setting to a coarser position and thereby keep the angle of attack of the blade near its optimum (approximately 3°) in terms of lift and drag, Fig. 5-130(b).

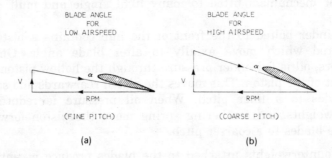

Fig. 5-130

THE CONTROLLABLE SPEED UNIT (CSU)

This unit is used with most controllable pitch propellers nowadays and although the basic principle of operation is common to all types of CSU, the specific mechanics of operation vary and it is neither possible nor necessary to cover these in detail in this manual.

One common type used in light aircraft, controls the blade angle through a unit consisting of a centrifugal governor, a governor valve, an oil pump and a hydraulic cylinder and piston assembly, (Fig. 5-131). The oil pump is used to boost the engine/propeller control mechanism. Linear movement of the piston which is governed by oil pressure, is converted into an angular movement of the propeller blades by a suitable linkage mechanism.

The governor is driven from the engine shaft and any movement of the governor weights under centrifugal force, is opposed by a spring, the loading of which is set through the position of the pilot's RPM lever (pitch lever) in the cockpit.

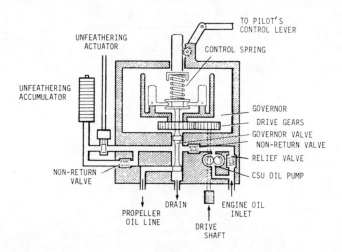

Fig. 5-131

The actual position of the governor valve is therefore determined by the engine RPM and the force from the spring. When both these forces are balanced following the setting of the pitch lever, the oil line to the unit is blanked off and oil is trapped at constant pressure in the cylinder of the pitch change mechanism.

If power is increased, e.g. through movement of the throttle, or if the propeller load is decreased, the engine will tend to speed up. At this stage, the governor will cause the pitch change mechanism to turn the propeller blades to a higher angle (coarser), so increasing the load on the engine and reducing the RPM to the original pre-set value.

When the RPM decreases below the pre-set value, the governor will cause the pitch change mechanism to turn the blades to a lower angle. This decreases the load on the engine and the RPM will increase until the original value is restored. Therefore the purpose of the CSU is to make automaic adjustments to the blade angle, and so maintain a constant RPM within the designed limits of the specific propeller pitch range.

This particular method of operation is convenient in the case of multi engine aircraft so that should an engine fail, the oil pressure will be reduced thus causing an increase in blade angle toward a minimum drag position. The final movement into what is known as the 'feathered position' (which is parallel to the relative airflow) is controlled by the pilot through the RPM lever in the cockpit and is often assisted by a strong spring or electric motor because the twisting effect of the counter-weights tends to reduce as the propeller slows down.

Aircraft Performance

This heading relates to the performance capability of an aircraft in differing flight situations including straight and level flight, climbing, and take-off and landing.

POWER CURVES

When an aircraft is in steady level flight, the basic condition of equilibrium must prevail, i.e. at any airspeed, the lift will equal the weight, and the thrust will equal the drag. In the case of propeller driven aircraft, the horse power required for this condition can be shown in the form of a performance graph based on actual drag curves for the particular aircraft type. This is illustrated in Fig. 5-132 which shows the parasite and induced drag curves for a representative light aircraft at various airspeeds.

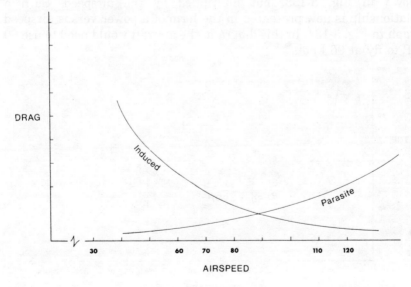

Fig. 5-132

The two types of drag are shown separately, and it should be remembered that whereas parasite drag increases as the square of the speed, the induced drag (due to decreasing angle of attack) decreases as the square of the speed. When these two types of drag are combined, they will produce a single curve as shown in Fig. 5-133.

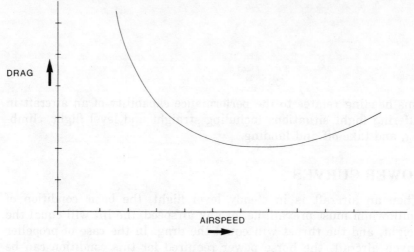

Fig. 5-133

Because the amount of power required at any airspeed is directly proportional to the product of the drag and the airspeed, the relationship between power and airspeed will be similar to that shown in Fig. 5-133, but multiplied by the airspeed. Such a relationship is now presented in the form of a power versus airspeed graph in Fig. 5-134. In this diagram, the aircraft would need to use 60 HP to fly at 96 knots.

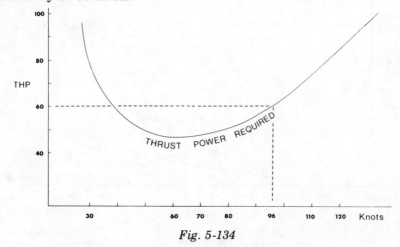

Fig. 5-134

The engine provides the power and the propeller provides the thrust to overcome the drag. With fixed pitch propellers, the efficiency of the engine/propeller combination varies with airspeed, and because the propeller is normally designed to be most efficient at normal cruising airspeed, the optimum efficiency of the thrust unit is usually achieved at this speed.

At airspeeds lower than the optimum, the thrust power available is less, due to the lower lift/drag ratio of the propeller blades, and at speeds higher than optimum, not only is the lift/drag ratio reduced, but the higher tip speeds also produce a less efficient thrust unit. This is shown by the thrust power available curve superimposed on the 'power required' diagram as shown in Fig. 5-135.

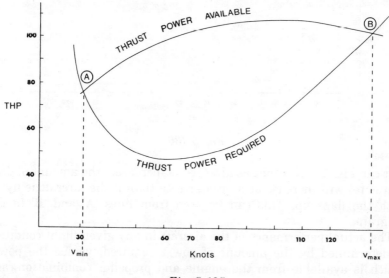

Fig. 5-135

A study of this diagram will reveal that at speeds lower than 32 knots the power required will exceed the power available and it can be seen that insufficient power will be available for level flight. Therefore 'A' on the diagram illustrates the minimum speed at which the aircraft can be flown in level flight. The maximum airspeed in level flight is where the power required curve intersects the power available curve at 'B'.

Note: The actual minimum speed at which an aircraft can be flown at any given configuration and power, is however usually governed by the speed at which the aircraft stalls, and is therefore more closely related to stability and control than it is to power.

EFFECT OF AIRCRAFT CONFIGURATION

If the configuration of the aircraft is changed by lowering flaps, the drag will be increased and more power will be required for the aircraft to maintain the same speed. Figure 5-136 illustrates this effect.

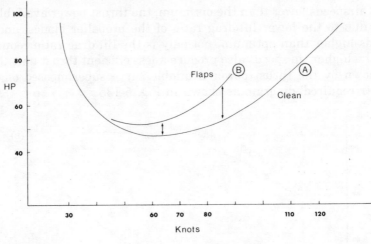

Fig. 5-136

It can also be seen that as airspeed is increased, the amount of drag (parasite) will increase at a greater rate than if the aircraft is flying with the flaps up. This can be seen from lines 'A' and 'B' in the diagram.

The actual performance of the aircraft in any given flight condition is determined by the amount of power required, versus the power which is available from the engine and propeller combination, and this performance is therefore affected by the aircraft configuration and the airspeed at which it is flown.

EFFECT OF TEMPERATURE AND DENSITY

The power delivered from a piston engine will be dependent on the weight of the fuel-air mixture taken into the cylinders during any particular operating condition.

The amount of air entering the engine will be determined by the size of the volume induced and the density of the air. The volume induced is related to the size of the carburettor system and the position of the throttle butterfly. The density which relates to the weight of charge is determined by the atmospheric pressure and temperature.

Since air density decreases with altitude, engine power will also decrease with altitude. The density of the fuel/air mixture will also vary with temperature and humidity in that the higher the temperature, and the greater the water content in the atmosphere, the lower will be the density. The second statement is not always easily understood, as at first sight, it would appear that water being heavier than air would increase the density. A simple explanation of this apparent paradox can be related to engine power output, by considering the fact that when water vapour, which is less dense than air is held in a parcel of air of a given volume, there will be less room for the air molecules. Since fuel flow rate is determined by the volume of air passing through the carburettor throat, this means that when water is present, the weight of the fuel/air mixture will be less, and therefore the engine will deliver less power.

Although the effect of an increase in humidity alone in relation to power output is quite small, in certain circumstances it could become significant, e.g. taking off when heavily laden from a small airfield in conditions of little wind and high temperature.

The combined effects of temperature and air pressure on air density are reflected in the effect of altitude on the power needed, and the power available, at any aircraft configuration and airspeed.

Most light training aircraft are equipped with normally aspirated engines (non-supercharged) and therefore the maximum power available will vary directly with air density and will therefore decrease from sea level upwards. Figure 5-137 illustrates the effect of lowering air density on the power required and power available curves.

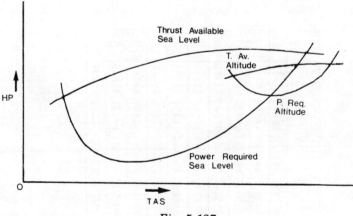

Fig. 5-137

The gradual closing of the power required and power available curves as altitude is gained will eventually mean that there will be no excess power available when the aircraft reaches a certain altitude. This altitude is known as the *absolute altitude* at which the aicraft is capable of level flight. When this altitude is reached, the power curves will have closed completely as shown in Fig. 5-138.

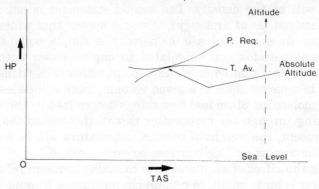

Fig. 5-138

RANGE AND ENDURANCE

In order to achieve the maximum range of the aircraft i.e. to cover the greatest distance given the amount of fuel carried, several aspects must be considered, and in the case of light aircraft, it is usually the effect of the wind which predominates.

In the practical sense, the pilot will refer to the 'Performance' section of the aircraft manual and determine from the appropriate tables or graphs which airspeed and altitude to use.

CRUISE PERFORMANCE

CONDITIONS:
Recommended Lean Mixture
2300 Pounds

PRESSURE ALTITUDE	RPM	20°C BELOW STANDARD TEMP			STANDARD TEMPERATURE			20°C ABOVE STANDARD TEMP		
		% BHP	KTAS	GPH	% BHP	KTAS	GPH	% BHP	KTAS	GPH
2000	2550	80	114	8.8	75	113	8.2	71	113	7.8
	2500	76	111	8.3	71	111	7.8	67	111	7.5
	2400	68	107	7.5	64	107	7.2	61	106	6.9
	2300	61	102	6.9	58	101	6.7	55	99	6.5
	2200	55	96	6.4	52	95	6.2	49	93	6.1
4000	2600	80	116	8.8	75	116	8.3	71	116	7.8
	2500	72	111	7.9	68	111	7.5	64	110	7.2
	2400	65	107	7.3	61	106	6.9	58	104	6.7
	2300	58	101	6.7	55	100	6.5	53	98	6.3
	2200	52	95	6.3	49	93	6.1	47	92	5.9
6000	2650	80	118	8.8	75	118	8.2	71	118	7.8
	2600	76	116	8.3	71	116	7.9	68	115	7.5
	2500	69	111	7.6	65	110	7.2	62	109	7.0
	2400	62	106	7.0	59	104	6.7	56	103	6.5
	2300	56	100	6.5	53	98	6.3	50	97	6.1
	2200	50	94	6.1	47	92	5.9	45	91	5.8
8000	2700	80	120	8.8	75	120	8.3	71	120	7.8
	2600	72	116	8.0	68	115	7.5	65	114	7.3
	2500	65	111	7.3	62	109	7.0	59	108	6.8
	2400	59	105	6.8	56	103	6.6	53	101	6.3
	2300	54	99	6.4	51	97	6.2	48	96	6.0
	2200	48	93	6.0	45	91	5.8	43	90	5.7
10,000	2700	76	120	8.4	72	120	7.9	68	119	7.6
	2600	69	115	7.6	65	114	7.3	62	112	7.0
	2500	63	110	7.1	59	108	6.8	56	106	6.6
	2400	57	104	6.6	54	102	6.4	51	100	6.2
	2300	51	97	6.2	48	96	6.0	46	95	5.8
	2200	46	92	5.8	43	90	5.7	41	89	5.5
12,000	2650	69	117	7.6	65	116	7.3	62	114	7.0
	2600	66	114	7.4	62	113	7.0	59	111	6.8
	2500	60	108	6.8	57	106	6.6	54	105	6.4
	2400	54	102	6.4	51	100	6.2	49	99	6.0
	2300	49	96	6.0	46	95	5.9	43	94	5.7
	2200	44	91	5.7	41	89	5.5	38	88	5.3

Fig. 5-139

The same will also apply when determining the power settings and altitude to fly when the maximum endurance is required, i.e. the longest time for which the aircraft can remain airborne with the fuel carried. Pilots' operating handbooks present information relating to range and endurance performance in different ways, and Figs 5-139 to 5-143 illustrate some common methods of presentation.

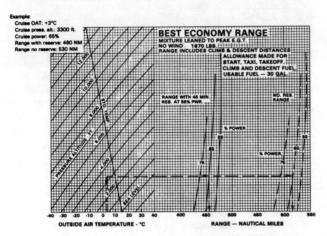

Fig. 5-140

RANGE PROFILE
45 MINUTES RESERVE
38.0 GALLONS USABLE FUEL

CONDITIONS:
2300 Pounds
Recommended Lean Mixture for Cruise
Standard Temperature
Zero Wind

NOTES:
1.   This chart allows for the fuel used for engine start, taxi, takeoff and climb, and the distance during climb as shown in figure 5-6.
2.   Reserve fuel is based on 45 minutes at 45% BHP and is 4.3 gallons.

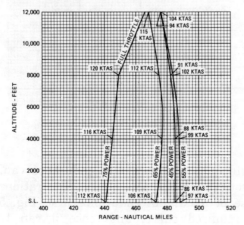

Fig. 5-141

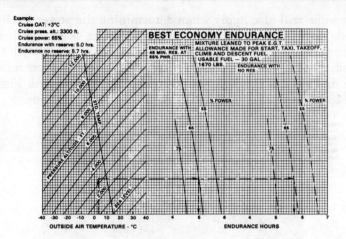

Fig. 5-142

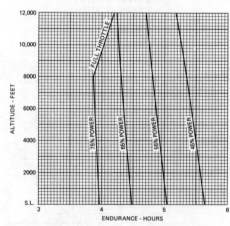

Fig. 5-143

The basic principles of range and endurance can, however, be understood by referring to the power curve illustrations which follow. Taking the case of maximum endurance first. Fig. 5-144 shows a typical power required curve, and since it can be stated that maximum endurance is a consideration of flying 'time', it would be obtained at that point on the graph where minimum power is required. This would require the lowest fuel flow to keep the aircraft in steady level flight. The dotted lines show that this condition would occur if the pilot flew at 60 knots.

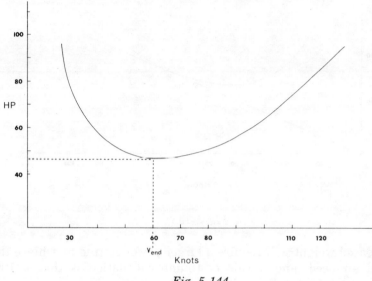

Fig. 5-144

Any increase of weight, altitude, or drag, would involve an increase of power to maintain this airspeed. Therefore, maximum endurance is achieved at the lowest weight consistent with maximum fuel being carried, the lowest altitude consistent with safety, and the least drag.

Weight and altitude are normally determined by the operational factors involved in the flight and cannot perhaps be adjusted by the pilot. Therefore, flying at the correct airspeed and keeping drag to a minimum are the two most easily altered factors over which the pilot has control when flying for endurance.

RANGE

Flying for range is a function of distance which involves *airspeed × time*. Therefore, the maximum range condition would occur where the ratio between airspeed and power required is greatest. The best airspeed/horse power combination will normally be interpreted from the aircraft manual, but for the purposes of understanding the principles involved the best range speed can be determined by drawing a straight line from the point of origin tangential to the power required curve as shown in Fig. 5-145. This point reflects a speed where the lift/drag ratio is at a maximum, in this case at 84 knots.

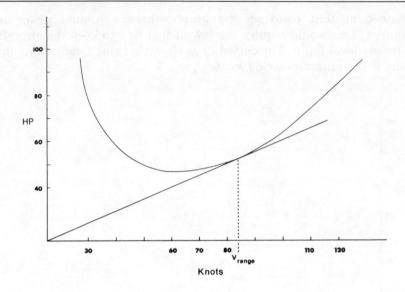

Fig. 5-145

Increased weight will require a larger power setting to achieve the desired airspeed, and a rule of thumb calculation is that a 10% increase in weight will result in a 10% reduction in range.

Although increase of altitude will permit the pilot to reduce the rate of fuel flow through the use of the mixture control, and so lead to small economies in fuel consumption, the effect of altitude on the range of small aircraft with normally aspirated engines is minimal. This is due to the quite small increase of engine efficiency with altitude coupled with the increased rate of fuel consumption during the climb to altitude, added to which, the advantage of a longer descent at a reduced fuel consumption at the end of the flight cannot always be guaranteed because of operational reasons such as weather and air traffic control requirements.

The ability to fly for maximum range in light aircraft by VFR pilots is therefore largely governed by the weather and airspace requirements in the form of airways etc.

For similar reasons, a pilot may not be able to derive the maximum benefits from a tailwind nor can he reduce the effects of a headwind. Nevertheless, during flight planning, he should appreciate that the prevailing wind component has a significant effect on range. For example, a 50 knot headwind component over a period of two hours will reduce the aircraft's range by a large amount, e.g. about 100 nm. The converse, where a tailwind is experienced, is equally true.

A further point is that a change in the basic range airspeed will improve the aircraft's range capability if strong winds prevail. This principle can best be illustrated by plotting the wind component on the power curve diagram and then drawing lines from the new points of origin tangentially to the power curve, as in Fig. 5-146.

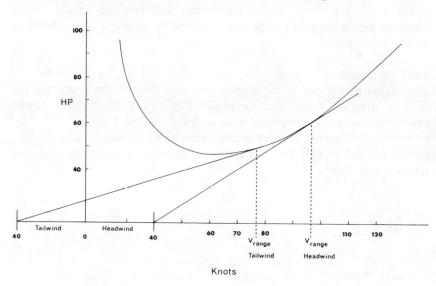

Fig. 5-146

To understand the results of this calculation, i.e. the benefit of a higher airspeed when flying into a headwind, one has only to consider the case of an aircraft flying at an airspeed of 60 knots into a 60 knot headwind – the result of this is a range of nil, but if it was flown at a higher airspeed it would at least travel some distance over the ground before using up its fuel supply.

Alternatively, the effect of a tailwind is beneficial to range and by flying at a proportionally reduced airspeed, the advantage of the tailwind will be experienced for a longer time and therefore range would be further improved.

Because light aircraft are not commonly flown in wind strengths which would produce a need to gain advantage from changing range airspeeds, the above paragraphs are offered more to illustrate a general principle rather than a note for practical guidance. Nevertheless, it can be seen that increasing or reducing the airspeed by some 10 knots may be beneficial in certain circumstances.

CLIMBING PERFORMANCE

To understand the factors involved in the climb performance of an aircraft, it is necessary to consider the power available and the airspeed at which the aircraft will be flown. A rate of climb will be achieved at any airspeed provided there is a surplus of available power above that which is required for level flight. It can therefore be stated that at any airspeed, the rate of climb depends on the 'excess power available', that is, the difference between the actual power which is available and the power required to maintain that speed in steady level flight.

RATE OF CLIMB

The excess power can be determined by reference to the power curves for the aircraft type. For example, Fig. 5-147 shows the power available and power required curves for a typical light aircraft and provided the aircraft is flown at any airspeed between 'A' and 'B', the power available will be in excess of the power required and the aircraft can climb.

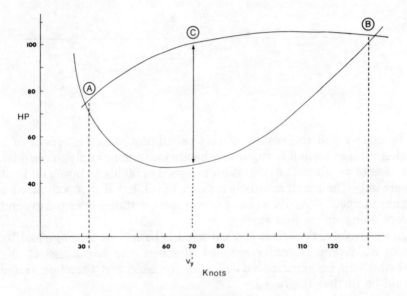

Fig. 5-147

However, the largest amount of excess power available will be when the aircraft is flown at an airspeed which corresponds to the largest vertical distance between the power required and the power available curves (point 'C' in the diagram). Therefore, in this case, the maximum rate of climb (V_y) will occur at 70 knots.

As in the case of level flight, anything which increases the drag will raise the power required curve, and anything which reduces the power available will lower the power available curve. From this, it can be seen that any increase in drag e.g. lowering of flaps, or reduction in density e.g. increase in altitude, will cause the curves to move together resulting in less excess power available and consequently reducing the rate at which the aircraft can climb.

ANGLE OF CLIMB

Whereas the rate of climb is dependent on the height gained in a given time, the angle of climb is determined by the height gained in a given distance, and so is most commonly related to obstacle clearance considerations during the take-off.

The airspeed for maximum angle of climb (V_x) will normally occur at about 10 knots less than the maximum rate of climb speed, but the small benefit accrued when using maximum angle of climb airspeeds rather than maximum rate of climb speed is very often difficult to measure with any degree of accuracy. It should be noted that although specific angle of climb speeds are normally quoted in the various aircraft manuals, no performance tables or graphs are detailed to show how such speeds affect the performance of an aircraft during the take-off and initial climb phase.

TAKE-OFF AND LANDING PERFORMANCE

The performance of an aircraft and the way it is handled during the take-off and landing phases is one of the most important factors affecting safe flight. The pilot under training, will initially be more concerned with the development of co-ordination and timing in relation to speed and control movements as well as judgment of distance and height. Although these accomplishments must be given priority, needing time and perseverance to acquire, the other considerations of take-off and landing planning in relation to such factors as wind, aircraft weight, altitude, density, ground surface and distance available, as well as weight and balance, are also vital aspects to the safety of any flight.

These variables are therefore discussed in the concluding paragraphs of this section, but before doing so, the terms, Take-off Run Available, Take-off Distance Available, Emergency Distance Available and Landing Distance Available and how they are used must first be understood. These can be defined as follows:

TAKE-OFF RUN AVAILABLE (TORA)

The distance from the point on the surface of the aerodrome at which the aeroplane can commence its take-off run to the nearest point in the direction of take-off at which the surface of the aerodrome is incapable of bearing the weight of the aeroplane under normal operating conditions.

TAKE-OFF DISTANCE AVAILABLE (TODA)

Either the distance from the point on the surface of the aerodrome at which the aeroplane can commence its take-off run to the nearest obstacle in the direction of take-off projecting above the surface of the aerodrome and capable of affecting the safety of the aeroplane, or, one and one half times the take-off run available, whichever is the less.

EMERGENCY DISTANCE AVAILABLE (ED)

This is the length of the take-off run available plus the length of any stopway available. The term *stopway* relates to any declared clear and relatively flat area which may exist immediately beyond the end of the runway in the direction of take-off.

LANDING DISTANCE AVAILABLE (LSDA)

The distance from the point on the surface of the aerodrome above which the aeroplane can be deemed to commence its landing, having regard to the obstructions in its approach path, i.e. the threshold, to the nearest point in the direction of landing at which the surface of the aerodrome is incapable of bearing the weight of the aeroplane under normal operating conditions.

These figures relate to specific take-off and landing directions at specified aerodromes as shown in the AGA section of the *U.K. Air Pilot*. It should be noted that the distances quoted in the *Air Pilot* are in metres, (Fig. 5-148.)

TOWN/ AERODROME CO-ORDINATES AND LOCATION	ELEV (ft.)	VAR	RUNWAY						DECLARED DISTANCES				SURFACE ELEVATIONS(ft.)			
			°MAG	°TRUE	DIMENSIONS (METRES)	S	STRENGTH	THRES ELEV (ft.)	TORA (m.)	ED (m.)	TODA (m.)	LDA (m.)	START OF TORA	END OF TORA	END OF ED	END OF TODA
1	2	3	4	5	6	7	8	9	10	11	12	13	14	15	16	17
Halfpenny Green 523102N 021536W 5 nm E by S of Bridgnorth.	293	8°W	04 22	035 215	890×46	T		259 271	739 752	835 830	865 890	701 710	259 271	271 259	267 263	264 268
			11 29	097 277	1,032×46	T		255 274	891 1,032	990 1,032	1,046 1,245	990 891	255 274	274 255	272 254	272 254
			16	156	1,178×46	T		276	1,096	1,178	1,230	1,012	276	280	282	282
			34	336				280	1,012	1,138 (day) 1,096 (night)	1,178	1,055 (day) 1,020 (night)	280	276	274	272

Fig. 5-148

The pilot will need to crosscheck these distances with the take-off and landing figures shown in the performance section of the aircraft manual, (typical examples are shown in Figs 5-149 and 5-150) making due allowances for the various effects of wind, weight, etc.

TAKEOFF DISTANCE (ft)

CONDITIONS:
Flaps Up
Full Throttle Prior to Brake Release
Paved, Level, Dry Runway
Zero Wind

NOTES:

Prior to takeoff from fields above 5000 feet elevation, the mixture should be leaned to give maximum RPM in a full throttle, static runup.
Decrease distances 10% for each 9 knots headwind. For operation with tailwinds up to 10 knots, increase distances by 10% for each 2 knots.
Where distance value has been deleted, climb performance after lift-off is less than 150 fpm at takeoff speed.
For operation on a dry, grass runway, increase distances by 15% of the "ground roll" figure.

WEIGHT LBS	TAKEOFF SPEED KIAS		PRESS ALT FT	0°C		10°C		20°C		30°C		40°C	
	LIFT OFF	AT 50 FT		GRND ROLL	TOTAL TO CLEAR 50 FT OBS	GRND ROLL	TOTAL TO CLEAR 50 FT OBS	GRND ROLL	TOTAL TO CLEAR 50 FT OBS	GRND ROLL	TOTAL TO CLEAR 50 FT OBS	GRND ROLL	TOTAL TO CLEAR 50 FT OBS
1600	53	60	S.L.	655	1245	710	1335	765	1435	820	1540	880	1650
			1000	720	1365	775	1465	835	1575	900	1690	970	1815
			2000	790	1500	855	1615	920	1735	990	1865	1065	2005
			3000	870	1650	935	1780	1010	1915	1090	2065	1170	2225
			4000	955	1820	1030	1965	1115	2125	1200	2290	1290	2475
			5000	1050	2015	1140	2185	1230	2360	1325	2555	1430	2770
			6000	1160	2245	1255	2435	1360	2640	1465	2870	1580	3120
			7000	1285	2510	1390	2730	1505	2970	1625	3240	...	...
			8000	1420	2820	1540	3080	1670	3370	...	...	...	...

Fig. 5-149

LANDING DISTANCE (ft)

CONDITIONS:
Flaps 40°
Power Off
Maximum Braking
Paved, Level, Dry Runway
Zero Wind

NOTES:
1.
2. Decrease distances 10% for each 9 knots headwind. For operation with tailwinds up to 10 knots, increase distances by 10% for each 2 knots.
3. For operation on a dry, grass runway, increase distances by 45% of the "ground roll" figure.

WEIGHT LBS	SPEED AT 50 FT KIAS	PRESS ALT FT	0°C		10°C		20°C		30°C		40°C	
			GRND ROLL	TOTAL TO CLEAR 50 FT OBS	GRND ROLL	TOTAL TO CLEAR 50 FT OBS	GRND ROLL	TOTAL TO CLEAR 50 FT OBS	GRND ROLL	TOTAL TO CLEAR 50 FT OBS	GRND ROLL	TOTAL TO CLEAR 50 FT OBS
1600	52	S.L.	425	1045	440	1065	455	1090	470	1110	485	1135
		1000	440	1065	455	1090	470	1110	485	1135	505	1165
		2000	455	1090	470	1115	490	1140	505	1165	520	1185
		3000	470	1115	490	1140	505	1165	525	1195	540	1215
		4000	490	1140	505	1165	525	1195	545	1225	560	1245
		5000	510	1170	525	1195	545	1225	565	1255	585	1285
		6000	530	1200	545	1225	565	1255	585	1285	605	1315
		7000	550	1230	570	1260	590	1290	610	1320	630	1350
		8000	570	1260	590	1290	610	1320	630	1350	655	1385

Fig. 5-150

The ground roll figures shown in Figs. 5-149 and 5-150 under 'Grnd Roll' approximate to the take-off run required, and the figures shown under 'Total to Clear 50 ft Obs' approximates to the take-off distance required.

Note: Many aircraft manuals give distances in feet, therefore care must be taken to ensure that conversion to metres is made before comparing them with the figures used in the *Air Pilot*.

The various items which affect take-off and landing performance will be considered under two separate headings:

- The take-off and initial climb;
- The approach and landing.

TAKE OFF AND INITIAL CLIMB PERFORMANCE

EFFECT OF WIND

Of the many factors which affect the performance of an aircraft during take-off, the effect of wind is by far the most significant in relation to the take-off run and take-off distance.

A headwind enables an aircraft to reach its take-off speed at a lower ground speed, whilst the effect of a tailwind requires the aircraft to attain a higher ground speed to achieve the take-off speed.

Figure 5-151 illustrates the effect of a headwind or tailwind component during the take-off run. For example a headwind component of 20% of the lift-off speed will reduce the ground run by approximately 35%. However, the reverse is true when taking off with a tailwind component, and it can be seen that a tailwind component of 20% of the lift-off speed will result in a 45% longer run than when no wind exists.

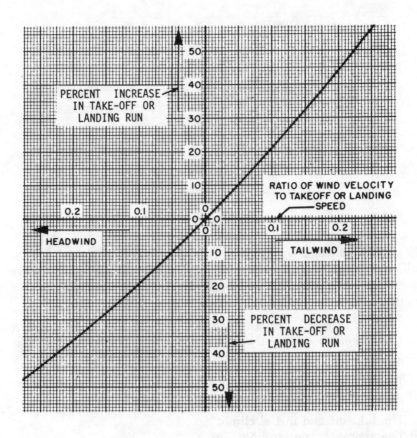

Fig. 5-151

Assuming a lift-off speed of 50 knots and a take-off run of 800 feet in zero wind, a tailwind of 10 knots will increase the length of the take-off by 45%, (45% of 800 is 360), thereby lengthening the total run to 1160 feet; a significant increase. It must also be appreciated that the gradient of climb following lift-off will be significantly steeper when strong headwinds exist, and very much flatter during conditions of light wind or tailwinds.

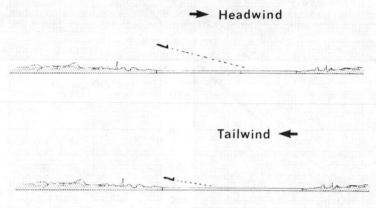

Fig. 5-152

EFFECT OF WEIGHT
It will be remembered from the facts concerning stalling that an increase of weight increases the stalling speed, and as the lift-off speed is related to the speed of stall (the lift-off speed quoted in aircraft manuals is normally 1.1 to 1.2 times the stalling speed), and from this, it will be clear that any increase in weight will lead to a higher lift-off speed.

The actual figures can be determined by reference to Fig. 5-153. As an example, a 20% increase in weight will increase the lift off speed by 10%. But this is not the whole story, and any increase in aircraft weight will have a threefold effect on the take-off performance.

- An increased lift-off speed;
- A greater mass to be accelerated;
- An increased retarding force.

Due to these 3 factors, the net result of increasing weight by just 10% will be to increase the take-off run of a light aircraft by at least 25% and also reduce the rate of climb.

PRESSURE, ALTITUDE, TEMPERATURE AND DENSITY
The effect of taking off from airfields significantly higher than sea level is to lengthen the take-off run, the take-off distance and reduce

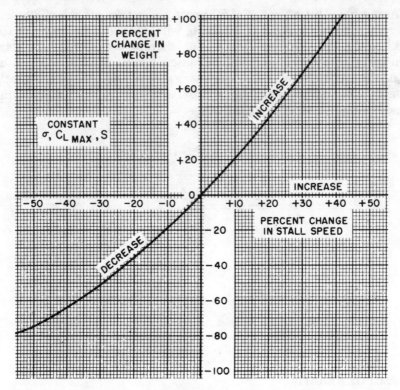

Fig. 5-153

the rate of climb. This is due to the reduction of power available as altitude is increased and also because of the reduced density, a greater true airspeed will be needed to achieve the indicated lift-off and climbing speeds.

Whenever the temperature is higher than standard for a particular altitude, the density, and therefore the aircraft performance, will be reduced (the expression 'high density altitude' is often used to describe this situation). Although the performance aspects of high density altitudes are normally absent when operating from relatively low altitude airfields in temperate climates, a pilot must have an appreciation of this effect so that he can operate safely when such conditions do exist.

Density altitude is calculated from pressure altitude corrected for non-standard temperature. Due to the variation in thrust/weight ratios between different aircraft the following figures can only be approximate:

● For every 1000 ft a.m.s.l. the take-off run is increased by 12%
● For every 10°C above standard (15°C) the take-off run is increased by 12%.

A high density altitude will also reduce the rate of climb, and the climbing angle will be significantly flatter.

USE OF FLAPS

The use of flaps during the take-off will lower the stalling speed and consequently the lift off can be achieved at a lower speed. Provided the amount of flap selected is small, it will generally reduce the length of the take-off run but may not produce any significant reduction of the take-off distance. This is because in most aircraft, the use of flap will reduce the lift-drag ratio and therefore reduce the rate of climb.

Due to variations between different aircraft in relation to the benefits obtained from the use of flaps, it will be necessary to refer to the aircraft manual to see under what conditions their use is recommended. Nevertheless, the use of flaps for take-off on soft or rough surfaces, will normally be beneficial and this subject is covered under the next heading.

GROUND SURFACE AND GRADIENT

Light aircraft commonly operate from grass surfaces, small airfields and landing strips, and sometimes also when the grass is longer than normal and/or the surface is wet, soft or covered with snow. Under these circumstances, the pilot should be particularly careful to consider what effects the ground surface will have on the performance of the aircraft.

The ground drag of an aircraft as it rolls along the surface is known as *rolling resistance* and the equation for this is:

$$R = \mu \times (\text{weight minus lift})$$

where

R = rolling resistance
μ = coefficient of friction for the particular surface being used.

The following table illustrates the approximate effects of this resistance on the length of the take-off run for small aircraft.

Surface	μ	Approximate increase in take-off run (%)
Short Grass	0.05	10
Long Grass	0.10	25
Soft Ground	0.10 to 0.30	25 to 100

Because this rolling resistance causes substantial increases in the length of the take-off run when using grass or soft ground surfaces, it will be important to get the weight off the wheels as soon as possible during take-off. It is for this reason, that a significant benefit can normally be obtained through the use of flap.

The slight increase in aerodynamic drag when moderate flap settings are used is normally outweighed by the lower lift-off speed, particularly as in small aircraft the speed, and in consequence the drag, is fairly low during the period from the commencement of the take-off roll to lift-off.

The above considerations also hold good when the aircraft is taking off from rough ground, though for a slightly different reason. In the case of rough ground, the primary need will be to protect the landing gear, therefore the lower the speed at which lift-off can be achieved, the less will be the stresses imposed upon the landing gear.

Another factor which must be considered during take-off is the surface gradient, for whereas normal aerodromes are relatively flat, many landing strips have gradients which can significantly affect the length of the take-off run. In this respect, a rule of thumb guide is that a 2° upslope will increase the take-off run by some 20%. Bearing in mind the difficulty in estimating this angle with any degree of accuracy without some form of precision instrumentation, considerable care must be used when taking off in these circumstances, particularly when other adverse performance conditions are present.

APPROACH AND LANDING PERFORMANCE

The factors to be considered under this heading will be the same as those considered under the take-off and initial climb. Their individual and collective effects on the approach and landing must be understood if the pilot is to become competent to operate his aircraft safely whatever the conditions.

EFFECT OF WIND

The effect of a headwind upon the final approach path is to steepen the descent gradient for a given approach speed. Conversely, a tailwind will make the approach path more shallow. Therefore, when a light wind or tailwind is present, there will be a greater risk of overshooting the intended touch down point.

Wind shear (wind gradient) – When winds are moderate to strong, turbulence often associated with rapid changes in wind speed and direction in the vertical and horizontal plane can be met during the final stages of the approach. In these circumstances, sudden gusts can cause rapid changes to the airspeed and strong up- or downdraughts may be encountered.

The main problem associated with these conditions is that the aircraft speed is relatively low during the approach stage and loss of airspeed coupled with a downdraught can present difficulties when large flap settings (high drag) are used. However, whenever strong winds are present, the need to use large flap settings is substantially reduced, therefore it will be advisable to use less flap and approach at a slightly higher airspeed to ensure better control over the aircraft's descent path.

As in the case of the take-off, the influence of wind on landing performance is very significant. The main effect of the wind is to reduce the ground speed during the landing, and so alter the length of the landing distance and landing run. (The landing run (or roll) can be summarised as the distance taken for the aircraft to come to a stop from the point of touch down.)

The effect of wind on aircraft deceleration during the landing run is similar to its effect on the take-off run, which can be seen by reference to Fig. 5-15 (i.e. a headwind which is 10% of the touchdown speed will reduce the landing run by approximately 20%, and a tailwind which is 10% of the touchdown speed will increase the landing run by 20%). For example, the effect of a 5 knot tailwind on an aircraft which touches down at 50 knots and requires a 1000 ft landing run in conditions of zero wind, will be to increase the landing run to 1200 ft.

EFFECT OF WEIGHT
The effect of weight in relation to the approach and landing requires that consideration must be given as to whether the approach speed should be increased if the all-up weight is increased, and by how much the landing run will be increased at the resulting higher touch down speed associated with the greater stalling speed.

Aircraft manuals base their recommended approach speeds on the maximum permitted all-up weight of the aircraft, so even if the aircraft is operating at its maximum all-up weight, there will not normally be any need to increase the approach speed on this account. However, the effect of weight on the landing run is significant, in that added weight means a higher touch down speed, the actual figures being: a 20% increase in weight will produce a 10% increase in touch down speed.

To this must be added the greater energy to be dissipated during the landing roll. This energy increases with increased weight and touch down speed and a 20% increase in weight will result in approximately a 20% increase in the length of the landing run.

PRESSURE ALTITUDE, TEMPERATURE AND DENSITY

Increases in pressure altitude, temperature and density altitude affect the landing run which will be increased due to the higher landing speed associated with a higher true airspeed.

In relation to the effects of density altitude a rule of thumb is to allow an additional 5% of the landing distance required, for each 1000 ft of airfield elevation.

The reduced engine power associated with altitude and density effect is normally not a critical factor during the approach to landing because of the reduced power settings needed. It must nevertheless be appreciated that altitude will have a very significant effect on the aircraft's rate of climb should a go-around be necessary, and in this situation it will be necessary to reduce drag to a minimum by raising flaps as quickly as possible after achieving a safe airspeed.

USE OF FLAPS

The primary purpose of using flap during the landing approach is to change the aircraft attitude for a given approach speed. With flaps down the nose position will be lower, thus allowing the pilot a better view along the descent path to the intended touchdown area. Without the use of flap, the modern streamlined aircraft would have the problems posed by a very flat approach attitude, right up to touchdown.

Flaps decrease the stalling speed of an aircraft, and thus give it a lower touchdown speed. Under normal conditions this makes the landing easier, and places less strain on the landing gear.

The use of full flap is usually recommended for normal approaches and landings, but during the early stages of training, or when strong gusty winds prevail, and particularly when strong crosswinds are present and powerful flaps are fitted, it may be advisable to restrict their operation to less than the fully down position. Flight/owner's manuals/pilot's operating handbooks often contain advice as to when the use of flap should be restricted.

In considering the use of flaps during strong winds it is useful to know that stalling speed reduction with flaps lowered is normally in the order of some 5 to 8 knots in most light aircraft. Compared to the 30 knot reduction in ground speed occasioned by a 30 knot wind, it can be seen that flaps play a minor and sometimes insignificant part in the landing when strong winds are present. Bearing in mind the adverse effect of large flap settings during strong downdraughts on the approach, one can more easily understand the need to arrive at a correct decision as to how much flap to use in relation to the effect of wind.

GROUND SURFACE AND GRADIENT

The length of the landing run will depend on the wind strength and direction, the touchdown speed, weight, the type of ground surface and whether it is flat or sloping, and finally the effectiveness of the braking system in relation to the surface conditions e.g. dry, wet or icy.

Clearly the correct touchdown speed is important, so too is the need to consider the effect of the nature of the landing area i.e. smooth concrete, long grass, soft ground etc. In doing this two more factors will play an important part. The first is the aerodynamic braking effect of drag, and the second is the surface braking effect of ground friction. Figure 5-154 illustrates that at the point of touchdown only part of the aircraft weight is exerted on the wheels, the remaining weight is supported by the residual lift which still exists for a short while after touchdown. As the aircraft slows down, more and more of the aircraft weight is placed on the wheels, and so rolling friction increases. The use of the aircraft brakes will further add to this. Clearly the minimum rolling friction will thus be experienced when the touchdown speed is high, where a tailwind exists and when the landing surface is smooth.

Whilst runway slope must be taken into account, the amount found at normal airfields will not normally have a significant effect on landing distance, or landing run, and in these circumstances it is usually better to land into wind and accept the gradient.

The use of the aircraft braking system reduces the length of the landing run most effectively on firm dry surfaces. Where the point of touchdown has been correctly planned and achieved, the use of brakes during the early part of the landing run will normally be unnecessary, but if a late touchdown occurs the brakes may be required to avoid the aircraft over-running the available landing area.

Although a 5% increase in touchdown speed increases the length of the landing distance by 10% what is not always so readily appreciated is that this 5% increase in touchdown speed actually produces a 10% increase in the kinetic energy to be dissipated. When landings are being made on wet grass surfaces, the brakes will be almost ineffective at higher speeds, and may even have an adverse effect by causing the aircraft to skid, so leading to difficulties in stopping as well as in keeping directional control.

On a firm dry surface a small increase in touchdown speed may easily be resolved by firm application of the aircraft brakes, but where the same touchdown speed occurs on a wet surface, the braking ability could have deteriorated to such an extent that it would be impossible to stop the aircraft in the surface length remaining.

If the landing is being made on long grass, a soft surface, or in slush or snow, the rolling friction will be high. Maintaining a

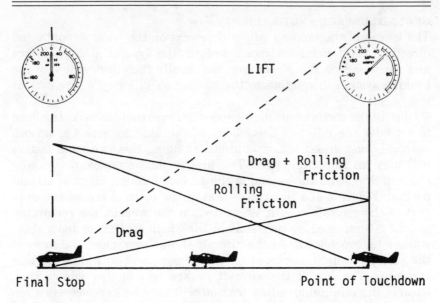

LIFT

Drag + Rolling
Friction

Rolling
Friction

Drag

Final Stop   Point of Touchdown

Fig. 5-154

relatively nose-high attitude in the early stage of the landing roll will also provide aerodynamic braking action, and in many aircraft will be quite effective in keeping the weight off the nosewheel. Application of brakes during this period may have little effect, but when brakes have to be applied, light to moderate pressure should normally be used immediately after touchdown, increasing to a stronger application as the aircraft slows down.

GROUND EFFECT

This occurs when the aircraft is close to the ground and extends from ground level up to a height approximately equal to the span of the aircraft's wing. It is within this layer that the induced drag is significantly less.

From a practical aspect, a pilot who allows the aircraft to become airborne at less than the recommended lift-off speed may easily be misled into believing that the aircraft has a greater climb capability than it actually has.

Bearing in mind the rapid increase in induced drag which will occur as the aircraft ceases to experience ground effect, it can be seen that the aircraft's rate of acceleration will momentarily decrease at this point, added to which there is the modifying action that ground effect has on the elevators in relation to longitudinal stability i.e. it produces a nose down moment. This will result in a tendency for the nose to rise as the aircraft climbs out of the ground effect layer and this may cause the airspeed to decrease until such time as this is rectified by the pilot.

To sum up, the pilot must bear in mind that when operating in the ground effect layer it is possible to get airborne with less thrust and lift than will actually be required after leaving this layer. It is for this reason that all pilots should know the correct lift-off speed in relation to the aircraft's weight at the time of take-off.

The result of entering ground effect during the landing flare and hold off phase will be an increased float period and an excess approach speed, particularly in conditions of a light wind, which will add considerably to this effect.

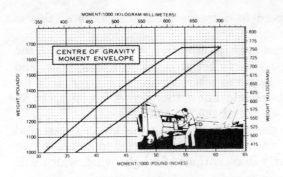

Weight and Balance

LIMITATIONS ON AIRCRAFT WEIGHT

A limitation is imposed on the all-up weight at which any aircraft is permitted to operate. This limitation depends on the strength of the structural components of the aircraft and the operational requirements it is designed to meet. If these limitations are exceeded, the operational efficiency will be impaired and the safety of the aircraft may be at risk.

The lift of an aircraft depends on the design of the wing, the airspeed, and the density of the air. The lift generated by the wing of the aircraft is the primary force available to counteract weight and maintain the aircraft in flight. If the lift is less than the aircraft weight in level flight and no additional power is available, the aircraft must descend.

The design of the wing on any particular aircraft limits the amount of lift available at any given speed and the available power from the engine limits the speed at which the wing can be made to move through the air. These two basic factors determine the amount of lift produced to balance the aicraft's weight.

When the aircraft is operated in atmospheric conditions where the air is less dense than the International Standard Atmosphere, the aircraft performance will be reduced. The effect of this performance reduction is particularly important during the take-off and initial climb. Therefore, before flight, the pilot must ascertain that the all-up weight of the aircraft is within the correct limits applicable to the conditions in which it is to be operated. He must also appreciate the probable adverse effect on aircraft performance if the permitted all-up weight or centre of gravity limits are exceeded.

Pre-flight planning should include a check of the aircraft performance charts to determine if the aircraft weight could contribute to a hazardous flight condition. Payload, passengers, baggage, cargo and fuel load must be adjusted to provide an adequate margin of safety. In this respect, it should be understood that in most general aviation aircraft it is not possible to fill all seats, baggage space and fuel tanks and still remain within the approved weight or balance limits. In many four seat aircraft, the fuel tanks may not be permitted to be filled to capacity when a full complement of passengers and baggage is to be carried. Aircraft are generally designed so that a full complement of passengers can be carried on short flights but not on extended flights when a full fuel load will be needed.

The effects on the performance characteristics of an over-weight aircraft are a:

- Higher take-off speed;
- Longer take-off run;
- Reduced rate and angle of climb;
- Lower maximum ceiling altitude;
- Shorter range;
- Reduced cruising speed;
- Reduced manoeuvrability;
- Higher stalling speed;
- High landing speed;
- Longer landing roll.

LIMITATIONS IN RELATION TO AIRCRAFT BALANCE

Balance refers to the location of the centre of gravity (c.g.) of the aircraft. It is of primary importance to the safety of flight. Whilst it is necessary to ensure that the maximum all-up  weight of an aircraft is not exceeded, the distribution of permissible weight, i.e. the balance of the aircraft, is vitally important.

It is not possible to design an aircraft in which the lift, weight, thrust and drag forces are always in a natural state of equilibrium during straight and level flight; the centre of pressure and the drag line vary with changes of angle of attack and the position of the centre of gravity depends on the load distribution. It is necessary therefore to provide a force to counteract unbalancing couples that may be set up by these forces. This is the function of the tailplane, which together with the elevators and trimmers, can offset any pitching moment set up by the movement of the centre of pressure or the drag line. It is also able to counteract any of the unbalance or unstable tendencies caused by movements of the centre of gravity, provided that these movements are confined within certain limits.

Therefore, the forward and aft limits of the centre of gravity range are determined by the capability of the elevators or stabilator to control the aircraft in pitch at the lowest speed of flight. These limits are established by the aircraft manufacturer and published on a weight and centre of gravity schedule which is issued for individual aircraft. Information relating to examples of working out weight and balance problems is normally contained in the flight/owner's manual/pilot's operating handbook. The weight figures are given in pounds or kilograms.

A forward centre of gravity limit is specified to ensure that sufficient elevator deflection *is* available at minimum airspeed e.g. during the round out for a landing.

The aft centre of gravity limit is the most rearward position at which the centre of gravity can be located for the most critical manoeuvre or operation. Aircraft static stability decreases as the centre of gravity moves aft, and the ability of the aircraft to right itself after manoeuvring, or after disturbances by gusts, is correspondingly decreased.

If, after the aircraft is loaded, the centre of gravity does not fall within the allowable limits, it will be necessary to shift loads before flight is attempted. The actual location of the centre of gravity can be determined by a number of factors under the control of the pilot. Positioning of baggage and cargo items, assignment of seats to passengers according to weight, and arranging for the fuel load to be carried, are all items under his control. The pilot may also be able to make selective use of fuel from various tank locations, a factor which may have to be considered in maintaining a safe condition of aircraft balance.

The all-up weight of an aircraft will vary during flight due to the consumption of fuel and oil. The alteration of all-up weight due to this fuel and oil consumption will usually change the position of the centre of gravity, unless the centre of gravity of the fuel and oil is coincident with the aircraft's centre of gravity. Fuel tanks are normally aligned close to the mid-point of the basic centre of gravity in order to keep the centre of gravity changes from this source to a minimum.

It must nevertheless be appreciated that in light aircraft the centre of gravity of the fuel carried, is generally ahead of the location of the passengers, and therefore as fuel is used the aircraft's centre of gravity will move rearward. Finally, any movement of the passengers or crew during flight will cause a change in the position of the aircraft centre of gravity.

The *Air Navigation Order* requires that before take-off, the commander of an aircraft shall satisfy himself that the load carried by the aircraft is of such weight, and is so distributed, that it may be safely carried on the intended flight. Therefore, before every flight, it is the captain's responsibility to ensure that his aircraft is loaded in such a manner that the all-up weight is not exceeded, and that the position of the centre of gravity remains within the limits for the particular aircraft.

In order to understand the principles of weight and balance calculations, a pilot will need to be familiar with the following terms:

Centre of gravity (c.g.) – The point about which an aircraft would balance if it were possible to suspend it at that point. It is the mass centre of the aircraft or the theoretical point at which the entire weight of the aircraft is assumed to be concentrated.

Centre of gravity limits – The specified forward and aft points beyond which the centre of gravity must not be located during flight.

Centre of gravity range – The distance between the forward and aft limits.

Arm (moment arm) – The horizontal distance, from the reference datum line to the centre of gravity of the item. The sign is (+) if measured aft of the datum and (−) if measured forward of the datum.

Datum (reference datum) – An imaginary vertical plane or line from which all measurements of the arm are taken. The datum is established by the manufacturer. After the datum has been established, all moment arms and the location of the permissible range must be taken with reference to that point.

Station – A location in the aircraft which is identified by a number designating its distance from the datum. The datum is therefore identified as zero. The station and arm are usually identical i.e. an item located at station +50 would have an arm of 50 inches.

Moment – The product of the weight of an item multiplied by its arm. Moments are expressed in pound inches or metric equivalent kgm.

Moment index (or index) – The moment divided by a constant such as 100, 1000, or 10000. The purpose of using a moment index is to simplify weight and balance computations where heavy items and long arms result in large unmanageable numbers.

Reduction factor – The constant which, when divided into a moment, results in an index.

Mean aerodynamic cord (MAC) – The centre of gravity limits are sometimes specified as a percentage of mean aerodynamic chord. The MAC is specified for the aircraft by determining the average chord of a wing.

The aircraft weight and balance schedule will contain information relating to the following terms:

Basic weight – The basic weight is the weight of the aircraft and all its basic equipment and that of the declared quantity of unusable fuel and unusable oil. In the case of aircraft of 5700 kg (12500 lb) maximum authorised weight or less it may also include the weight of usable oil.

Basic equipment – This consists of the unconsumable fluids, and equipment, which are necessary for the operation of the aircraft in any role for which it is certified.

Variable load – Variable load is the weight of the crew and of items such as the crew's baggage, removable units, and other equipment the carriage of which depends on the purpose for which the operator intends to use the aircraft on that particular flight.

Disposable load – This is the weight of all persons and items of load, including fuel and other consumable fluids carried in the aircraft, but excluding the basic equipment and variable load.

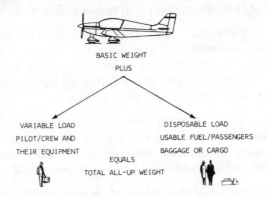

BASIC WEIGHT
PLUS

VARIABLE LOAD
PILOT/CREW AND
THEIR EQUIPMENT

DISPOSABLE LOAD
USABLE FUEL/PASSENGERS
BAGGAGE OR CARGO

EQUALS
TOTAL ALL-UP WEIGHT

WEIGHT AND CENTRE OF GRAVITY CALCULATIONS

To obtain the total loaded weight, it is necessary to add, to the basic weight, the weights of the variable and disposable load items to be carried, for the particular role for which the aircraft is to be used.

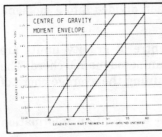

Fig. 5-155

Flight/owner's manuals vary in their methods of presenting weight and balance information but most of them show a weight and balance envelope (see Fig. 5-155) so that a pilot can quickly check if the weight and balance is within the limits after making his calculations. These calculations must commence by referring to the weight and balance schedule for the particular aircraft. The following information outlines the steps to be taken to determine the actual weight and balance of the aircraft.

Referring to the weight and balance schedule and the aircraft flight/owner's manual:

1. List the aircraft basic weight, variable load and disposable load.
2. Multiply the weights by their arms to get the moment of each item.
3. Add the respective weights to get the total loaded weight of the aircraft.
4. Add the moments to get the total moment.
5. Divide the total moment by the total weight to obtain the arm of the centre of gravity of the aircraft.
6. Compare the total weight obtained in step 3 with the maximum authorised all-up weight.
7. Compare the calculated centre of gravity arm obtained in step 5 to the approved centre of gravity range of the aircraft.

If both the weight and position of the centre of gravity are within the permitted limits, the aircraft is safe to fly. If, however, the actual weight is greater than the maximum authorised weight or the calculated centre of gravity position is outside the permitted limits, the disposable load must be adjusted accordingly.

Although it will be sensible to enter the weights of the various items first and then check that the total weight is within limits before carrying out the moment arm calculations, it must not be assumed that because the actual total weight is below the maximum all-up weight allowed that the centre of gravity will also be within the permitted limits.

Remember the calculations must determine two items:

● The total all-up weight;
● The actual position of the centre of gravity.

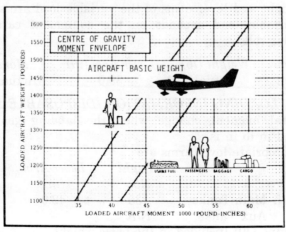

Fig. 5-156

Example of a Weight and Centre of Gravity Schedule

Reference	: BA/123
Produced by	: Balanced Aircraft Ltd.
Aircraft designation	: Pivot 00.
Nationality and registration marks	: G-BZZZ
Constructor	: General Aviation
Constructor's serial number	: 432L.
Maximum authorised weight	: 768 kg (1690 lb)
Centre of gravity limits	: Refer to flight manual reference No. AV50

PART A BASIC WEIGHT

The basic weight of the aircraft as calculated from the weighing report supplied by General Aviation reference W/Bal. 00 dated 27 March 1985 is   : 1190 lb

   The centre of gravity of the aircraft in the same condition at this weight with landing gear extended is   : 38.5 in aft of datum

   The total moment about the datum in this condition is   : 45815.0 lb in

Note: The datum is at fuselage station 0.0 and is situated at the front face of the firewall. This is the datum defined in the flight manual. All lever arms are distances in inches aft of datum.

   The basic weight includes the weight of 21 lb unusable fuel and total oil and the weight of items as indicated on the attached Basic Equipment List (not included in this example).

PART B VARIABLE LOAD

The weight and lever arms of the variable load are shown below. The variable load depends on the equipment carried for the particular role.

Item	Weight (lb)	Lever Arm (in)	Moment (lb in)
Pilot	Actual	39.0	(Actual Wt. × 39.0)

PART C LOADING INFORMATION (DISPOSABLE LOAD)

The total moment change when the landing gear is extended in lb in is   : N/A

The appropriate lever arms are:

Item	Weight (lb)	Lever Arm (in)	Capacity (Imp. Gals)
Fuel: Main Tanks	135	42.0	18.75
Aux Tanks	N/A	–	–

Engine Oil: Included in the basic weight.

Note: In some cases this may not be included in the basic weight and in these circumstances will have to be included in the disposable load calculation.

Baggage: In Cabin 120 (max) 60.0
Passengers: Row 1 Actual 39.0
Fuel density 7.2 lb/gal and oil density 9.0 lb/gal.

Note: To obtain the total loaded weight of the aircraft, add to the basic weight the weights of the variable and disposable load items to be carried for the particular role.

This Schedule was prepared (date) .... and supersedes all previous issues.
Signature .... etc. etc

The following weight and balance calcula-tions are worked out with reference to the example Weight and Balance Schedule given above. The aircraft load in this case consists of the pilot, one passenger, full fuel tanks and no baggage.

Weight x Arm = Moment

	Item	Weight (lb)	Arm (in)	Moment (lb in)
Basic Weight	Aircraft	1190.0	+ 38.5	45815.0
Variable Load	Pilot	160	+ 39.0	6240.0
Disposable Load	Fuel	135	+ 42.0	5670.0
	Oil (included in the basic weight)			
	Passenger (one)	160	+ 39.0	6240.0
	Baggage	nil	–	–
	Total	1645.0	–	63965.0

Dividing the total weight into the total moment gives the position of the centre of gravity, in this case it is +38.88in aft of the datum. Reference to the centre of gravity moment envelope contained in the flight/owner's manual (Fig. 5-157) shows that the maximum all-up weight permitted is 1690 lb, therefore the calculated weight of 1645 lb is within limits. A further check of the moment envelope shows that at 1645 lb with a total moment arm of 63965 the loaded aircraft is within the authorised weight and balance envelope and can be operated in the 'utility category'. If the weight and moment had fallen in the 'normal category' section of the envelope, the weight and balance would still have been within limits but certain manoeuvres, spinning for example, would not be permitted.

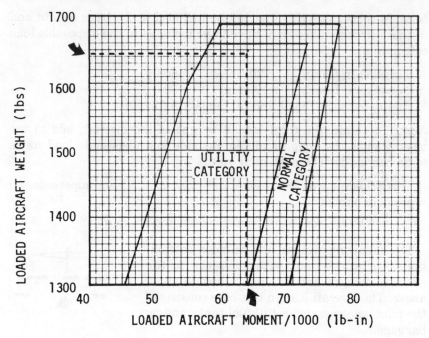

Fig. 5-157

WEIGHT AND BALANCE IN RELATION TO AIRCRAFT CATEGORY
The term category in relation to 'utility', 'normal', and 'aerobatic' indicates the types of manoeuvres which can be carried out in a particular aircraft in that category. Its meaning in this case is quite different from the definition of category in the *Air Navigation Order*, which relates to the purposes for which the aircraft can be used, e.g. transport category, private category, aerial work etc.

The terminology used to define whether certain manoeuvres are permitted varies in different countries. In the U.K. the terminology as laid down in the *British Civil Airworthiness Requirements* is, aerobatic, semi-aerobatic and non-aerobatic. Many countries however use the terms aerobatic, utility and normal. These terms do not always relate to each other in an identical fashion. The term aerobatic is virtually synonymous in all countries, and the terms non-aerobatic and normal also mean the same thing, however the term utility is not the same as semi-aerobatic. Semi-aerobatic means that the aircraft is permitted to carry out certain standard aerobatic manoeuvres, but an aircraft in the utility category would only be permitted to carry out spinning and certain other manoeuvres as listed in the flight/owner's manual. (Note that spinning is classified as an aerobatic manoeuvre.)

Some aircraft are permitted to operate in either one of two categories and sometimes in all three. The reason for this is to widen the operational use of the aircraft, for example, the manufacturer may wish to produce an aircraft which is capable of meeting basic training requirements and also be used as an air tourer. This latter purpose would be better accomplished if it could carry say, four persons and their baggage. Whereas it would be possible to design the aircraft with the appropriate seating and baggage space, the operation at the all-up weight will normally put a restriction on the more vigorous flight manoeuvres such as spinning, etc.

Nevertheless, if the aircraft is operated at a lower all-up weight and within a specified restricted centre of gravity range, this could safely permit limited aerobatic manoeuvres such as spinning to be carried out. In some aircraft the weight and range of the centre of gravity may be restricted still further, to make it possible to extend the operational capability of the aircraft to carry out normal aerobatic manoeuvres.

In view of these variations to the operational category of the aircraft, it will be necessary for the pilot to establish the particular category in which the aircraft falls when the weight and balance calculations have been made prior to flight.

A final cautionary note concerns the stowing of baggage. It is not sufficient just to ensure that the baggage weight and stowage position does not cause the weight and balance limit to be exceeded. If it is not secured properly, a shift in the position of loose baggage during flight can negate the purpose of the balance calculations and possibly jam or interfere with the aircraft controls or lead to injury of the pilot or the passengers in the case of an accident.

SECTION 6

Airframes and Aero Engines

The Aircraft Structure

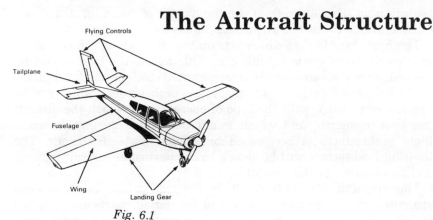

Fig. 6.1

AIRFRAME STRUCTURE

The airframe structure of a fixed wing aircraft can generally be stated to be made up of five principal units:

- The Fuselage;
- Wings;
- Stabilisers;
- Flying Controls;
- Landing Gear.

These airframe components can be constructed from a wide variety of materials and are joined together by bolts, screws, rivets, welding and/or adhesives or other bonding materials.

The structural members have to be of sufficient strength to carry the loads and stresses which are a normal part of an aircraft's operation. For example, a single member of the aircraft structure may be subjected to a combination of stresses, i.e. end loads, side loads, tension or compression and torsion.

Although the strength and ability to flex are major requirements of most components, there are others such as cowlings or fairings which do not carry loads but which are designed to provide smooth streamlined qualities in order to reduce the drag forces which occur as a result of movement through the air.

When designing an aircraft every part must be considered, together with the method of fitment, in relation to the load to be imposed upon it. Determining these loads is an essential part of a subject called stress analysis. Although knowledge of this subject is not a requirement for the private pilot, it gives a pilot a greater appreciation of the importance that loads and stress play in the operation of the aircraft if he is aware of some of the basic considerations concerned with stress analysis.

The *basic load* is that which acts on the structure of the aeroplane in a condition of static equilibrium. This means the load caused by the weight of the aeroplane in unaccelerated straight and level flight.

The designer determines the maximum probable load which will be applied, compatible with the type of operation for which the aircraft has been designed, and which might be applied during abnormal flight manoeuvres or occasioned by sudden gusts in the air. The limiting load factors will be shown in the particular aircraft manual and by placards in the cockpit.

The strength of any aircraft is limited by the need to keep structural weight to a minimum, and the various parts are designed to fail only at an ultimate load which is normally fixed at 1.5 times the maximum applied load. The ratio of the ultimate load to the maximum applied load (1.5) is known as the *safety factor*.

The *load factor* is expressed in multiples of gravitational pull or *g*, and in normal straight and level flight will be 1. If a force is applied equal to 2*g* the load factor will be 2. For example, an aircraft weighing 1000 kg would weigh 2000 kg if the load factor was increased to 2.

Apart from load factor, there are other stresses to which all aircraft are subjected, and before defining these in simple terms, it would also be helpful to realise that although the designer arranges for the individual aircraft components to meet all load and stress requirements compatible with normal flight and the operational purpose of the aeroplane, every pilot has the physical strength to exceed these limitations by brutal operation of the controls.

It should also be realised that:

> The forces of acceleration normally called *g* can, on reaching a certain level, cause the blood to be drained from a person's head. This action will cause the person to *black out* and become unconscious. The average level for this to happen would be about 5*g*, although physical training and other methods can increase this level.

Having said this, it must be further appreciated that a person of normal physical strength can apply forces to the aircraft controls which can cause a change in direction which will produce an acceleration in excess of 8*g* and although the application of this force would cause a pilot to become unconscious in a second or two, the airframe would already have been subject to a load factor greater than 8. Bearing in mind that most small general aviation aircraft are designed to withstand positive g forces of between 3.8 and 4.4 and less on certain occasions, it will be appreciated that a pilot could therefore apply forces to the aircraft structure which are greater than those for which it was originally designed. Additionally, fatigue due to aircraft age and/or repeated stress loadings may cause a structure or component to fail at an earlier stage than that to which it was originally designed. These points must be borne in mind by pilots when carrying out manoeuvres involving higher than normal loadings.

Given these facts, it is clear that pilots should have a basic understanding of the types of stresses which may occur to an aircraft. For example, the application of a force to a unit area of material will induce within that material something called *stress*, and such stress is always accompanied by a deformation within the material, called *strain*.

The five major stresses which act upon the parts of an aeroplane can be described as follows.

STRESSES

TENSION

The stress that results from a force which acts along a straight line so as to cause 'stretching'.

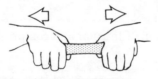

Fig. 6-2

An example of this would be the effect of the propeller pulling the aircraft forward, and the effect of air resistance which tries to hold it back. The result is a tension which tends to stretch the aircraft.

COMPRESSION

The stress that results from a 'crushing' force. In other words, the stress that tends to shorten or squeeze the parts of an aircraft, e.g. the nose wheel strut whilst the aircraft is on the ground.

Fig. 6-3

TORSION

Torsion is a twisting stress and an example of this can be seen in the action of the propeller turning, an action which causes the fuselage to want to turn in the opposite direction.

Fig. 6-4

SHEAR

Shear is the stress that results from a force tending to cause one layer of material to slide over an adjacent layer. For example, if two strips of metal or wood were bonded together by a lap joint, then if the two strips were pulled, i.e., placed in tension the bonded joint would be in direct shear.

Alternatively, one could consider two components of an aircraft which are riveted together which, when placed in tension, will develop a shearing stress in the rivets.

BENDING

Bending is a combination of tension and compression stress as seen in Fig. 6-5.

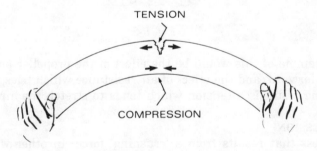

TENSION

COMPRESSION

Fig. 6-5

Apart from the strains imposed by steady loads and stresses, there is also the factor of fatigue. Most parts of an aircraft are subject to strain brought about by steady loads and by vibration and flexing. The fatigue resistance of a material is that property which enables it to withstand cycles of steady and fluctuating stresses applied over a period of time.

Fatigue failure of the aircraft component is caused by stress and microscopic changes in the structure of the material. This is one reason why a careful pre-flight inspection is necessary prior to each flight in order that any deterioration or cracks in the visible components or surfaces can be attended to as soon as possible, rather than waiting until the next ground engineer's inspection period.

FUSELAGE CONSTRUCTION

The fuselage is the main structure or body of the aeroplane and provides the necessary space for the crew, flying controls, instrumentation, system controls, equipment, passengers and cargo. The fuselage of single engined aircraft also provides a housing for the engine. The two general forms of fuselage construction are known as the *truss* type and the *monocoque* type.

The truss type can be described as being made up of a system of members and beams connected by struts and bars which give it rigidity. This also provides a frame which is normally covered by fabric. The fuselage frame is usually made from steel tubing or aluminium alloy which is welded, riveted and/or bolted into one rigid piece.

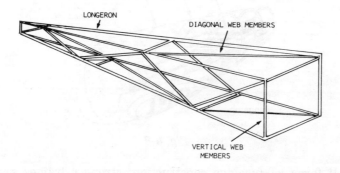

Fig. 6-6

The monocoque type of construction utilises frame assemblies and bulkheads to provide the shape of the fuselage and to which a skin of metal sheeting is riveted. However, as no bracing members are employed in this form of construction, the skin has to be of sufficient strength to keep the fuselage rigid and also carry the stresses. Whilst a thin light skin is acceptable in relation to weight and stress limits for small narrow fuselages, it is limited in its application to larger fuselages because the required thickness gauge of the skin makes the weight to strength ratio unacceptable.

Because of this, a variant of the true monocoque construction has been developed which still uses frames and bulkheads but in addition,

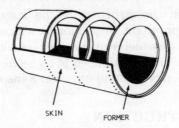

Fig. 6-7

the skin is braced by longitudinal members called longerons. This type of assembly is known as *semi monocoque*.

The materials employed are normally a combination of aluminium and steel. Primary stresses and bending loads are taken by longerons which usually extend across several of the vertical frames. Longerons are also supplemented by other longitudinal members called stringers and these are thinner, lighter and more numerous. Figure 6-8 shows an example of semi monocoque construction.

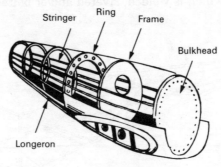

Fig. 6-8

In all forms of fuselage construction, stronger frames and bulkheads are used at those points where concentrated loads are normally applied, e.g. the attachment location of wings, tailplane and engine mountings etc. Although high localised stresses imposed on the fuselage are catered for in the design and construction, a point to note is that although maximum baggage load is placarded in the cargo compartment of light aircraft, it must be appreciated that cargo floors may be subject to loads from cargo items which have small area, but high density. In these circumstances, high loads are concentrated on small areas, and when such items are carried, it may be necessary to use 'spreader bars' to displace the total weight over a greater area.

Frames and bulkheads are often referred to as braces, formers, or rings, but they all essentially perform the same task of acting as the central members for the longerons, stringers and skin. The longerons and stringers act as pick-up points to which the skin is rivetted, and they also prevent tension and compression from bending the fuselage.

Stringers are normally constructed of aluminium alloy and are manufactured in a wide variety of shapes by extrusion, forming or casting. The metal skin is rivetted to the longerons, bulkheads and other members and provides additional bracing for the whole assembly. It also carries part of the load and so varies in thickness depending on the designed load to be carried and the calculated stresses at various locations along the fuselage. Twisting loads on the fuselage are mainly resisted by the skin in which shear stresses are directly produced and, in regions between the formers, bulkheads and stringers, areas of tension are developed.

The main advantage of a semi monocoque construction lies in the fact that loads and stresses are spread over the whole construction rather than being taken by the bulkhead, frames, and skin. This means that even if considerable damage is incurred, the whole assembly is more likely to hold together.

In the final assembly, provision is made for access doors for the crew, passengers, cargo and for ease of inspecting certain aircraft components and systems.

WING CONSTRUCTION

The aircraft wings provide the lifting surface for the aeroplane. The actual design, size, thickness and shape will depend on a number of factors, e.g. the particular use for which the aircraft is designed, and the desired speed range etc.

Wings are attached to the fuselage in a variety of locations both longitudinally and vertically. The term *high wing*, *low wing*, and *mid wing*, all refer to the particular wing location in the vertical sense, and the exact longitudinal position is usually determined by the required position of the mean line of lift of the wings and the centre of gravity of the aircraft.

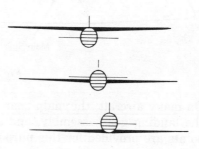

Fig. 6-9

Descriptive terms are also used to describe the plan shape of the wings and Fig. 6-10 shows a variety of common shapes.

Many aircraft have wings designed on the cantilever principle, i.e. with no bracing struts or wires. Others, notably of the high wing or biplane type, utilise struts and other forms of bracing to provide

Fig. 6-10

structural rigidity when attached to the fuselage.

The skin may be of fabric, wood, or aluminium, and carries loads and lifting stresses. The complete structure is normally made up of main and secondary spars, interspaced with stringers all running spanwise along the length of the wing from root to the tip. Additionally, ribs and formers are arranged chordwise from the leading edge to the trailing edge to give greater rigidity and provide a streamlined shape.

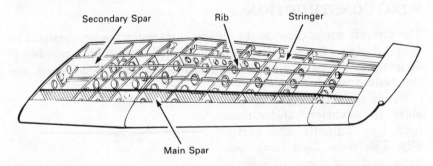

Fig. 6-11

On many aircraft, the main spar accepts the loads transmitted from the landing gear assembly, and special reinforcing and attachment points are provided for this purpose.

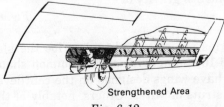

Strengthened Area

Fig. 6-12

During flight, the applied lifting loads are taken primarily along the skin from which they are transmitted to the ribs and then to the spars. Wings generally have two spars, one located along the deepest section of the wing, approximately one third back from the leading edge, and the other about one third forward from the trailing edge. Notwithstanding the type and design of the wing used, the spars are the strongest component of a wing and when other structural members of the wing are placed under load, they transmit most of the resulting stress onto the spars.

Wings are subject to air loads which produce lateral and chordwise flexing and they must therefore be strong enough to withstand the torsion and bending stresses involved. Additional strengthening will also be required in the regions where flaps and ailerons are attached and where fuel tanks are contained.

THE TAIL UNIT

The complete tail section normally consists of a vertical stabiliser with a moveable rudder hinged at the rear and a horizontal stabiliser to which the elevators are attached.

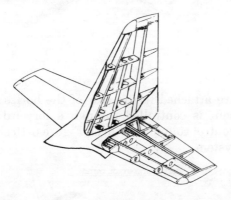

Fig. 6-13

The tail unit may be streamlined at the end of the fuselage by a cone-shaped attachment or the fuselage itself may be faired to produce the same streamlined effect.

The tail unit components are constructed in a similar manner to the main wings and are formed by spars, ribs, stringers and a skin. Stress will be applied to the various sections in the same manner as the wing and the bending, torsion and shear forces created by aerodynamic loads are passed between structural members and the skin, each member absorbing some of the stress and passing the remainder to other members. Stress felt by the tail unit will eventually be transmitted to the fuselage structure through the attachment points.

AILERONS, ELEVATORS AND RUDDER

These components are the primary group of control surfaces designed to enable the pilot to control the aircraft about its longitudinal, lateral and vertical axes. They consist of hinged surfaces which are closely similar in their methods of construction to the wings. The ailerons are attached to the trailing edge outer section of the aircraft wings and their movement is activated through a control column or control wheel in the aircraft cockpit. Figure 6-14 shows a typical aileron control system.

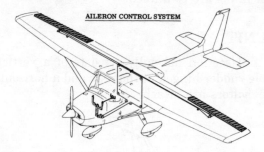

AILERON CONTROL SYSTEM

Fig. 6-14

The elevators are attached to the rear of the horizontal stabiliser and their movement is controlled through a forward or backward movement of the control column or wheel. Figure 6-15 shows a typical elevator control system.

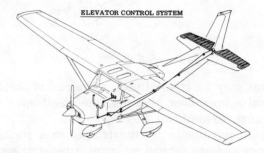

ELEVATOR CONTROL SYSTEM

Fig. 6-15

The rudder is attached at the rear of the vertical stabiliser (fin) and its movement is controlled by a rudder bar or pedals located close to the floor of the cockpit. A typical rudder system is shown in Fig. 6-16.

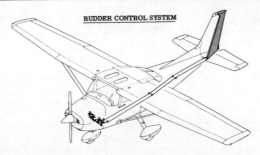

Fig. 6-16

Sometimes, in place of elevators, the whole horizontal stabiliser is hinged about a central axis. This type of control surface is often used to provide a more powerful control in pitch at low airspeeds where the smaller elevator surfaces may be inadequate. Such a unit is known as a *stabilator* and it performs the function of both the fixed stabiliser and the elevators.

Adjustable stops are used to limit the range of control surface movement. Usually there are two sets of stops for each control surface, one set at the cockpit control and the other situated adjacent to the control surface, (Fig. 6-17).

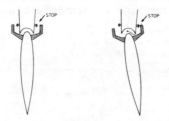

Fig. 6-17

TRIMMING CONTROLS

Trimming controls are fitted to reduce any sustained control loads experienced by the pilot. These consist of either a strong spring which is fitted directly to the control column or rudder bar, (the tension of which can be adjusted by the pilot,) or a small aerofoil attached to the particular control surface. A typical elevator trim assembly is shown in Fig. 6-18.

Small gaps or holes have to be arranged at the forward ends of control surfaces to route the control rods or cables to their attachment points. These apertures will also allow ingress of water, etc., and therefore drain holes are provided at the rear lower end of the control surfaces. It must be appreciated that only a small accumulation of

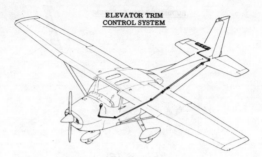

Fig. 6-18

water, ice, etc. inside a control surface will upset the control balance and could lead to flutter. Further to this, and in the case of the tailplane surfaces, any accumulation of water, ice, etc. will also have a significant effect in moving the aircraft's centre of gravity further aft and perhaps lead to a dangerous situation.

CONTROL SYSTEMS

The systems which operate the control surfaces of small aircraft, normally consist of cockpit controls, and cable assemblies which are routed through the fuselage or wings via a system of pulleys, fairleads and linkages.

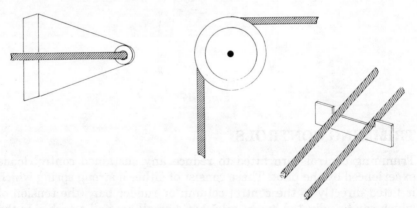

Fig. 6-19

In order to adjust cable tension during the assembly and life of the control system, it is normal to incorporate turnbuckles at the cable ends adjacent to the control surface. Various types of turnbuckles are in common use, but essentially, they consist of a barrel with internal screw threads at either end. One end has a right hand thread and the other a left hand thread. When fitting the control cables and adjusting the tension the cable terminal is screwed into either end of the barrel an equal distance, and as a safety factor, not more than three threads should be exposed on either side of the barrel.

To ensure that vibration or wear does not loosen the cable terminals from the barrel ends, a locking wire is used. Safety wiring is a method of wiring two or more units in such a manner that any tendency of one to loosen is counteracted by the tension of the wire.

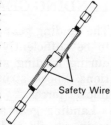

Safety Wire

The turnbuckles used adjacent to control surfaces are normally exposed so that they can be easily examined by a pilot and this is an important item to be included during the pilot's pre-flight inspection of the aircraft.

FLAPS

These auxiliary control surfaces are normally manually or electrically operated, but a few aircraft use a pneumatic or hydraulic system.

The flap system shown in Fig. 6-20 utilises electricity for its operation and is actuated via a control in the cockpit. The number of degrees of flap movement is shown either on a gauge or through the use of a gated slot in which the selector lever is operated.

Fig. 6-20

When flaps are operated manually, a thumb release button is attached to the operating lever and the number of selections is normally limited to two or three positions.

Note: Prior to starting the engine, all controls including the flaps should be checked visually and moved to ensure that they operate in the correct sense, that they move smoothly and freely and their water drain holes are clear. Any stiffness or jerkiness experienced during their travel indicates that excessive strain has been imposed upon them during a previous flight, or that they have been subject to damage on the ground, or that their pulleys or fairleads are fouled.

When this is apparent, the aircraft should be placed unserviceable and a report made to the engineering staff.

LANDING GEAR (FIXED)

The landing gear supports the aircraft whilst on the ground and has to be sufficiently strong to cope with the vertical forces imposed during landing and the lateral forces induced by crosswind conditions. Shock struts of various designs are fitted to absorb ground impact forces.

Landing gear arrangements used in light aircraft consist of two main wheels and either one nosewheel or one tailwheel. When a nosewheel is fitted, some form of linkage is generally incorporated to permit nosewheel steering and so facilitate directional control on the ground. Brakes installed in the main wheel assemblies enable the aircraft to be slowed or stopped during movement on the ground.

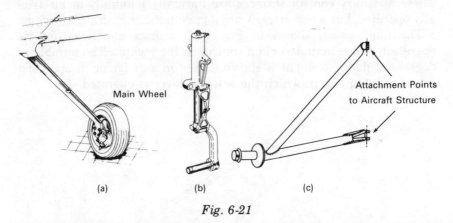

Main Wheel

Attachment Points
to Aircraft Structure

(a)   (b)   (c)

Fig. 6-21

Figure 6-21 illustrates three common types of landing gear struts. That shown in (a) is a spring steel leaf normally used for the main landing gear assembly on small high wing aircraft. Illustrated in (b) is an oleo pneumatic assembly normally fitted as the main landing gear on low wing aircraft and also generally employed for nosewheel structures. The type shown in (c) is a braced assembly which incorporates some form of shock absorbing system through the use of an elastic bungee arrangement at the points where the end fittings are attached to the aircraft main structure.

The landing gear strut is equipped with an axle attached to the lowest portion to provide for attachment of the wheels. Those which utilise an oleo assembly have a piston and cylinder system which is used to absorb the shocks during landing and taxying. A fitting consisting of a fluid filler inlet and air valve is located near the upper end of the shock strut to allow the piston and cylinder assembly to be filled with hydraulic fluid and inflated with air. For efficient operation, the correct level of fluid and air must be maintained and the pilot will need to visually check the shock strut for proper inflation during each pre-flight inspection.

The majority of the oleo type assemblies are fitted with torque arms to maintain correct alignment of the wheel (Fig. 6-22). The top of the hinged V unit is attached to the oleo cylinder casing and the bottom is connected to the wheel fork unit. When fitted as nosewheel assemblies, the torque arms are also equipped with a *shimmy damper* consisting of a small piston unit.

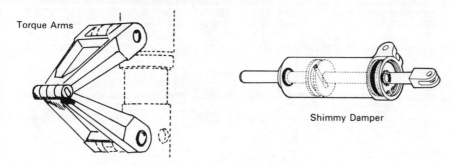

Torque Arms

Shimmy Damper

Fig. 6-22

Any damage to the torque arm, or loss of pressure from the shimmy damper will result in *nosewheel shimmy*. This is a form of vibration resulting from the nosewheel swivelling a few degrees either side of the centre line. If this occurs at relatively high speed immediately after landing, it can be reduced by increasing the back pressure on the control column. At low speeds however, the elevator effectiveness is markedly reduced and the best method will be to apply forward pressure on the control column to place more weight on the nosewheel. In any event, whenever this shimmy has been experienced, it should be reported to a ground engineer for remedial action.

BRAKE SYSTEMS

The correct functioning of the brake system is extremely important as the brakes are used to slow down and stop the aircraft. Additionally, they are also used for steering the aircraft when turning in confined spaces as well as occasionally counteracting strong crosswind effects during landing and taxying.

Although some of the older types of light aircraft use a cable system to activate the brakes, the most common method used today is hydraulic, and it is normally an independent system, i.e. one which has its own reservoir of fluid and which is entirely independent of any other hydraulic system which may be fitted to the aircraft. The system permits the brakes on both main wheels to be applied either singly or together. When brake pressure is only applied to one wheel, the action is known as differential braking.

Independent braking systems are powered by a master cylinder usually fitted via a linkage to each brake pedal (which is usually also the rudder pedal). The complete system comprises a reservoir, one or two master cylinders, linkages, fluid lines and a brake assembly attached to each main wheel. Figure 6-23 is a typical outline diagram of a braking system.

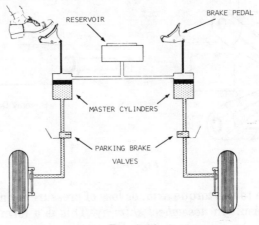

Fig. 6-23

Although some brake systems are activated by the use of a hand lever, the most common system to be found on light aircraft is one which is operated via pressure applied to brake pedals which form part of the rudder pedal system. Additionally a parking brake is fitted to ensure the aircraft can be left adequately braked after use, and the aircraft manual will give details on the method of using the different systems.

A pilot must check the serviceability of the braking system by visually inspecting the brake disc assembly attached to the main wheels, to ensure that it is clean, securely attached, and that no hydraulic leaks are evident.

AIRCRAFT TYRES

The function of aircraft tyres is to support and cushion the aircraft on the ground. Although they are subjected to considerable strain as the aircraft touches down when they are rapidly accelerated from rest to

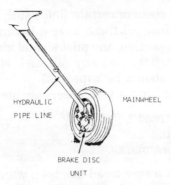

HYDRAULIC PIPE LINE

MAINWHEEL

BRAKE DISC UNIT

Fig. 6-24

the running speed of the aircraft, the greatest wear occurs when harsh braking is used or strong sideways forces are applied during changes of direction on the ground.

Early types of tyre had smooth surfaces but later types are now commonly constructed with patterned or circular grooved treads as they give more adhesion on wet, smooth runways.

The friction effect of the ground, particularly during landing or during sharp braking will cause the outer casing to move around the wheel disc. If this movement is allowed to become too great, the inflation valve neck of the inner tube will be ruptured or torn off. Therefore, it is common practice to paint a mark (known as a *creep mark*) on the wheel disc, and on the side wall of the tyre, so that the two marks are in line. If a gap appears between these two marks, the tyre must be considered unserviceable and will need re-fitting. However, the full width of the mark represents the maximum permitted creep and a sensible pilot would normally place the aircraft unserviceable shortly before this limit is reached.

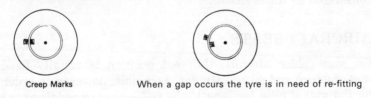

Creep Marks

When a gap occurs the tyre is in need of re-fitting

Fig. 6-25

Correct tyre pressure is also very important, as under-inflated tyres will suffer damage to the side walls, particularly during turning and breaking and they will also have a greater rate of creep. Over-inflated tyres can cause excessive vibration whilst taxying, uneven tyre wear, and high pressure bursts.

Tyres must be kept clean of certain fluids such as oil, petrol, glycol and hydraulic fluid, since all these have a harmful effect on rubber. During a pre-flight inspection, the pilot should visually check for any signs of incorrect inflation, and any oil, fuel, etc. which may have dripped onto the tyre should be wiped off.

Other reasons for placing a tyre unserviceable are:

- Wear of the tyre tread
- Bulges in the casing
- Deep cuts and score marks.

The extent to which a tyre tread has been worn is not always easy to assess and may be overall or localised. However, the following descriptions can be used as a guide in determining the serviceability of a tyre.

WEAR

Plain tread tyres should be considered as unserviceable if the grey cushion rubber or casing cords can be seen. Patterned tread tyres may be used until the tread is worn to the depth of the pattern. Ribbed tyres (circular grooved tread) may be used until worn to within 2 mm of the bottom of the two central grooves.

BULGES

The presence of any bulge usually indicates that a partial failure of the casing has occurred and in these circumstances, the tyre should be considered as unserviceable.

CUTS AND SCORES

Acceptable damage may be considered as that in which the cut or score mark does not reveal the casing cords. If the damage is such that any part of the casing cord is revealed, the tyre must be considered as unserviceable.

AIRCRAFT SEATS

On some older aircraft, the seat position is usually fixed during manufacture and no adjustment is possible, however, in order to cater for individual pilot leg length, the rudder bar or pedals are capable of forward or rearward adjustment.

On many modern aircraft the seat position is adjustable, forwards and backwards. Additionally, many seats can be raised or lowered and the seat back angle can often also be altered to meet individual pilot requirements. Levers or handles positioned underneath or adjacent to the seat are used for the different adjustments, and it is particularly important to ensure that after any adjustment, the seat or seat back position has been securely locked in place.

Each seat is equipped with either lap straps or a form of harness to secure the body. Current legislation defined in the *Air Navigation Order* requires that the front seats occupied by the pilot and front passenger are equipped with a form of harness which includes an upper torso body restraint (shoulder harness.) On some earlier aircraft, these may not be practical, and in these cases, provision is made for an exemption to be granted from the requirements of the *ANO*.

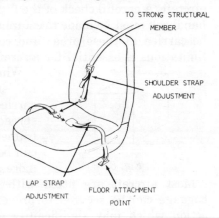

Fig. 6-26

Normally, seat straps and safety harnesses are attached directly to the airframe structure, (normally the floor) and the attachment points are located on a member sufficiently strong to meet the stresses imposed by the aircraft being suddenly arrested at landing speeds.

Before attaching the straps or harness about the body, the seat should first be adjusted, as once the straps are secured, it may be impossible to alter the seat position.

Shoulder harnesses are often of the inertia reel type which give freedom to movement of the upper torso and only lock when an impact force is sustained. In the case of non-inertia reel systems, the shoulder harness may normally be left loose during ground operations and whilst in level flight at altitude. However, it should be tightened prior to take-off, landing, or when flying in turbulent conditions, or carrying out steep turns, stalling or other unusual manoeuvres.

BAGGAGE – STOWAGE AND MAXIMUM WEIGHTS ALLOWED

Structural limitations and weight and balance considerations dictate

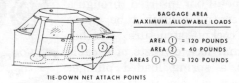

Fig. 6-27

the weight limit of any load carried in the baggage areas of light aircraft. A careful check of the flight/owner's manual/pilot's operating handbook must be made to establish the maximum weight which may be carried in these areas and compliance with the manufacturer's limitations is essential for aircraft safety.

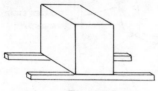

Fig. 6-28

When an item of high weight density i.e. small surface area to weight, is carried, consideration should be given to spreading its load across the fuselage frames instead of between them. This can be accomplished by the use of two or more spreader bars.

Most aircraft are fitted with tie-down points so that items of baggage can be secured to prevent them shifting during flight, an action which may significantly alter the position of the centre of gravity and lead to difficulty in controlling the aircraft. Bear in mind that baggage which gradually moves rearward may not adversely affect the pilot's control over the aircraft during cruising flight, but when speed is reduced for the approach to a landing, the reduced effectiveness of the elevators may cause the pilot to lose control in pitch. Further to this, baggage which is firmly secured is less likely to move rapidly forward and injure the occupants in the event of the aircraft being rapidly brought to a stop, for example, during landing or take-off incidents or accidents.

CONTROL LOCKS – TYPES AND PURPOSE

Various devices are in use to lock the flying controls when the aircraft is left unattended on the ground and so prevent them from damage as a result of wind gusts. Common types in use are external control surface locks, and internal metal tubes and/or spring loaded locking bars.

The external control surface locks are usually in the form of wood blocks which slide into the openings between the ends of the moveable surfaces and the aircraft structure. Sometimes, a pair of wood blocks are used and once in position, these are screwed together by a butterfly nut.

The most simple internal lock consists of a shaped metal bar inserted through a hole in the control column tube and a part of the cockpit structure. Another type of internal lock consists of a cable system with a spring loaded plunger which engages a hole in the control surface mechanical system and which

Fig. 6-29

can be engaged or disengaged via a lever or plunger.

Most internal locks are designed so that when they are in the locked position, a metal attachment arm covers the ignition switches or prevents the throttle from being moved forward, thus acting as a safety feature to prevent inadvertently taking off with the controls locked. External locks usually have a red streamer attached to them to clearly alert the pilot to their presence.

The Aero Engine

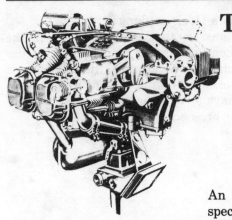

An aircraft engine has to meet specific requirements in relation to reliability and durability and be capable of sustained high power output and operate for long periods of time between overhauls. Added to this, and in relation to operating costs and performance considerations, it must meet exacting design requirements involving low weight per horse power and economy in fuel consumption.

The fundamental principle of operation of an aero engine is the utilisation of air, which when heated by the combustion of a fuel, expands, and in so doing, is able to do work. In other words, the aero engine is a machine which converts heat energy into mechanical energy which is then utilised to drive a propeller and other ancillary systems.

The basic components of an aero engine are shown in Fig. 6-30 and consist of a number of cylinders and pistons, with connecting rods to a crankshaft. One end of the connecting rod is attached to the base of the piston, and the other to a crankshaft, which converts the straight up and down action of the piston into a rotary motion which turns the propeller.

To enable the necessary cycle of events to occur, an induction and carburation system, an ignition system, and an exhaust system, are required. These systems respectively control the air and fuel supply, provide a spark to ignite the fuel, and guide the exit of the expelled products of combustion. Due to the relative movements of many of the engine components, a lubrication and oil cooling system will also be needed to reduce friction, and disperse heat created between the moving parts.

THE FOUR-STROKE CYCLE

Piston engines used in aircraft operate on the principle of the *Otto* cycle, a name derived from the inventor Nicholas A. Otto who built the first successful engine operating by means of pistons moving back

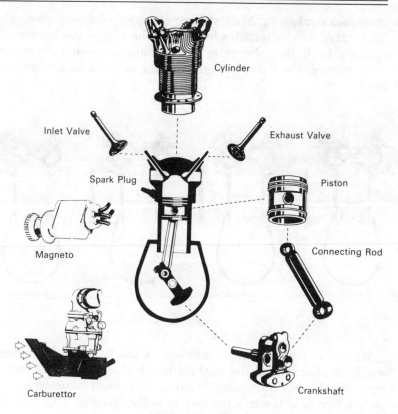

Fig. 6-30

and forth within cylinders (*reciprocating*).

One cycle is comprised of four strokes and it can be used with one or more cylinders. The most common layout nowadays is with 4 or 6 cylinders laid out horizontally as illustrated in Fig. 6-31.

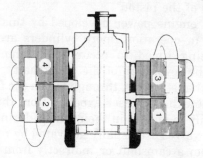

Fig. 6-31

The four strokes are termed *intake* (or *induction*), *compression*, *expansion* (or *power*) and *exhaust*. Figure 6-32 shows an illustration of these four strokes. In 'A' the fuel/air mixture is fed through an opened inlet valve as the piston moves from the top to the bottom of the cylinder. In 'B' the inlet valve is closed and the piston commences to move towards the top of the cylinder (the cylinder head) compressing the mixture.

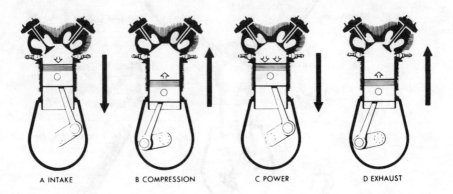

A INTAKE   B COMPRESSION   C POWER   D EXHAUST

Fig. 6-32

When the piston is approximately at the top of the cylinder, the sparking plug ignites the mixture which then burns at a controlled rate. As the burning gases expand, they exert a pressure on the piston, forcing it towards the bottom of the cylinder. This is shown in 'C' and is known as the power stroke.

Just before the piston completes this stroke, the exhaust valve opens and the burned gases are forced out of the cylinder as the piston returns to the top. This cycle then continues to repeat itself throughout the period the engine is running. It should be noted that the power stroke occurs once, and the crankshaft revolves twice, for every four strokes of the piston.

To increase the engine power developed by this cycle and create more smoothness in operation, more cylinders are added with the power strokes being timed to occur at different but successive intervals during the revolution of the crankshaft.

The inlet and exhaust valves, through which the fuel/air mixture is introduced and the exhaust gases expelled from the cylinders of the engine, slide rapidly to and fro in their guides during the operation of the engine. These valves are usually activated by rocker arms driven either directly from a camshaft or indirectly from the camshaft via push rods.

As the power developed by the engine is a function of the amount of fuel/air mixture which can be forced into the cylinder during the intake stroke, it can readily be appreciated that the amount of power developed depends, among other things, on the size of the intake port and the length of time the inlet valve is open. Because the inlet stroke occurs once for every two revolutions of the crankshaft, it can be seen that when the engine is running at 2500 revolutions per minute (a typical high cruising RPM), the intake valve will open 1250 times per minute or some 20 times per second. Therefore it is clear that a major problem in obtaining a given power output is in getting sufficient mixture into the cylinder during each intake stroke, i.e. to improve its volumetric efficiency.

VALVE TIMING

One way in which this can be improved is to arrange the valve cycle so that the inlet valve opens just before the piston reaches the top of its stroke (Top Dead Centre) and closes just after it reaches the bottom of its stroke (Bottom Dead Centre). This is technically known as *valve lead* and *valve lag*.

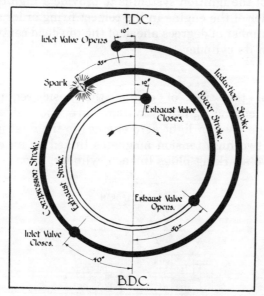

A Typical Timing Diagram

Fig. 6-33

Figure 6-33 shows diagrammatically how this is arranged. Notice that the exhaust valves open just before the exhaust stroke commences and close later. This is to increase the time available for the cylinder to be scavenged of the burnt gases. The smaller the volume of burnt gases remaining, the greater will be the amount of fuel/air mixture introduced into the cylinder during the inlet stroke.

The time when both inlet and exhaust valves are open in conjunction is known as the *valve overlap period*.

It can be observed that the moment when the sparking plug is activated is just prior to the commencement of the downward movement of the piston (power stroke). This is to give the burning gases a chance to expand and create maximum pressure on the crown of the piston at the moment it commences its downward stroke. Although it would appear that the effect of valve overlap can at best give only a slight improvement to the power output of the engine, it should nevertheless be appreciated that in view of the minute period of time for which the valves are open during each cycle, any increase in this period will produce a significant increase to the amount of fuel/air charge induced into the cylinder.

IGNITION SYSTEMS

The purpose of the ignition system is to provide a high tension spark to each cylinder of the engine in the correct firing order and at a predetermined number of degrees ahead of the top dead centre position of each piston in its cylinder.

PRINCIPLES

Regardless of the type of engine the basic requirements for reciprocating engine ignition systems are the same. The most common system used in light aero engines is the dual ignition type, consisting of two high tension magnetos linked by an electric cable harness to two sparking plugs in each cylinder.

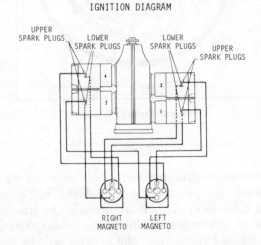

Fig. 6-34

MAGNETOS

The magneto is a type of self contained engine-driven generator which is not connected in any way with the aircraft's main electrical system but uses a permanent magnet as a source of initial energy. Nevertheless, the aircraft battery is used initially to activate the rotating element of the magneto via the starter system, although manually swinging the propeller has the same effect should the battery be discharged.

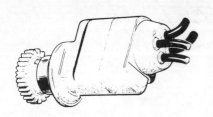

Fig. 6-35

Once the engine has been started, the starter system is disengaged and unlike a car ignition system, the aircraft battery has no further part in the operation of the engine, i.e. if the battery master switch were to be turned off, the engine would continue to run normally. Naturally, with the engine turning, the alternator or generator will ensure the battery is charged.

The magneto develops the high voltage needed to force a spark to jump across a gap in the sparking plug. This spark ignites the fuel/air mixture and is arranged to occur in each cylinder at a specific moment in the four-stroke cycle.

The electrical current is produced by the engine being geared to move a magnet within the magneto housing, past a conductor, which has a wire coil wrapped around it. The mechanical rotation of the magnet induces an electric current to flow in the coil. A secondary coil with a far greater number of turns of wire is wrapped around the primary coil and this transforms the primary voltage to a value high enough to allow a powerful electric spark to jump across the gap in the sparking plug electrodes. This is the 'spark' which ignites the mixture in the cylinder and occurs immediately prior to the power stroke.

To arrange for the spark to occur at the right time, the magneto system is equipped with a set of electric current breaker points which open and close via the action of a cam geared to the rotary movement of the crankshaft. A current distributor assembly is also incorporated to feed the current to the correct cylinder sparking plug at the proper time in the cycle of piston strokes.

During engine starting, the starter motor turns the engine relatively slowly and because of this, the electrical current induced by the magneto assembly is very weak. Therefore, in order to boost up the voltage, one of two methods is normally used. These are separately known as an 'impulse coupler' or an 'induction vibrator'.

Basically, the impulse coupler has a coiled spring attached to an

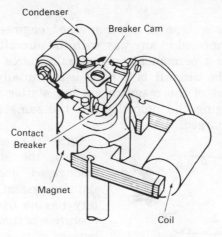

Fig. 3-36

engine accessory drive shaft. When the engine commences to turn over as the starter is engaged the spring tightens, until it is fully compressed. At this stage it automatically releases and spins the magneto rapidly enough to develop a strong spark to the plug in the cylinder undergoing compression. This system has the advantage of not depending on external power.

The induction vibrator requires current drawn from the aircraft battery which then passes through the magneto's primary coil, building up into a high voltage which when released at the proper time delivers a consecutive stream of sparks at about 200 impulses a second. In either method, the booster system automatically disengages once the engine starts.

IGNITION SWITCHES

The aircraft ignition system is controlled through ignition switches in the cockpit, and because two separate ignition systems are fitted, there will be two ignition switches for each engine.

The types of ignition switch used in small aircraft vary between the tumbler type and the rotary type. Nowadays, the most common is a rotary type operated through a key which has four positions, OFF, LEFT, RIGHT and BOTH. Selecting the switch barrel via the key to the LEFT or RIGHT position activates one magneto system whereas when the BOTH position is selected, both magneto systems are in operation together.

Fig. 6-37

The ignition switches are different in at least one respect from all other types of electric switch in that when the ignition switch is in

Fig. 6-38

the OFF position, the circuit is *closed* from the switch to the ground. In other electrical switches, the OFF position normally *opens* the circuit. For this reason, propellers must be treated as live at all times, because if a *ground* connection is broken for any reason, the circuit becomes live. Whereas this is a good safety factor during flight, it can clearly be seen that an inherent danger will exist when the engine is switched off on the ground, and a fault develops in the circuit.

CARBURATION

Petrol and other hydrocarbon fuels will not burn at all unless they have a sufficient supply of oxygen. This oxygen supply is provided by mixing the fuel with air, and so that this mixture can burn properly within an engine cylinder, the ratio of fuel to air must be maintained within certain limits.

The chemically correct ratio is fifteen parts of air to one part of fuel, but in small engines, which use a float type carburettor to produce the required mixture, this ideal ratio may not be achieved for various reasons. One reason is that it is not always possible to deliver the same mixture strength to each cylinder due to their different positions relative to the carburettor and the resultant variation in the length of piping from the carburettor to the inlet valves at the cylinder heads.

CARBURATION PRINCIPLES

On small aero engines a carburettor assembly is used to meter the airflow through the engine's induction system and to regulate the amount of fuel discharged in the induction airstream. Basically it utilises the principle of a venturi inside a cylinder which causes a drop in pressure, resulting in fuel from the adjacent float chamber being sucked into the induction airstream. The amount of air permitted to pass through the induction system is controlled by a butterfly valve connected to

Fig. 6-39

the pilot's throttle lever in the cockpit.

Fuel jets are positioned in the venturi to meter the correct amount of fuel and are fed from the adjacent float chamber. Figure 6-40 shows a diagrammatic illustration of a carburettor assembly.

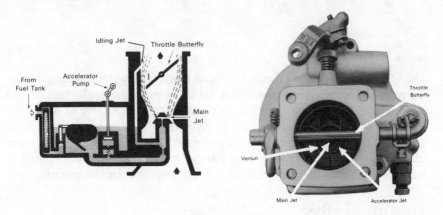

Fig. 6-40

As the pressure surrounding the discharge nozzle is lowered, a differential pressure is created between that in the float chamber and that in the venturi. This results in fuel flowing from the chamber to the fuel jets. As fuel leaves the chamber, the float lowers, lifting a needle in the inlet orifice permitting a continuous replenishment of the chamber from the aircraft fuel tanks.

The size and shape of the venturi passage depends on the size of the engine and when the carburettor is positioned so that air passes through it in an upwards direction to the cylinders, it is known as an *updraught* carburettor. The converse of this arrangement is called a *downdraught* carburettor. The updraught type is the one most commonly used in small aero engines.

Apart from the main metering jet, each carburettor has certain other fuel control units to provide for operating under various conditions and power settings. These units normally consist of at least the following:

● Idling jets;
● Accelerator pump;
● Idle cut-off valve;
● Mixture control system.

These different units operate to meter the fuel flow at different power outputs and may act alone or in conjunction with each other.

IDLING JETS

At low engine speeds the throttle is nearly closed and, as a result, the velocity of the air through the venturi is low so there is little drop in pressure. Under these conditions, the differential pressure between the float chamber and the venturi section is insufficient to operate the main metering system (main jet). Therefore, most carburettors have an idling system, which normally consists of one or more small orifices adjacent to the throttle butterfly, see Fig. 6-40. From this illustration, it will be seen that as the throttle is closed, a depression or venturi effect is created at '1' allowing a sufficient rate of flow for the idling condition.

ACCELERATOR PUMP

When the throttle is opened, the airflow through the carburettor increases. Unless the throttle is opened very slowly the initial increase in rate of airflow is more rapid than the increase in fuel flow. This leads to a lag before the engine power increases.

The accelerator pump system which normally consists of a plunger assembly in the carburettor attached to the throttle linkage provides extra fuel during that period in which the throttle is being opened. This provides a more balanced fuel/air ratio and consequently smoother engine acceleration.

IDLE CUT-OFF VALVE

This system is normally incorporated with the manual mixture control system (discussed later) and is provided so that the engine can be stopped without leaving a combustible mixture in the induction passages, cylinders, and exhaust system. This is a situation which could easily occur if the engine were stopped by turning off the fuel or ignition switches.

The idle cut-off system utilises a tapered needle which moves into the fuel passage between the float chamber and the carburettor when the mixture control lever is moved to the position marked IDLE CUT-OFF.

MIXTURE CONTROL SYSTEM

As altitude increases, the air becomes less dense, for example, the air at 18000 feet is only half as dense as that at sea level. This means that a cubic foot of space contains only half as many air molecules at 18000 feet as at sea level. However, the action of the carburettor venturi is such that it draws nominally the same volume of air at a given throttle setting regardless of altitude. This means that the amount of fuel being drawn through the carburettor jets will also remain the same. Since the same amount of fuel is supplied to the engine, but the air density is less, the mixture will become richer as altitude increases*. Therefore, to maintain the correct fuel/air ratio, the pilot must be able to adjust the amount of fuel being mixed with the incoming air as altitude increases. This is achieved by moving the mixture knob or lever situated in the cockpit.

A common system now used in light aircraft incorporates a simple shut-off needle in the body of the carburettor. The needle is tapered, and moving the mixture control knob or lever towards the lean position causes the needle to move further into an orifice and so reduce the amount of fuel flowing through the main jet, (Fig. 6-41). This reduction of fuel flow corrects the fuel/air ratio.

The design philosophy of the current light aero engine demands an adequate knowledge of mixture control operation in order that the engine can be handled efficiently and correctly. This is particularly true for flight operations conducted above 4–5000 feet where engine rough-running can easily occur if the mixture control is not used correctly. Although in the early stages of training, a student will be unlikely to operate at heights above 5000 feet, he will be more likely to do so when he has acquired his private pilot's licence and undertakes longer cross-country flights.

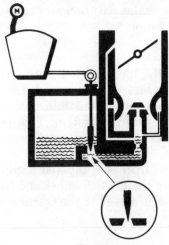

Fig. 6-41

It must also be appreciated that the fuel consumption figures obtained from the tables and graphs in flight/owner's manuals are normally based on the *correct* use of the mixture control system. A student who does not learn and understand the correct use of the mixture control during training will not always be capable of

---

* In actual fact it can be shown that the mixture strength for a venturi type carburettor varies as $\sqrt{(p/w)}$, where p is the air density and w is the fuel density.

conducting safe flight operations once outside the supervision of the training environment.

Basically the mixture control is used to vary the fuel/air ratio for two important reasons:

1. The fuel/air ratio in all reciprocating aero engines is set to give an over rich mixture, and the actual degree of richness varies with the throttle setting, being greatest at full power operation. The purpose of this arrangement is to reduce the possibility of detonation, pre-ignition and overheating occurring in the cylinders. However, when operating at cruise power settings with an engine in normal condition, the possibility of these things occurring will be remote, therefore, it is acceptable for the pilot to achieve greater fuel economy by using the manual mixture control to achieve the correct mixture strength. Further to this, the excess fuel flow as a result of an over rich mixture leads to plug fouling and excess carbon forming on the piston heads and valves. This is particularly so since AVGAS 100LL came into common use. Therefore, good engine handling dictates the use of correct mixture control operation in order to maintain the efficiency and life of the engine.

2. As the aircraft climbs, the surrounding air density decreases, and without some means of adjustment, the fuel/air ratio will become over rich, and the engine will suffer a loss of power. This power loss will be indicated by a gradual drop in RPM (when a fixed pitch propeller is fitted) followed eventually by rough running.

There are several ways of determining the correct setting for the mixture control when it is appropriate to use it. However, the following list represents the simplest method in small training aircraft which are not normally fitted with cylinder head temperature gauges or exhaust gas analysers.

● Set the throttle as required;
● Accurately note the RPM;
● Move the mixture control towards the LEAN position slowly;
● If mixture control is required, it will be indicated by a rise in RPM.
● If a rise in RPM occurs, continue moving the mixture control towards the LEAN position until the highest RPM figure is achieved at which point further movement of the mixture control would cause a drop in RPM.
● Once the RPM peak is passed, move the mixture control slightly towards the RICH position until the peak RPM is restored (this is to ensure that the engine is not in a critically lean condition where detonation may occur).
● The above steps will need to be repeated whenever altitude or power are changed.

The above procedure can be used to obtain *best power mixture* and also to avoid the engine running rough during a climb to an altitude in excess of 5000 feet. Further, it will give a more economical fuel consumption at cruise power settings below 75% power at any altitude, and reduce the possibility of excess carbon deposits being formed on the plugs, piston crowns, and in the cylinders.

Although this manual is not designed to give a comprehensive and detailed explanation of engine efficiency and fuel/air ratios, the following information will be of interest and value to any pilot under training.

In an internal combustion engine, the greatest heat energy derived from the burning of the combustible mixture occurs at a fuel to air ratio of one part fuel to fifteen parts air, or expressed another way, 0.067 lb fuel to 1 lb of air. This is the chemically correct or ideal mixture strength where all the fuel and air is converted into heat energy i.e. no fuel is wasted. If this fuel/air ratio is changed so that the proportion of fuel to air is increased, then excess fuel will be passed through the engine in an unburnt state.

The mixture of 0.067:1 is a theoretical point that can only be demonstrated on a single cylinder in a laboratory. In engines with more than one cylinder, the variations in fuel distribution between the cylinders make it difficult to evaluate the fuel/air ratio in each cylinder. This matter of distributing correct and equal amounts of fuel and air to the various cylinders is one of the greatest problems facing the aircraft engine manufacturers. Because of the unequal fuel/air ratio delivered to the various cylinders, the pilot who practises using an extremely lean mixture setting, so increasing the proportion of air to fuel without the benefit of additional engine instrumentation, could bring about a situation where, for example, all cylinders in the engine are operating at normal temperatures except for one hot cylinder, where the exhaust valve and seat could be overheating badly.

By calibrating and adjusting the carburettor to give a slightly over-rich mixture, the engine designer is able to overcome the problem of having one or more cylinders receiving a mixture ratio which is too lean. By further enriching the mixture, the designer can guard against detonation, pre-ignition and excessive cylinder head temperatures when the engine is operating at very high power settings. It can be seen from this that all aero engines generally operate with an enriched mixture throughout the power range from idling through to full power.

Figure 6-42 illustrates the effect of excess fuel or excess air on engine power. It will be seen that the engine produces its best power at a fuel/air ratio of approximately 0.080 lb of fuel to 1 lb of air and therefore this represents a mixture setting where the demands of efficient power production and fuel economy are both fairly well satisfied.

Although it is possible to achieve greater fuel economy by reducing the mixture strength to 0.067, it is difficult to ensure that this fuel/air ratio will reach all the cylinders of an engine equipped with a simple carburettor. Indiscriminate leaning is not conducive to efficient and safe engine handling, and special instrumentation such as exhaust gas analysers would be necessary. These types of instrument are not normally fitted in simple training aircraft, so a good general purpose fuel mixture will be as shown at 0.080 in the diagram.

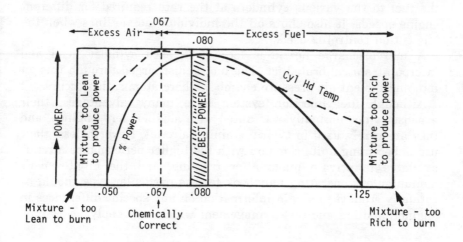

Fig. 6-42

The information contained in this manual illustrates some of the principles involved in mixture control, but, the flight/owner's manual or the engine manual for the specific aircraft or engine type must be the basic reference document when employing mixture control techniques. Finally, it must be clearly understood that the figures for range and endurance as given in tables or graphs in aircraft manuals are normally only applicable when mixture control is utilised.

FUEL INJECTION SYSTEMS

Direct fuel injection systems meter fuel directly into the cylinder and have many advantages over a conventional carburettor system. They reduce the possibility of induction icing since the drop in temperature due to fuel vapourisation (which causes approximately 70% of the temperature drop during mixing of air and fuel at cruise power setting) occurs in or near the cylinder. In addition to this, a direct fuel injection system provides better engine acceleration and improved fuel distribution, leading to greater economy of operation.

Each cylinder has its own individual fuel line and thus the overheating problems associated with normal carburettor systems and caused by uneven fuel distribution to the cylinders, are reduced. This reduces the need to provide a richer mixture than necessary so that the cylinder receiving the leanest mixture will operate properly.

Fuel injection systems vary in detail but basically they consist of a fuel injector, flow divider and fuel discharge nozzle. The fuel injector monitors the volume of air entering the system and meters the fuel flow. The flow divider keeps the fuel under pressure and distributes the fuel to the various cylinders at the rate required for different engine speeds. It also shuts off the individual nozzle lines when the idle cut-off control is used.

A fuel discharge nozzle is located in each cylinder head and incorporates a calibrated jet. The fuel is discharged through this jet into an ambient air pressure chamber where atomisation occurs.

Although fuel injection system have many advantages, their expense is not normally warranted with smaller aero engines, and they are rarely used in typical training aircraft. Nevertheless, their use is becoming quite common with the higher performance aircraft available to private pilots after training, and the flight/owner's manual/pilot's operating handbook for the particular type should be carefully studied to obtain information on any specific differences in engine handling and fuel management which may apply.

DETONATION AND PRE-IGNITION

Normal combustion within the cylinder occurs when the mixture ignites and burns progressively. This produces a normal pressure increase forcing the piston smoothly towards the bottom of the cylinder.

NORMAL BURNING

Fig. 6-43

There is however, a limit to the amount of compression and degree of temperature rise that can be tolerated before the fuel/air mixture reaches a point at which it will ignite spontaneously without the aid of

DETONATION

Fig. 6-44

the sparking plug. This causes an instantaneous combustion, i.e., an explosion, and when this occurs, an extremely high pressure is created within the combustion area. This is called detonation and it is very damaging to the piston top and valves.

In automobile engines, detonation can be identified by a *pinking* noise and the driver can take action to eliminate this by reducing power or changing gear. In aero engines, this characteristic pinking noise cannot be heard, and therefore, the engine designer arranges for the mixture to be richer than normally necessary. This acts as a coolant to prevent the mixture reaching a critical temperature. When the engine is operating at below approximately 70% power, detonation will not normally occur, but it should be borne in mind that the use of fuel of a lower grade than recommended, or over weakening the mixture can produce detonation under most power conditions.

Pre-ignition, as the name implies, means that normal combustion takes place before the sparking plug fires. This condition is often due to localised hot spots (e.g. carbon deposits) becoming incandescent and igniting the mixture. Although pre-ignition can be the result of detonation, it can also be caused by high power operation in lean mixture. Pre-ignition is usually indicated by engine roughness, back firing or a sudden increase in cylinder head temperature.

The best '*in flight*' measures for correcting detonation or pre-ignition are to enrich the mixture, decrease power and/or open the engine cowl flaps (if available).

CARBURETTOR ICING

Under certain atmospheric conditions when the air humidity and temperature are within a particular range, ice will form in the induction system and affect carburettor operation. This will take the form of a reduction in power, rough running, or both, and in severe cases the engine may stop.

It is important that pilots know about induction icing and the manner in which it is formed as well as the precautions to be taken to avoid it and the remedial measures which can overcome the problems.

There are three types of induction system icing and these are:

● Impact icing;
● Fuel (or refrigeration icing);
● Throttle (or venturi icing).

IMPACT ICE

Impact ice is formed by super-cooled water vapour or droplets striking the external induction aperture or filter and freezing on impact. It can also occur inside the induction channel to the carburettor. This type of icing can also affect fuel injection systems as well as those using a normal float type carburettor.

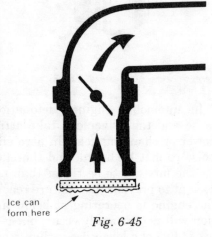

Ice can form here

Fig. 6-45

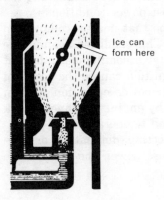

Ice can form here

Fig. 6-46

FUEL ICE

Fuel ice can form at and downstream from the point where fuel is mixed with the incoming air. It occurs if the entrained moisture in the air (and sometimes in the fuel) reaches the icing range (usually 0°C down to −8°C), as a result of the cooling which takes place when the fuel is vapourised. If the temperature drops below −8°C, the moisture forms directly into ice crystals which pass through the system with little or no effect on the engine power, but if the temperature in the system drops to between 0°C and −8°C water will be precipitated from the incoming air and freeze on the walls of the induction passages, throttle butterfly, or any other protrusion in the carburettor passages.

This will effectively reduce the size of the carburettor passage, causing a change to the fuel/air ratio, leading to loss of power and rough running. If the build up of ice is allowed to continue, the rough running will worsen and the engine may stop. Fuel icing is rare in fuel injection systems as the fuel/air mixture is injected directly into the cylinders, which have a considerable heat content.

THROTTLE ICE

This is caused by the sudden drop in temperature as the air expands when passing the venturi and butterfly section of the carburettor passage. In conventional float type carburettors, throttle icing usually occurs in combination with fuel icing which serves to compound the rate of ice accretion.

RECOGNITION

In all forms of induction icing, the main recognition features are, a drop in engine power, followed by rough running. However, because a pilot monitors the RPM less frequently than the ASI or altimeter, he may more quickly recognise the presence of induction icing when in level flight, by noticing a decrease of airspeed for a constant altitude, or a loss of altitude for a constant airspeed.

REMEDIAL ACTIONS

Impact ice, which forms around the engine air intake will normally only occur during flight in cloud or heavy rain at freezing temperatures. The ambient temperature at which impact ice can be expected to build up ranges between 0°C and −8°C in layer type cloud, but can be experienced at temperature as low as −20°C in cumulus cloud.

Pilots should be particularly alert for this type of icing whenever flying in rain, sleet, snow or clouds, especially when ice is seen building up on the windscreen or wing leading edges. It should also be understood that impact ice can occur to the same extent with fuel injection or float type carburation systems. However, most fuel injection systems are equipped with an alternative intake air source situated within the engine cowling, and this should be used according to the aircraft manufacturer's recommendations.

TYPES AND EFFECTS OF CARBURETTOR HEATING SYSTEMS

Fuel and throttle ice can occur whether the aircraft is in or clear of cloud and this is an important point to bear in mind. To combat fuel or throttle icing, it is now normal to equip the aircraft with a carburettor hot air system, or alternatively in some older models of aircraft, a warm air system is employed. This distinction is quite an important one, for whereas hot air systems can normally provide a very substantial amount of heated air into the carburettor passage, the warm air system can only increase the air temperature by a few degrees.

It is apparent from previous statements that if the air temperature in the vicinity of the venturi and butterfly section is say −10°C, it is unlikely that ice will stick to the side walls, butterfly etc. If under these conditions, a few degrees of temperature rise were applied through the use of the warm air system, the temperature would be raised to within the icing range and ice could build up rapidly. No remedial action will be possible unless the aircraft can change altitude, and so effect a change in the outside air temperature. This latter course of action is a somewhat limited remedy as the standard temperature lapse rate is only about 2°C per 1000 feet.

With hot air systems application of carburettor heat will almost always raise the carburettor air temperature well above that at which freezing can occur and can therefore be used either as a precaution against ice formation, or, as a very effective remedy to clear any ice which has already formed.

The most common type of hot air system utilises a heat exchanger incorporated with the exhaust assembly. In some aircraft the carburettor heat is supplied from the same heat exchanger unit as the cabin heat system. The exact form and operation of hot air systems will be particular to the aircraft make and the aircraft manual should be studied carefully to obtain a precise knowledge of its operation.

In all cases, however, it can be generally stated that when symptoms of carburettor icing occur, the pilot should apply full heat to remove it, and then return the control to the cold position. The use of hot air will automatically reduce the engine power by a small amount, due to it being less dense than cold air. This will also result in an increase in the rate at which fuel is consumed.

If a small amount of ice is present, application of hot air will cause a drop in RPM followed almost immediately by a rise. This will denote that the ice has been cleared, following which, cold air can be re-selected.

If icing symptoms return within a short while, the ice should be cleared as described before and consideration should be given to changing the power setting. This latter action will affect the rate at which fuel is being vapourised and in consequence change the temperature in the carburettor passage. For example, if the normal air temperature in the carburettor is −6°C, a sufficient increase in RPM would reduce it to below the icing range and avoid the need to keep the hot air applied through the flight. Although the fuel consumption would be a little higher at the increased power, it would still be more economical than with hot air permanently in use.

It should be appreciated that the use of full heat can increase the fuel consumption by as much as 20% which means that the aircraft's range and endurance would also be reduced by 20%. On long flights, this could result in a significant reduction to operational safety margins.

Note: If carburettor ice has been allowed to build up to any appreciable amount, the correct use of hot air will transform this into water which will be promptly fed directly into the engine causing the rough running to temporarily worsen. In the case of a particularly large build up, the engine could temporarily stop firing. If this occurs, the air should be left in hot, and flying speed maintained. The engine will return to normal firing within a few moments.

OIL SYSTEMS

The primary purpose of engine lubricating oils is to reduce friction and therefore wear between the moving parts. In principle, oil prevents metal to metal contact, and provided the oil film remains unbroken, metallic friction is replaced by fluid friction.

Oil also acts as a cushion and reduces shocks between metal parts. This is particularly important for such components as the engine crankshaft and connecting rods which are subject to high loads when the engine is running.

Additionally, as oil circulates through an engine, it absorbs heat and this is particularly important in the case of the pistons and the internal walls of the cylinder. The oil film between the piston and cylinder wall also produces a seal to prevent gases leaking from the combustion chamber. Finally, during its circulation, oil collects dirt introduced into the engine from the atmosphere and also the carbon particles produced by combustion, these are collected by the oil filter thereby reducing abrasive wear on the internal parts.

PROPERTIES OF OIL

There are several important properties which an engine oil must possess. It must flow freely over a wide range of temperature yet not become so fluid at high temperatures that its viscosity breaks down resulting in too thin a film of oil between moving parts. It must therefore remain viscous enough to withstand high operating temperatures and high bearing pressures. It must also have a high flash and fire point, that is to say, the temperature at which it will produce ignitable vapours and support a flame.

Aviation oils are classified numerically, and the numbers used indicate the degree of viscosity. A high viscosity oil flows slowly and a low viscosity oil flows freely. It is important that the correct grade of oil as recommended by the engine manufacturer is used throughout the life of an engine. Further to this, it should be appreciated that different grades are recommended for the same engine dependent on the average climatic temperature. i.e. in winter or cold climates, a grade of lesser viscosity will be recommended.

LUBRICATION METHODS

Piston engine lubricating systems are of two specific types, those which use a wet sump and those which have a dry sump. The wet sump type stores the oil as an integral part of the engine casing, and the components are lubricated by a pressure pump or simply by splashfeed.

The dry sump type has a separate oil tank located in a convenient position adjacent to the engine. Oil is supplied from the tank by a pressure pump, and having passed through the engine is returned to the tank by a separate scavenge pump.

PUMPS, SUMPS AND FILTERS

Apart from the differences involved in having a sump located at the lower portion of the engine or a separate tank installation, oil systems generally incorporate a supply pump, which forces oil from the sump or tank into and around the moving parts of the engine via drilled passages. Because it is essential to keep the oil as clean as possible, filters are fitted into the system and these absorb the dirt, carbon particles and other foreign matter. Normally the elements of these filters are replaced at regular maintenance intervals and the condition of the engine can often be determined by the type and amount of particles they collect.

Apart from absorbing foreign matter, two important chemical changes take place in the oil during use. These are firstly, *oxidation* which occurs due to contamination from corrosive lead salts produced during combustion, and secondly, the chemical effect of water vapour condensing inside the engine as the oil cools after the engine is stopped. These effects cannot be removed by any system of filters, and for this reason alone, it is important to adhere to the oil change periods recommended by the manufacturer.

TYPICAL SYSTEMS

Apart from the method of storing oil, the wet sump and the dry sump systems are closely similar, and the wet sump type has been chosen for description in the following paragraphs.

The oil is collected and stored in a sump which forms the lower end of the engine casing. An oil pump driven by the engine draws oil out of the sump through an oil screen, (Fig. 6-47). The oil flows through to the pressure side of the pump and then to the engine. It should be appreciated that the oil pump has to provide the correct oil pressure

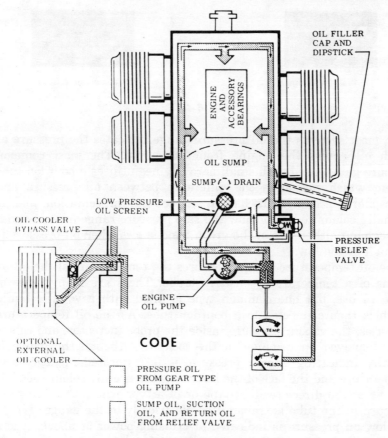

Fig. 6-47

over a range of RPM settings, therefore a relief valve is integrated into the system. If the pump pressure is too high, it is relieved by allowing some of the oil to flow directly back into the sump while the remaining oil travels through an oil cooler (on most lower power engines the oil cooler is an optional item) and then via galleries and passages into the engine.

RECOGNITION OF OIL SYSTEM MALFUNCTION
Two gauges are usually mounted in the cockpit which show the pilot the temperature of the oil and the oil pressure being maintained in the system. It should be noted that the oil temperature shown on the gauge is the temperature of the oil as it leaves the oil cooler, however, some low horsepower engines are not equipped with an oil cooler, and in this case the oil temperature gauge reflects the oil temperature immediately the oil is drawn out of the sump where it has had time to cool before redistribution.

Oil Pressure Gauge

Oil Temperature Gauge

Fig. 6-48

On most systems the oil pressure gauge indicates the pressure at which oil enters the engine from the pump. The most common pressure gauge used with small aero engines utilises a bourdon tube system which measures the difference between oil pressure and atmospheric pressure. It has a simple dial presentation and is normally colour coded to show the safe pressure range (green) and a red segment either side of the green band shows when oil pressure is too high or too low.

The oil temperature gauge measures the temperature of the oil by means of a temperature sensitive probe. There are many types of probe in use, but one common type is filled with a volatile liquid which is then connected to a bourdon tube. As the oil temperature increases, the vapour pressure inside the probe increases, and this is then displayed on a gauge in the cockpit. Although the gauge is actually indicating vapour pressure, it is calibrated in degrees of temperature and the face of the instrument is usually colour coded. It may be of the direct reading type or of a type where the change of pressure in the tube is transmitted electrically to the gauge.

If low oil pressure is indicated at cruising power or above, it is a sign of likely engine failure resulting from too little or no oil available, leaking oil lines, burned out engine bearings or failure of the oil pump. However, because it is possible for an oil pressure or temperature gauge itself to fail, it is advisable to carefully note the readings from the oil temperature gauge in order to decide whether it is the oil system or the gauge which is at fault. For example, if the quantity of oil in the system is low, or is not being properly circulated, a rapid rise in oil temperature will result. If on the other hand, the oil temperature gauge continues to give a normal reading whilst the oil pressure gauge indicates a low pressure it will be a fairly good indication that the oil pressure gauge has become unserviceable.

Finally, the modern aero engine is extremely clean in operation and if, during a pre-flight inspection, oil is seen coating parts of the engine or cowlings, the flight should be cancelled and the fact reported to an engineer.

FUEL SYSTEMS

The aircraft fuel system is designed to store fuel and deliver it to the carburettor in the correct quantity and at sufficient pressure to meet the demands of the engine in all normal flight conditions. A properly designed fuel system ensures a positive and continuous flow of fuel throughout changes in altitude, or sudden acceleration and deceleration of the power plant.

FUEL TANKS

Generally, there are two or more fuel tanks (or fuel cells as they are sometimes called) incorporated into even the simplest fuel system.

Some tanks are constructed of metal and are known as rigid tanks, others are constructed of non-rigid material and depend on the structure of the wing cavity into which they are inserted to support the weight of the fuel within them. A relatively new method of storing fuel in wings is a cell constructed integrally within the wing and this is therefore part of the aircraft structure. This type of construction is often referred to as a *wet wing*.

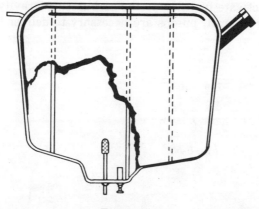

Fig. 6-49

The materials used in tank construction can be aluminium alloy, synthetic rubber, nylon etc. – it must be one which does not react chemically with aviation fuel.

Normally, a sump and drain is provided at the lowest point of the tank and the fuel supply line, which is fitted with a filter, is arranged to terminate at some point higher than the sump. This latter arrangement reduces the possibility of any sludge or sediment which may be present, from blocking the filter.

The top of each tank is vented to the outside air so that atmospheric pressure can be maintained in the tank as the fuel is used up. If this vent becomes blocked for any reason, a suction (reduced pressure) will be created in the area above the head of the fuel and reduce the normal rate of fuel flow. Such a reduced pressure area can eventually cause the flow to cease completely and the engine will stop.

In order to prevent fuel surging about in the tank, due to changes of attitude during flight, the tanks are normally fitted with baffles. An expansion space is also designed into the top of the tank to cater for the expansion of fuel volume whenever the temperature increases. Aircraft certification requirements demand that the fuel caps or the areas adjacent to them are clearly marked with the fuel capacity and fuel grade designation.

FUEL DISTRIBUTION
The basic components of a typical fuel system consist of fuel tanks, fuel lines, selection valves, filters, pumps, quantity indicators, and fuel pressure gauges.

Two significant differences occur in light aircraft fuel feed systems due to the position of the wings where the fuel tanks are normally located. In a high wing aircraft, a simpler system is possible, utilising gravity to activate fuel flow to the carburettor (gravity feed system). In low wing aircraft, pumps are necessary to deliver the fuel to the carburettor.

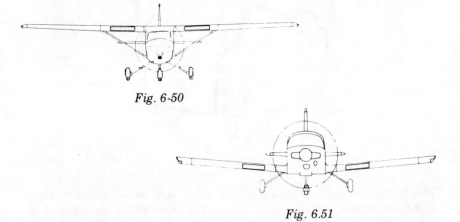

Fig. 6-50

Fig. 6.51

In low wing aircraft, therefore, an electric pump is fitted to pump fuel from the tanks through the lines to the carburettor for starting purposes. Once the engine has started, the mechanical pump driven by the engine takes over and is used to maintain the required fuel pressure. In this system, a fuel pressure gauge is a normal requirement in order to check that the fuel pump is operating properly.

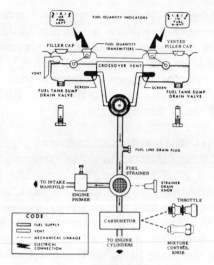

Fig. 6-52

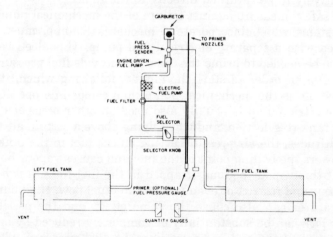

Fig. 6-53

FUEL SELECTION METHODS

From each tank, a fuel line leads to a selector valve in the cockpit. This valve is used by the pilot to either select fuel from the appropriate tank(s) or to shut off the supply.

The fuel valve passages and fuel lines must be of sufficient bore to accommodate the maximum flow demand required by the engine when operating at full power. It is vital when selecting the appropriate tank, to ensure the selector valve is positively seated in the correct position, otherwise the pipe bore will be partially obstructed and only a reduced rate of flow will be possible. This reduced flow could be such that the engine will operate normally at low to cruising power but will be insufficient to meet the engine demand at high power such as at take-off. In this case, a marked loss of power and possible engine stoppage will occur.

With some fuel systems it is recommended that the electric fuel pump is ON and/or the mixture is returned to the RICH position prior to re-selecting fuel tanks during flight.

FUEL, PUMPS (MECHANICAL AND ELECTRICAL)

A mechanical fuel pump is fitted to those systems in which the fuel tanks are positioned at or below engine level. The pump is used to provide a continuous supply of fuel from the tank to the carburettor and it is normally mounted on the accessory section of the engine.

For safety reasons, engine driven fuel pumps are normally designed to be capable of supplying more fuel than the particular engine requires. They are therefore fitted with a relief valve system which permits unused fuel to return to the inlet side of the pump, or alternatively to be returned directly to the tank.

As a safety measure against failure of the mechanical pump, those fuel systems which incorporate a mechanical pump, must also be equipped with a separate electrical fuel pump. This electrical pump will also be needed to prime the lines and provide fuel pressure to the carburettor in order to start the engine, following which, it can be switched off as the mechanical pump then comes into operation.

The electric pump is usually also used on other occasions such as during tank re-selection, and when flying above a certain altitude. At high altitudes, the air pressure acting on the fuel in the tank is low. This lowers the boiling point of the fuel and causes vapour bubbles to form. If this vapour becomes trapped in the fuel lines, a *vapour lock* may occur and restrict or even prevent any fuel flow. High outside air temperatures can also cause the same effect, and the possibility of vapour lock can be substantially or completely reduced by operating the electric pump and so increasing the fuel pressure within the tanks and fuel lines.

Although small high wing aircraft do not require fuel pumps as they rely on gravity to provide the fuel pressure, those high wing aircraft with more powerful engines and greater performance will usually be equipped with an electrical pump to assist in overcoming starting and vapour locking problems.

When electric pumps are not employed for priming purposes during starting, a hand operated pump known as a *priming pump* is fitted in the cockpit. After the fuel has been turned on, the fuel flows through the primary system and operation of the manual pump forces fuel directly into the induction system, by-passing the carburettor.

FUEL GRADES AND COLOURING

Fuel is a substance which, when combined with oxygen, will burn and produce heat. Liquid fuels are generally accepted as the most ideal fuel to use in internal combustion engines, but the liquid needs to be vaporised or partially vaporised in order to burn properly.

Aviation gasoline (AVGAS) is a liquid which contains chemical energy. This is converted into heat energy during combustion which in turn produces a pressure on the piston heads, and in so doing produces the mechanical energy to turn the propeller.

AVGAS consists almost entirely of hydrocarbons, that is, compounds composed of hydrogen and carbon. Even though great care is taken during the refining of fuel, some impurities in the form of sulphur, and absorbed water will always be present. This water content cannot be avoided because fuel is exposed to the moisture contained in the atmosphere and which enters the tanks via the vent openings.

The volatility of a fuel (its tendency to vaporise) is controlled during manufacture. If fuel vaporises too readily it can cause vapour in the fuel lines and so decrease the rate of fuel flow. If the fuel does not vaporise readily it can cause difficult engine starting, uneven fuel distribution to the cylinder and retarded engine acceleration.

Automobile fuel is not controlled during manufacture to the same tolerances as aviation fuel, nor is its storage and transportation subject to the same quality control, therefore automobile fuels should not be used in aero engines (except where permitted by the Airworthiness Section of the C.A.A.).

During compression and combustion it is possible under certain conditions for detonation to take place. Detonation is an uncontrolled rate of burning which is akin to an explosion, and to reduce this possibility AVGAS incorporates a fuel additive known as tetraethyl lead (TEL). This TEL does, however, have certain corrosive properties which can lead to chemical deposits on the sparking plug electrode, valves, and pistons, and therefore its use has to be kept to a minimum.

Fuel grades

Aero engines vary widely in the power they can produce. Some aircraft use small engines as low as 65 HP (489 kW), whereas others have HP outputs which run into thousands. Because of the markedly different requirements and performance of these various engines, it is necessary to produce varying grades of aviation fuel, and these are identified by a numerical code system. This grading system differentiates between fuels which have low or high anti-knock (anti-detonation) qualities. The higher the grade the greater the compression the air/fuel mixture can stand without detonating, and therefore it is particularly important for a pilot to see that his aircraft is provided with the correct grade of fuel recommended by the manufacturer.

To assist in identification, all aviation gasoline contains a coloured dye and the allocation of different colours to different fuel grades is standardised throughout the world. Small aero engines now operate on AVGAS Grade 100LL (the LL stands for low lead content) which is coloured blue, and is easily recognisable by looking into the tank through the filler orifice.

INSPECTION FOR CONTAMINATION AND CONDENSATION

Fuel contamination occurs when any material other than that provided for in its specification is introduced into the fuel. This material generally consists of such items as, water, rust, sand, dust or micro-organisms (microbia).

Although rigorous precautions are taken to ensure that fuel pumped into an aircraft contains as little water as possible, an aircraft fuel containing no water is almost an impossibility. This is due primarily to the affinity which hydrocarbon fuels have for water.

All aviation fuels absorb moisture from the air and contain water in liquid form. Whenever the temperature of the fuel is decreased, some of the condensed water comes out of solution and falls slowly to the bottom of the tank. Whenever the temperature of the fuel increases, water is drawn from the atmosphere to maintain a saturated solution. Therefore changes of temperature result in a continuous accumulation of water. In temperate climates the rate of this accumulation is fairly low, but it will be accelerated during aircraft operation due to the significant change of temperature with altitude.

Additionally and during changes of ambient temperature, water can condense out as liquid droplets on the inside walls of the tank and then settle into the fuel. Keeping the aircraft tanks topped up particularly overnight when temperature changes are usually most rapid or on those occasions when the aircraft is not being used for several days will greatly reduce this condensation effect.

Rust from storage and ground pipelines is an additional contaminant and a higher degree of filtration is required to eliminate it.

Dust and sand may accumulate in small quantities via tank openings and whenever fuel is being transferred. These particles tend to gravitate towards the lowest point in the fuel system. The entry of rust, dust and sand particles into the aircraft fuel lines, is normally reduced by the fitting of filters at suitable points in the system.

Microbia, are more prevalent in unleaded fuels such as those used in turbine engines, but can to a smaller extent develop in AVGAS particularly in climatic conditions of heat and high humidity. Micro-organisms tend to mat together and form a slimy brown layer in the fuel. The growth of these bacteria can cause blocking of filters and fuel screens.

FUEL STRAINERS AND DRAINS
In order to reduce the possibility of fuel contamination, all fuel systems are equipped with fuel strainers and drain points which are easily accessible.

Strainers are installed in the fuel tank outlets and sometimes in the tank filler necks. These are normally of a fairly coarse mesh and prevent only the larger particles from entering the fuel system. Other strainers which are of a finer mesh are usually provided in the carburettor fuel inlets and in the fuel lines.

In light aircraft, a main strainer often called a *gascolator* is fitted at the lowest point of the fuel system and fuel which has left the tank has to flow through this strainer before reaching the carburettor. Its purpose is to trap water and other foreign matter.

The strainers usually consist of a small metal, glass or perspex bowl which can be opened during a pre-flight inspection to drain fuel and with it any water or sediment. A typical gascolator is shown in Fig. 6-54.

Fig. 6-54   Fig. 6-55

Because it is practically impossible to drain all the water held in the tanks by straining the fuel system, it is also necessary to fit each fuel tank with a separate drain unit. These are installed at the bottom of the tank sump and when these are of the *finger* or quick drain type (Fig. 6-55), they should be manually operated for a short while at frequent periods. The particular aircraft manual will contain the operating instructions for their use during pre-flight inspections. Because fuel system designs differ significantly it is advisable to use the information contained in the particular flight/owner's manual/pilot's operating handbook rather than rely on some generally accepted procedure.

It must also be appreciated that merely opening a strainer or fuel drain and allowing fuel to flow out onto the ground will not in itself reveal the presence of water. It is only by collecting the fuel in a small glass or perspex cup or jar that the presence of water in the system can be detected. Water being heavier than fuel, will separate and settle in the lower portion of the container. If water is discovered then the tank and/or fuel system should be drained until no indications of water are present.

Fuel

Water

Fig. 6-56

A further point with regard to straining procedures is that after refuelling, it is advisable to allow at least 15 minutes before opening any strainers or drains. This is to allow sufficient time for any water to settle down to the bottom of the tanks, and the lowest point of the fuel system.

RECOGNITION OF MALFUNCTION/MISMANAGEMENT

Any situation in which fuel is available in the tanks but is not able to reach the engine, is known as *fuel starvation*. The components which are most likely to malfunction and cause fuel starvation are the pumps and filters. Mechanical pump failure, although rare, is nevertheless capable of producing a hazardous situation unless the back-up electric fuel pump procedures are quickly performed.

For example, a fuel pump failure at altitude will normally allow sufficient time for the electric pump to be switched on and take over the task of maintaining fuel pressure and an adequate supply of fuel to the engine. However, aircraft manuals recommend that electric pumps are checked on the ground and switched on prior to take-off and landing, thus permitting a supply of fuel to the engine even if the mechanical pump fails.

It must be appreciated that if the electric pump is OFF and the mechanical pump fails, the engine will stop only after most of the fuel has been drawn from the lines. This will therefore mean a significant delay following the switching on of the electric pump during which pressure is restored, the fuel line primed, and fuel is delivered to the carburettor. If the aircraft is at low altitude, such as when

ON

OFF

Fig. 6-57

taking-off or landing, there could be insufficient time available for the engine to restart.

Blocked filters will naturally starve the engine of fuel, but as most aircraft have more than one tank, the greatest hazard will occur if the carburettor filter itself becomes blocked. Rigid maintenance cycles and meticulous re-fuelling procedures usually ensure that blocked filters are a very unusual occurrence, but should foreign matter block filters during flight, it can sometimes be dislodged by sharply rocking the wings or pitching the aircraft.

Fuel system malfunction

Sudden loss of power without any accompanying mechanical noise or vibration is usually indicative of fuel starvation or exhaustion. Indications of impending power failure due to lack of sufficient fuel can normally be obtained via the fuel contents and fuel pressure gauges.

In the event that the fuel gauge still shows a reasonable quantity of fuel, it may be that the mixture control is in a *too lean* position. This for example could occur following a descent at low or nil power from high altitude and when the throttle is re-opened to the cruise power position.

When the aircraft is equipped with an electric fuel pump this should be switched on immediately if the appropriate tank gauge is still giving a positive indication of fuel in the tank.

In those cases where a tank has inadvertently been run dry, the manufacturer's instructions should be followed in relation to the correct procedure to be followed when changing fuel tanks during flight, e.g. the switching on of an electric pump before tank re-selection may be recommended or alternatively its use may be recommended only after the tank change has been made.

Fuel system mismanagement

By far the most common reason for engine failure is mismanagement of the fuel system. This can result in the engine stopping due to fuel exhaustion or fuel starvation.

In relation to fuel exhaustion, past experience with fuel gauges in light aircraft has revealed that when the fuel contents are low, it is often impossible for a pilot to know with sufficient accuracy how much fuel is left for him to decide whether or not to continue his flight and consequently pilots should exercise the greatest caution in fuel management.

A useful general rule to apply to the operation of light aeroplanes is that pilots should not rely on the quantity of fuel left in the tanks when the gauges indicate one third full or less in straight and level flight. The more obvious general precautions that should be taken include physical checks of the amount and grade of fuel in the tanks before take-off, and the accurate calculation of the amount of fuel required for the intended flight including that needed for taxying, take-off, climb to cruising altitude, plus a sensible allowance to cover a possible diversion en route due to weather or other reasons.

The general definition of fuel starvation is, any occurrence which interrupts, reduces or terminates the correct supply of fuel to the engine, even though there is sufficient fuel in the tanks. Fuel starvation may occur for a variety of reasons and it is essential that all pilots be thoroughly conversant with their aircraft fuel system and the correct fuel management procedures before take-off and during flight.

A summary of fuel management pointers is listed below. These should be carefully studied and applied.

● Make adequate pre-flight preparation to ensure that sufficient clean fuel of the correct grade is on board the aircraft for the distance to be covered and the time to be flown, plus an adequate reserve.

● Know the total usable fuel on board. Most aircraft fuel tanks carry a quantity of unusable fuel and this cannot be included when calculating the fuel amount which is to be consumed during a flight.

● Before flight, make a visual inspection to assess the fuel quantity in the tanks. Complete trust in the fuel gauges has often resulted in fuel depletion before reaching the destination and accidents in consequence.

● Make a thorough drain check of the fuel sumps, prior to flight following the fuel draining procedures as recommended in the aircraft manual.

● During the pre-flight inspection, ensure that all tank vents are undamaged and clear of obstructions.

● Positively determine that manual priming pumps are closed and in the locked position prior to flight.

● When practical, check fuel flow from all tanks prior to take-off. Never select a tank immediately before take-off or landing, but always allow time after selection to ensure that the fuel supply to the carburettor is being maintained.

● Know and understand the positions of the fuel selector valves. Markings should be clearly legible, and the valves should be easy and smooth to operate with a positive detent action.

● Be completely familiar with the operation of the electric fuel pumps.

● When switching from one tank to another, double check the quantity of fuel available as shown by the appropriate fuel gauge and after switching, re-check that the new position of the fuel selector valve is the correct one.

● After switching tanks, monitor the fuel pressure (when pressure gauges are fitted) for a short while to ensure that fuel is flowing correctly from the selected tank(s).

COOLING SYSTEMS

The temperature generated in the gases within the cylinders of an aero engine during the use of maximum cruising power may be in the order of 2000°C and even greater than this at maximum power. Although the internal combustion engine is a heat machine which converts the chemical energy of the fuel into mechanical power, it does not do so without some loss of energy.

THE PURPOSE OF COOLING SYSTEMS

This loss of energy may amount to 60 to 70% of the original energy in the fuel, and unless most of this waste heat is rapidly removed, the cylinders may become hot enough to cause damage to the engine or even complete failure of the power plant.

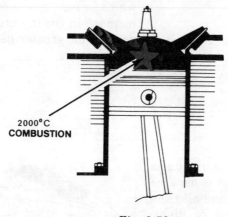

2000°C
COMBUSTION

Fig. 6-58

There are four main reasons why excessive heat should be avoided and these are:

- It weakens the engine components and so shortens engine life
- It reduces the efficiency of the lubrication system
- It can cause detonation to occur
- It affects the behaviour of the combustion of the fuel/air charge.

METHODS OF COOLING

Cooling systems are therefore designed to transfer the excess heat from the cylinders to the air, however, this is not simply a matter of arranging for the cylinders to be placed in the airstream. For example, Fig. 6-59 shows that when air passes around a cylinder, flow breakaway occurs at the rear and this portion of the cylinder will receive inadequate cooling which will lead to a localised hot spot and possible detonation with subsequent damage to the cylinder wall etc.

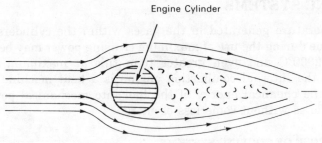

Engine Cylinder

Fig. 6-59

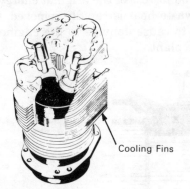

Cooling Fins

Fig. 6-60

To improve the normal cooling action of the air, the external area of the cylinder is fitted with fins which give it a considerable increase in cooling area and also provide for greater heat transfer by radiation.

Air is forced into cowling ducts from the increased pressure area behind the propeller and also due to the forward speed of flight, thus providing a cooling air pressure system which is then ducted by baffles to achieve the maximum cooling effect on the cylinders.

Cowling Ducts

Fig. 6-61

Increased cooling capacity and the avoidance of local hot spots is obtained by carefully designed cowlings and baffles which collect air and direct it around the cylinders.

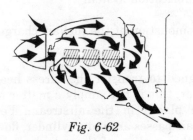

Fig. 6-62

The cylinder baffles are metal shields designed and arranged to direct the flow of air evenly around all parts of the cylinders. This even distribution of the airflow aids in preventing local hot spots in any one cylinder, or more than one cylinder from becoming excessively hotter than the rest. The air is then expelled out of the cowled area via apertures at the bottom and rear of the engine compartment.

In the case of higher power engines with a greater number of cylinders and therefore a larger amount of excess heat to remove, it is normal to control the volume of air passing through the cooling system by using cowl flaps which can be adjusted by the pilot during flight so exercising greater control over the cylinder temperatures. Figure 6-63 is an illustration of a cowl flap system. Closing of the cowl flaps reduces the volume of airflow passing through the engine compartment, and opening the flaps increases the volume of air leading to increased cooling.

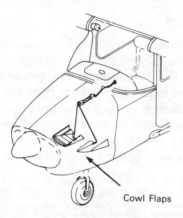

Cowl Flaps

Fig. 6-63

Some cooling installations use a liquid coolant to remove excess heat from the power plant, but these are not in common use with light aircraft. Glycol is the normal coolant used with this method, and after circulating around the engine, it is directed through a radiator to cool it down before it continues its cooling cycle.

OPERATION OF THE AIR COOLING SYSTEM

A cylinder head temperature gauge is fitted when cowling flaps are an integral part of the cooling system. This instrument is normally colour coded and indicates cylinder head temperature. Cowl flaps are either manually or electrically operated from a lever or switch in the cockpit.

Fig. 6-64

Whenever the engine is running, pilots should be careful to monitor this gauge, particularly during extended ground operations, or when the aircraft is climbing or descending. The aircraft manual usually gives information on the best cylinder head temperature to maintain, and sometimes this is indicated by colour coding on the gauge.

If at any stage of a flight, the cylinder head temperature gauge shows excessively high readings, the pilot should take any or all of the following actions:

- Ensure the cowl flaps are fully open.
- Enrich the mixture.
- Reduce the power being used.
- If possible, increase the airspeed.

VACUUM SYSTEM

The power plant fitted to an aircraft is also harnessed to drive ancillary systems, one of which is the suction system which is the source of power for the operation of the gyroscopes fitted into the attitude indicator and heading indicator. Sometimes the gyros in the turn and balance indicator or turn co-ordinator are also operated by the suction system, but current practice is to drive the gyros of these latter instruments by electricity thereby providing a safety factor should the suction system become inoperative during flight.

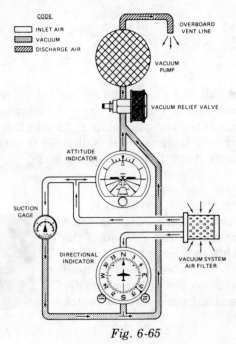

Fig. 6-65

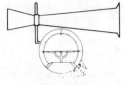

Fig. 6-66

The vacuum system in earlier aircraft was operated by means of an external venturi, and this method is still used by a small number of light aircraft in use today. The more modern method of operating a vacuum system is by means of a suction pump driven by the engine.

In high performance aircraft, electricity is universally used to drive all the gyroscopic instruments as this has a distinct advantage in those aircraft which operate at high altitudes where the reduced density can cause problems in providing sufficient power to operate a gyroscope.

The vacuum system spins the instrument gyro by sucking a continuous stream of air against specially shaped indentations in the rotor (buckets) and so causes the gyro to spin at a very high speed. This air is drawn in through an aperture in the instrument case and then passes out via the suction pump into the atmosphere.

The degree of vacuum normally required to drive the gyros is between $3\frac{1}{2}$ and $5\frac{1}{2}$ inches of mercury and this is usually controlled by a vacuum relief valve located in the supply line. When turn and balance indicators are also driven from the suction source, they are fitted with an additional regulator valve as they require a lower suction pressure than the attitude and heading indicators.

SUCTION PUMP

The engine driven suction pump used in light aircraft is usually of the vane type. This can be mounted on the engine block and driven by the engine crankshaft via a pulley and belt arrangement. The size of the pump used and its capacity, varies according to the number of instruments to be operated.

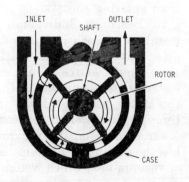

COMPONENTS OF THE VACUUM SYSTEM

These consist of the pump, an air/oil separator (oil recuperator), a vacuum regulator, a relief valve, filters and a suction gauge.

Oil recuperator

The oil recuperator is a metal box unit containing a filter or baffle. In this unit, the lubricating and cooling oil from the pump is separated from the air, following which, the oil is returned back to the engine sump, and the air vented back to atmosphere. The latest type of suction pump is self lubricating, and when this type is used, an oil recuperator is not required.

Vacuum regulator

This is essentially a pressure relief valve in reverse. A spring loaded valve can be adjusted to meet the required suction and if the vacuum in the system builds up above this pressure, (as it will at high engine RPM), the valve is lifted off its seat permitting atmospheric pressure to enter the system and thereby regulate the amount of vacuum developed.

A check valve is also normally fitted in the system to prevent a reverse flow of air should the engine backfire and so reverse the pump flow direction. This might cause serious damage to the instruments.

Vacuum gauge

This gauge is fitted in the cockpit and is often colour coded so that the pilot can see at a glance the value of the vacuum being created in the system. Many of these gauges incorporate a red *doll's eye* which appears whenever the pump fails or the engine is shut down.

Filter system

Air filters are used to prevent foreign matter from entering the system and damaging the gyro bearings. Individual filters may be installed for each instrument or a master air filter may be used. The master air filter acts as a single source of air supply to all the instruments connected to the system. When this filter becomes dirty, the total airflow through the system is reduced and results in a lower reading on the vacuum gauge, thus it has the advantage of giving an early warning of vacuum loss, which would not be so clearly noticed if an individual filter to each instrument was used.

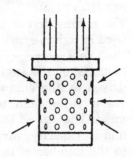

RECOGNITION OF MALFUNCTION

This will be recognised by the vacuum gauge reading too high, too low, or failing to show a reading at all. Incorrect suction will normally be caused by dirty filters or by incorrect operation of the suction relief valve. A zero reading on the suction gauge will be evidence that the vacuum pump has failed or the gauge has become unserviceable but because the instrument gyros run down within a few minutes a vacuum pump failure will normally be initially recognised by erratic, sluggish or incorrect readings from the gyro instruments.

ELECTRICAL SYSTEM

Electrical energy is widely used to provide power for many of the aircraft systems. Such systems or services typically comprise: the radio, lighting equipment, pitot heater, flaps, starter motor, retractable landing gear, some flight and engine instruments, and similar items.

Aircraft manuals normally give details on the operation of each system and include a simple wiring diagram of the electric circuit and the services supplied by it.

Light aircraft are normally equipped with what is known as a direct current single wire, negative ground electrical system. The circuit commences through a single wire carrying the positive current and is completed by grounding each electrical service to the airframe structure. In the wiring diagram (Fig. 6-67), the ground or earthing connection is shown by the symbol $\equiv$.

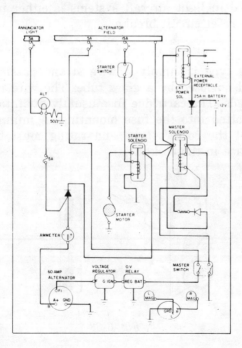

Fig. 6-67

The circuit is powered by an electric current obtained from either a generator or an alternator. Older aircraft use generators but alternators which are more efficient at low RPM than generators, are normally fitted to all new aircraft. A battery supplies power for engine starting and acts as a reserve source of supply should the generator or alternator fail. During normal operation of the engine the generator/alternator charges the battery as required.

Other components are the master switch which is used to bring the electrical power on line and a voltage regulator which controls the rate of charge from the generator to the battery. An ammeter is fitted to the system to indicate the rate of current flowing either to or from the battery. Voltmeters which measure the electrical force which is available to deliver the current are sometimes included in the system.

An optional component is an external power source socket, which can be used to plug an external power supply into the electrical system during periods of ground maintenance when the engine is not running or to conserve the aircraft battery when starting the engine.

As a precaution against fire risk or damage to equipment from overloading, each electrical circuit is normally provided with a fuse or thermal trip contact breaker. The type of fuse or contact breaker most commonly used in light aircraft systems is either in the form of a cartridge or a reset circuit breaker.

TYPES OF FUSES

The cartridge type is simply a wire strand passing between two terminals and enclosed by a glass tube. The wire burns out if the circuit overloads. The cartridge fuse usually fits into a cap which is screwed or slotted into the fuse mounting. A minimum number of spare fuses of the correct type and rating must be carried in a convenient place in the cockpit.

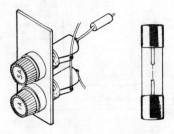

Fig. 6-68

The circuit breaker fuse is normally of the *press to reset* type. If the electrical circuit overloads, the push button pops out and isolates the circuit from the electrical supply.

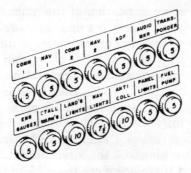

Fig. 6-69

Basically, there are two types of circuit breaker. One type has to be re-set manually by pressing the push button which protrudes from its mounting and is known as a manual re-set circuit breaker. The other, known as an automatic reset circuit breaker, uses a bimetallic strip which consists of two metals of dissimilar thermal expansion which are bonded together and attached to a fixed base. If the circuit becomes overheated the strip curls back from the contact point, and the circuit is broken. When the strip cools down, the strip straightens again and presses against the contact point reactivating the circuit. This type of device is often used in the case of fuel gauges or turn and balance indicators, the readings from which could be vital to a pilot during flight.

Whenever a fuse burns out or a manual circuit trips, and there are no indications of damage to the system e.g. odour or smoke, allow at least two minutes for the circuit to cool down before replacing the fuse or resetting the circuit breaker. After this, if the fuse again burns out or the circuit breaker trips, the pilot should switch off the services supplied through the circuit and report the unserviceability after landing.

ALTERNATORS/GENERATORS

The alternator or generator will normally supply all the power needed to drive the various services incorporated in the electrical system. The electrical pressure that causes electricity to flow is measured in *volts* and the rate at which electricity flows is measured in *amperes* (usually shortened to amps).

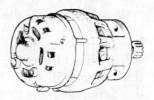

Fig. 6-70

Light aircraft normally use 14 or 18 volt systems and the current capacity of the particular generator or alternator used varies between 35 and 60 amperes.

The ammeter gives an indication of the amount of electric power being used by the electrical services and the more services in use the higher the amperage taken. For example, assume a typical light single engined aircraft which has a 14 volt system and a 25 amp hour battery with an alternator capable of generating 60 amperes. When the engine is switched off and the alternator is not charging, the battery would supply the service with 25 amps for one hour after which it would be fully discharged. Alternatively, it could supply electric current at the rate of 1 amp for 25 hours.

With the engine running and the alternator charging, a rate of 60 amps is supplied and therefore more than 25 amps is available with any excess power being used to charge the battery. If the rate at which current is used is more than 60 amps, the alternator supply would be exceeded and current would automatically be taken from the battery which would eventually become discharged. It is therefore important to monitor the ammeter to ensure that the rate at which current is being used does not exceed the supply from the alternator.

Originally, generators (which supply direct current, DC) were used in aircraft because direct current is used in most of the aircraft's electrical services. However, modern technology has produced a type of generator known as an alternator. Although this initially produces alternating current, it is internally rectified into direct current for use by the aircraft electrical system. Other advantages are that alternators are lighter, more compact and capable of functioning effectively at idle power settings, thereby preventing a current drain from the batteries during taxying and low-powered descents.

BATTERIES – CAPACITY AND CHARGING
It has already been stated that battery capacity is measured in amp hours which in effect is a measure of the amount of electrical energy that the battery contains when in a fully charged condition. Batteries are also rated by their voltage, (electrical pressure) and those used in most aircraft are either of the 12 or 24 volt type. A 12 volt battery is used with a 14 volt system and a 24 volt battery is used with a 28 volt system. The reason the battery has a slightly lower voltage than the electrical system in which it is used is related to the charging operation. For example, if 14 volts are applied to a 12 volt battery it will become fully charged, but if less than 12 volts are being applied, the battery will resist the charge and try to send the power back to the generator or alternator. In other words, it will refuse to be charged. Therefore by having a charging system of slightly higher voltage than the battery, this situation is avoided.

The voltage output from the generator or alternator is kept at the correct level by a voltage regulator. This component is therefore a voltage limiting device, which is also designed to prevent the battery trying to force electricity into the generator when the generator output falls below that designated for the system.

Should the voltage regulator fail, the generator may supply a greater voltage than that which the system was designed for. This would result in the battery becoming overcharged, with a risk of more permanent damage.

The most common battery used in light aircraft is the lead-acid type which creates electricity by reaction between the lead plates and the liquid electrolyte (dilute suphuric acid).

In order to protect the aircraft structure from any inadvertent spillage of acid the battery is normally housed in an enclosed compartment or box. A vent from this box to atmosphere is then arranged to exhaust the gases, hydrogen and oxygen, which form whenever the battery is being charged.

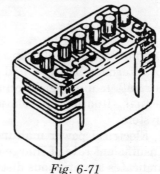

Fig. 6-71

RECOGNITION AND PROCEDURES IN THE EVENT OF MALFUNCTION
The failure of any electrical service could be an indication of an overload in the circuit causing the fuse or circuit breaker protecting the particular circuit to blow. In this case, the fuse or circuit breaker should be inspected and at least two minutes should be allowed before replacing the fuse with another one of the correct amperage rating or re-setting the circuit breaker.

Apart from a situation in which the particular protection device fails, there is also the question of whether the generator or alternator is supplying the necessary power to operate the electrical service, or to charge the battery. This will be indicated by the ammeter and a typical ammeter presentation of this situation is shown in Fig. 6-73(a).

Fig. 6-72

When the engine is not running, the electrical services will be driven by power taken from the battery and the ammeter will indicate the amount of amps being used indicating discharge. Once the engine is running, the generator or alternator will be operating and providing power for the electrical services and also to charge the battery as required, during which, the ammeter will show the rate at which the battery is being charged.

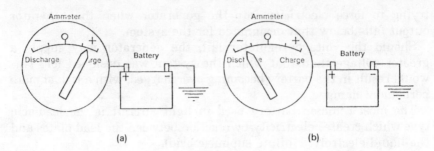

(a)   (b)

Fig. 6-73

Ammeter presentation may vary according to whether a generator or alternator is fitted and the pilot will need to study the particular aircraft manual to interpret the ammeter readings and assess the actual situation in relation to the status of the electrical power system.

Electrical power malfunction usually falls into two categories, i.e. insufficient rate of charge or excessive rate of charge. If the ammeter indicates a continuous discharge rate, the generator or alternator will be supplying either insufficient power, or no power to the system. In this case, the use of electric services should be reduced to the absolute minimum, and the flight terminated as soon as safely possible.

In the event that an excessive rate of charging is occurring, the battery will overheat and evaporate the liquid electrolyte at an excessive rate. Also, if the fault lies in the voltage regulator, the electronic components e.g. radio etc. could be adversely affected.

Most modern aircraft are equipped with an overvoltage sensor which will shut down the alternator and illuminate a warning light in the cockpit to more quickly warn the pilot of this situation.

The actual procedures applicable to particular models of aircraft when a generator or alternator malfunctions will vary and the pilot must study the flight/owner's manual/pilot's operating handbook to ascertain the actions which should be taken.

THE VARIABLE PITCH PROPELLER

Most small training aircraft are equipped with fixed pitch propellers which normally rotate at the same speed as the engine crankshaft. With this type the engine and propeller revolutions are shown by a revolutions per minute gauge (tachometer or RPM gauge) fitted to the aircraft's instrument panel.

Aircraft fitted with more powerful engines will normally be equipped with variable pitch propellers with an integrated component known as a controllable speed unit. This type of installation will utilise a manifold pressure gauge and a tachometer to indicate the amount of engine power being used for a particular RPM.

To understand the principle of the manifold pressure gauge, one must first consider that when the engine is not running, the air in the manifold system is relatively stationary and the pressure inside the intake manifold is the same as the outside atmosphere. However, when the engine is running, the throttle butterfly controls the amount of air entering the engine. If the throttle butterfly is wide open, the amount of air being ingested by the engine is at a maximum and in the case of a normally aspirated engine (non supercharged) the maximum manifold pressure will be slightly less than that of the outside air pressure. If the throttle is now partially closed, it will act as a restriction to the engine's air supply and at any given RPM there will now be a smaller pressure drop on the intake side of the butterfly but a further reduction of pressure will occur on the engine side of the butterfly. In effect, the engine will be acting as a pump and pulling the air through the venturi and past the butterfly.

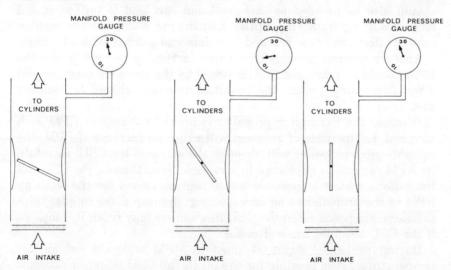

When the engine is not running, the pressure inside the manifold system and cylinders is the same as atmospheric pressure.

When the engine is idling or at low power, a depression occurs on the engine side of the butterfly.

With the throttle wide open, the air pressure (manifold pressure) is almost equal to the atmospheric pressure for the altitude being flown.

Fig. 6-74

Changing the throttle position will vary the manifold pressure which is available to the cylinders during the intake stroke, therefore the power developed will depend on the manifold pressure available. If the manifold pressure is kept constant and the propeller revolutions are increased, this also will produce more power. This is because the number of power strokes per unit time is increased. It can therefore be seen that an increase of power can be obtained by increasing the manifold pressure or increasing the RPM because either of these actions will increase the mass flow of air through the engine and hence the horsepower produced.

HANDLING AND LIMITATIONS

The actual combinations of manifold pressure and RPM to use during cruising, climbing or descending flight will vary in different circumstances, but the flight/owner's manual or pilot's operating handbook will contain advice on the best combinations to use for the different conditions.

Nevertheless, the pilot should appreciate in general that when operating the engine in the high power range, the use of high manifold pressure and low RPM is inadvisable because with this combination, there is a strong possibility that detonation will occur. On the other hand, the use of a high RPM and low manifold pressure should also be avoided as this condition can lead to broken piston rings resulting from ring flutter and during a descent the sudden cooling effect can cause cracked cylinders and warped exhaust valves.

Another general point is that when increasing to high power the RPM should be increased first, followed by the manifold pressure and when decreasing power, the manifold pressure should be reduced first.

Whereas the fixed pitch propeller is prone to change of RPM with airspeed, i.e. increase of airspeed will cause an increase of RPM, the variable pitch propeller will, through the action of the CSU, maintain its RPM regardless of change in airspeed. Nevertheless, the CSU has limitations and it is possible on certain occasions for the limiting RPM of the propeller to be exceeded e.g. in steep dives coupled with excessive airspeeds when the CSU mechanism may reach its stops, or if the CSU becomes unserviceable.

During prolonged flight at constant RPM and cold outside air temperatures, it is possible for the oil in the CSU system to become very viscous and result in sluggish operation of the CSU. To avoid this, the pilot should exercise the CSU by momentarily changing the RPM at frequent intervals, and in any event, the RPM must be carefully monitored whenever operating at high airspeeds or during sudden application of the throttle to high manifold pressure settings.

GROUND CHECKS

Apart from the normal care which should be taken whenever engine power checks are carried out on the ground, the variable pitch propeller should be exercised at least once through its full range or in the case of feathering propellers as recommended in the aircraft manual.

This is to check that the CSU is operating satisfactorily and that the oil in the CSU is circulating properly prior to flight. The exact details of this procedure will be given in the flight/owner's manual or pilot's operating handbook for the particular aircraft type.

ENGINE HANDLING

The modern aero engine is extremely rugged and reliable but like most pieces of machinery, it can be damaged by improper handling. Embryo pilots must also understand that the penalties for mishandling an aircraft engine are far greater than mishandling a car engine.

GROUND CONSIDERATIONS

The three most important factors relating to engine handling during ground operation are:

- Care of the propeller;
- Oil and cylinder head temperatures;
- Avoidance of sparking plug fouling.

Care of the propeller

When taxying over rough ground or transitting from grass to tarmac areas or vice versa, the propeller ground clearance must be borne in mind. In nosewheel aircraft which are heavily laden, the propeller tip may only be some six to nine inches above the ground surface and the effect of crossing even shallow ground depressions will reduce this clearance. Additionally, sudden bursts of power will often cause the nosewheel oleo to depress, lowering the propeller tip still further.

Rough ground should therefore be taxied over very slowly and ridges and depressions on the surface should wherever possible be crossed at an angle of 45° and, during this crossing, the control column should be held back to reduce the weight on the nosewheel.

Engine run-ups must be performed in areas which are clear of loose stones and similar debris. The vortices which are shed from the propeller tips are very powerful at high power settings and can easily pick up stones and similar material drawing them up onto the propeller blades. Due to the speed of propeller rotation, even small gravel can cause significant nicks and scratches to the propeller blade, as well as damaging the airframe and tailplane surfaces.

Oil and cylinder head temperatures

The engine in a modern aeroplane is closely cowled to reduce airframe drag and increase the overall aircraft efficiency. Consequently, there is very little space inside the cowling and adequate cylinder cooling is only obtained by air being forced into the cowled area by the action of the propeller and the speed of the aircraft during flight.

During normal ground operations, the RPM are low and little cooling effect is available from the airflow when the aircraft is being taxied or during those periods when the aircraft is stationary. Although the oil circulating through the engine will disperse some of the heat, there will be times during hot summer temperatures or periods of prolonged ground running when the engine temperature could rise to an unacceptable degree. Therefore, under these circumstances, particular care must be taken to monitor the oil temperature (and when fitted, the cylinder head temperature) gauge at frequent intervals.

Whenever practical, the aircraft should be headed into the wind to obtain maximum cooling effect and if cowl flaps are fitted these should normally be in the fully open position. If at any time the oil or cylinder head temperatures reach the red line, the aircraft should be taxied to the nearest suitable area (to avoid obstructing other aircraft) and the engine shut down for a suitable period to allow the temperatures to drop.

Avoidance of sparking plug fouling

Since the advent of 100LL AVGAS with its higher content of tetraethyl lead, spark plug fouling occurs more easily, and although this fuel contains a lead scavenging agent, it can only function provided the temperature of the spark plug nose core has a minimum temperature of 425°C. In order to maintain this temperature, the engine RPM should not be set lower than 1200 (taxying excepted). At this RPM, the engine will also run cooler and the alternator/ generator output will be higher.

INDUCTION AIR FILTER

Although the oil system, through use of filters and regular oil changes, plays an important part in removing any dirt from the engine, dirt and dust from the atmosphere is continuously entering the engine via the induction intake. To reduce the amount of dirt which enters from this source, an induction air filter is fitted and this too must be cleaned or replaced at regular intervals. In the main, the greatest amount of dust in the atmosphere is concentrated in the lower levels and particularly at ground level.

Choked air filters can reduce the rate at which air enters the engine and will have a significant effect in reducing the amount of power being delivered. When carburettor heat systems are fitted, the cold air comes in directly through the normal intake filter, but when hot air is selected, the filter is bypassed and unfiltered heated air is taken into the engine's induction system. In consequence therefore, any dirt or grit in the air will be ingested and cause damage to the cylinder walls, pistons and piston rings etc. Because of this, it will be necessary to keep the use of the hot air system to a minimum during engine operation on the ground and it should only be selected briefly to check the integrity of the system and to clear any ice which may form whilst the aircraft is on the ground.

HIGH POWER OPERATION

In view of the comment made under 'Oil and cylinder head temperatures', it will be obvious that ground running of the engine at high power will be conducive to overheating leading to scored cylinders and broken or jammed piston rings.

Excessive ground running should be avoided in hot or temperature climates and the time taken in starting up, and taxying is usually long enough for the engine to become sufficiently warm for the run-up checks to be carried out. The manufacturer's recommendations in relation to engine run-ups to check the magnetos and associated systems should be strictly followed.

When cowl flaps are fitted, it is particularly important to ensure that they are (with the exception of very cold outside air temperatures), in the fully open position prior to and during the run-up procedures. It is rarely necessary for full power run-ups to be carried out except for specific servicing purposes.

LIMITATIONS

The reliability and efficiency of the modern aero engine is extremely good and is made possible by:

- The advent of advanced technology in design and the materials used;
- Improved lubricants and fuels;
- Correct maintenance techniques.

The airworthiness authorities take these factors, among others, into consideration when they establish an engine's specific servicing period and determine the length of time it can remain in service (engine life) before a complete overhaul is required. However, this safety principle can be completely destroyed if the pilot adopts incorrect engine procedures or neglects to handle the engine properly.

The refinements brought about to aero engines over the years have therefore led to the pilot becoming an important link in the chain of safety between the engine manufacturers, airworthiness authorities and the operation of an aircraft.

The present day owner's/flight manuals and pilot's operating handbooks give sufficient information in the form of recommendations and limitations so that the pilot is aware of the correct engine handling procedures applicable to his aircraft. Neglecting this information can only lead to trouble and expense in the form of reduced engine life or partial or total engine failure. Because any form of engine failure during flight could lead to disastrous consequences the need to abide by the correct handling procedures and to operate the engine within the manufacturer's laid down limitations cannot be stressed too highly.

INTER-RELATIONSHIP OF ENGINE INSTRUMENTS

The instruments used to show either individually or collectively the operating condition of the engine vary in type and number. All small training aircraft will be equipped with a tachometer, oil temperature and oil pressure gauge. Other types of engine instruments may include those which measure fuel flow, fuel pressure, cylinder head temperature, exhaust gas temperature, manifold pressure and carburettor air temperature. Although each of these instruments is calibrated to give the pilot individual information, the correct use of these instruments to determine the health of the engine may sometimes require cross referring from one to another.

For example, if the oil pressure gauge drops to zero or to a significantly low reading, it could be showing a lack of oil in the system, or alternatively, it could be that the gauge has become unserviceable. However, if loss of oil is the problem, the oil temperature gauge will begin to rise to an abnormally high figure in a very short period of time. A cross reference of this short will therefore be helpful to a pilot in his assessment of how to handle the situation.

Another example can be given in relation to the manifold pressure gauge and the carburettor air temperature gauge, i.e. if an aircraft with a normally aspirated engine and variable pitch propeller enters a climb, it is normal for the manifold pressure to decrease for a given throttle setting. However, in aircraft equipped with a constant speed propeller, a reduction of manifold pressure for a constant power setting can also be an indication of carburettor icing. Therefore, in this case, reference to the carburettor air temperature gauge may establish whether the manifold pressure is decreasing because of carburettor icing, or increase of altitude or both.

EFFECT OF MISUSE OF CONTROLS

The main engine controls in small training aircraft consist of the throttle, mixture, carburettor air, ignition switches and fuel selector valves. Others which may be fitted are cowling shutters to regulate the cylinder head temperature, a pitch lever to adjust the RPM, and an alternative air control in place of the carburettor heat system. Misuse of any of these can lead to a temporary problem or permanent damage to the engine.

As an example, it should be noted that the throttle must be handled smoothly and never rammed open as this can lead to the engine cutting due to an incorrect fuel/air mixture supply or detonation due to a sudden increase in the cylinder gas temperatures.

It is important to appreciate that although aero engines can withstand extremes of temperature, if any rapid and extreme temperature change occurs, it can lead to distortion of both the fixed and moving parts. For example, one reason why it is recommended that the throttle should be slowly opened to the halfway position at frequent intervals during a glide is to avoid sudden and extreme changes in temperature occurring when returning to cruise or climb power.

Another example in misuse of engine controls can be related to mixture, in that use of the mixture control to lean the mixture when the engine is operating at more than 70% power below a specific altitude will induce the possibility of detonation, and incur engine damage. The usual altitude below which leaning should not be attempted at high engine power is 5000 feet, but nowadays, some engine manufacturers have lowered this recommended figure to 3000 feet.

Because of the differences between aircraft types, the only advice that can be given in a manual of this nature is to carefully follow the operating instructions given in the appropriate flight/owner's manual, pilot's operating handbook and during flight to double check that the correct movement or selection of a control has been made in accordance with the operating circumstances.

INDICATIONS OF UNSATISFACTORY RUNNING

To a certain extent, the contents of this sub-heading overlap those given under 'Inter-relationship of engine instruments', and apart from a total and sudden failure of the engine, the usual symptoms of unsatisfactory running can be divided into two classes – that in which vibration is the main indication, and that in which the engine runs roughly.

Vibration is usually an indication of propeller unbalance due to damaged blades or a loosening of the propeller attachment bolts. If vibration is encountered at any time during a flight, a temporary remedy to reduce the vibration may sometimes be obtained by changing the RPM or airspeed. However, during flight, it is usually impossible to determine the exact cause of the vibration, and, because propellers are subject to enormous stresses even during normal operation, it will always be advisable to proceed to the nearest airfield. If severe or even moderate vibration cannot be reduced, the pilot will need to give serious consideration to carrying out a forced landing without power.

Engine roughness may either be continuous or intermittent, and if rough running of any sort occurs, the first step should be to quickly check the engine instruments for some indication of the source of the trouble. If there is a specific indication e.g. fluctuating fuel pressure, the source of the problem will most probably lie in the fuel supply and may be the result of too little fuel in the selected tank or a malfunctioning mechanical fuel pump, in which case the pilot can take appropriate action by changing to another tank and/or switching on the electric fuel pump. However, as is often the case, the engine instruments may not give any indication as to the root of the problem, in which case, a systematic check should be made in an attempt to discover the cause. The various steps in this procedure should include the following:

● Select hot or alternative air (as applicable to type). If a carburettor or intake icing is the cause, a small power loss will occur followed by an increase in power and smooth running of the engine.

● If a large amount of ice is present, the engine will run more roughly or even stop momentarily after hot air has been applied. If either of these happens, remain in hot air and allow sufficient time (normally a few seconds) for this remedy to be effective. If it is necessary to continue the flight with hot air selected to prevent re-occurrence of icing, the mixture control should be re-adjusted to compensate for the richer mixture.

● If fuel or icing is not the cause and the normal leaning technique has been used, return the mixture control to the rich position or alternatively, if full rich, operate the mixture control to obtain a leaner mixture. Take care to abide by the manufacturer's recommendations in relation to high power and altitude.

● Remember that climbing in full rich above a certain altitude will inevitably cause engine roughness as will a return to cruise power following a descent after the mixture has been leaned for operation at a significantly higher altitude.

● If the fault does not reveal itself by the foregoing actions, then the next item to be investigated is the magneto system. A low cruise power should be selected and each magneto checked in turn. If the engine runs smoothly on one magneto but rough when both are selected, then select the single magneto which gave the smooth running and proceed to a suitable airfield.

● In some cases, a rough running engine caused by an ignition system problem will smooth out at a lower altitude and this could be caused by an ignition leak, usually in the harness. The most common ignition problem is, however, the occurrence of spark plug fouling and in this case, leaning the mixture or changing the power setting may be a temporary solution.

Whenever any form of engine roughness or vibration occurs, the pilot should not become distracted from flying the aircraft, abiding by the principles of good airmanship, and if the problem cannot be resolved, he should consider the need to re-plan and land at the nearest suitable airfield.

Another important indication of unsatisfactory engine performance which is often unnoticed or overlooked is the excessive consumption of oil or fuel. Either of these will indicate problems such as faulty or worn valves, piston rings etc. and whenever excessive consumption is evident, it should be reported to a ground engineer so that early action can be taken to avoid a serious in-flight situation developing.

STARTING AND STOPPING

The basic engine starting and stopping procedures are detailed in the flight/owner's manual or pilot's operating handbook, and in normal circumstances they should be followed exactly as listed.

For various personal reasons, some pilots develop their own procedures which vary from those given in the particular aircraft manual. It should nevertheless be appreciated that the engine manufacturer has far greater knowledge and experience in relation to the best way of starting his product than any individual pilot. This knowledge is obtained during manufacture and testing supplemented by the feed back of information relating to any starting problems from those engaged in using the particular type of engine and its associated systems during their normal flying operations.

STARTING METHODS

As stated in the previous paragraph, the method used for starting a particular engine in normal circumstances should comply with that recommended by the manufacturer. However, variations from the recommended procedure may be necessary when starting an engine which has been overprimed with fuel (flooded) or in the case of a *hot* engine, i.e. one which has only recently been shut down. It may also be necessary to vary the usual starting procedure when a very cold ambient temperature exists.

The aircraft manual may list alternative starting methods to use in these circumstances but if it does not, the following procedures can be generally applied and because the basic starting procedures between engines fitted with float type carburettors or fuel injection systems are different, these are dealt with under separate headings as follows.

Float type carburettor engines

Starting in cold temperatures – When a cold aero engine is started, it will require some priming either through means of a manual or electric pump. In the event of very cold ambient temperatures the volatility of fuel is significantly reduced and a greater amount of priming will therefore be necessary. In the case of manual primers, this may mean that two or three times the number of 'shots' than are normally used will be required.

The turning over of the propeller during this priming operation will enhance the distribution of fuel to the cylinders, but because of the associated hazards of handling the propeller during starting operations, this should only be carried out by persons qualified in hand swinging aircraft propellers.

When starting difficulties occur, many pilots tend to pump the throttle, and whereas this may sometimes help, the value of this action varies according to whether an accelerator pump is fitted e.g. many aero engines of less than 125 HP are not fitted with an accelerator pump, in which case, pumping the throttle will only increase the amount of air entering the system and lead to a weaker mixture, and greater difficulty in starting.

Due to the many makes and models of aero engine, it is difficult to generalise in the actions to be taken when starting in very cold weather conditions. However, it can be stated that the use of a priming pump is normally more effective than just pumping the throttle. This is because the priming line usually takes fuel into the cylinders or at least directly onto the engine side of the butterfly valve whereas pumping the throttle squirts fuel into the area of the carburettor venturi. An additional point is that with an updraught carburettor (the one most commonly used in small aero engines), any excess fuel from pumping the throttle drains down into the cowling area and a backfire from the engine during starting can easily ignite this and cause an engine-bay fire.

Starting a hot engine (or one that has been overprimed) – Complete the normal starting procedure with the mixture control in the 'idle cut-off' position. When the engine starts, smoothly return the mixture control to the 'rich' position.

Fuel injection engines

Starting problems with these engines are normally related to hot engines. This is due to the fact that with the closely cowled modern engine, the air trapped in the cowlings is heated after shut-down by the residual heat from the engine. On a hot day, this heated air within the cowling may take some hours to dissipate.

The fuel injected engine is equipped with very small bore lines which are routed across the engine and into the cylinders, and after the engine is shut-down, the heated air causes the fuel contained in these lines and fuel metering components to expand and vaporise. The expanding vapours will either be pushed back to the fuel tank if the fuel selector cock is left on or through the fuel metering components into the induction manifold from where they escape to the outside atmosphere.

When a 'hot start' situation occurs, the best starting method will therefore be:

1. Set the mixture to 'idle cut-off'
2. Throttle fully open
3. Electrical fuel pump 'on' (high position).

Wait for approximately 20 seconds and allow the electric fuel pump to force fuel through the heat soaked lines under the cowling. Because the mixture is in the idle cut-off position, the fuel is mainly prevented from entering the cylinders and instead it is re-cycled back into the fuel tank.

The reason for having the throttle fully open is because some fuel injected engines incorporate a switch in their throttle linkage to prevent the electric pump from operating in the 'high' position when the throttle is retarded.

After 20 seconds, the continuous flow of fuel will purge the vapour and cool the lines within the engine cowling, following which, the electric pump should be switched off, mixture and throttle adjusted and a normal starting procedure (without priming) can be implemented. No priming will be necessary because a small amount of fuel will have made its way past the mixture idle cut-off position and into the fuel nozzles during the purging operation.

SAFETY PROCEDURES

The pilot is responsible for ensuring that adequate safety precautions are taken prior to and during engine starting. The aircraft's position must be such that there is sufficient clearance from obstructions, buildings, other aircraft and refuelling installations, so that after starting, it can be safely taxied clear of the area in which it is parked.

The brakes should be firmly applied, or where brakes are not fitted, suitable chocks should be in position in front of the main wheels. With nosewheel aircraft, it is inadvisable to use a nosewheel chock due to its close proximity to the propeller.

Although it is often impractical to have a fire extinguisher available (apart from that in the aircraft), it is certainly advisable to have one ready in case of an engine induction fire during the start up procedure.

The area all around the aircraft to a safe distance should be clear of persons and an aural warning of start up should be made as an automatic precaution to reduce the dangers of people approaching too close to the propeller. During start-up and afterwards, the pilot must remain vigilant to spot any persons coming close to the aircraft particularly in the region of the propeller. Should such a situation occur, it is by far safer to immediately switch off the engine rather than waiting for persons to realise the danger of their actions.

During the start-up procedure and after the engine is running, the pilot's seat should be occupied by a competent person. On no account should the aircraft be left unattended.

When power for starting is supplied by external means (*trolley accumulators*), the pilot should remain alert and poised to turn off the ignition switches should the person operating the external power source and unplugging it from the aircraft come too close to the propeller.

HAND SWINGING A PROPELLER

In the event that a propeller has to be hand swung, it is important that the person handling the propeller has had the necessary training, and that the following points are complied with:

- The aircraft should be positioned on a level non-slip surface such that the person swinging the propeller can obtain a firm foothold for both feet, i.e. there should be no water puddles, oil spots, soft mud or loose stones near the propeller area.
- The propeller should not be handled until the pilot and the person carrying out the hand swinging have established that the ignition switches are 'off'.
- The propeller should be grasped near the tip of the blade and with metal propellers it is advisable to use a glove.
- The direction of pull should make an angle of not less than 30° with the propeller's plane of rotation.
- The propeller should be pulled firmly over compression with a follow through movement of the hand in conjunction with a body and leg movement backwards from the propeller arc. The body must never be allowed to enter the propeller arc at any time during this movement.

The following table sets out the usual procedure to be adopted by the pilot and the person swinging the propeller.

If an engine has not been run for some time, or if it is cold, it may be necessary to have the propeller pulled over by hand for several revolutions. This should be done with the ignition switches 'off', the

Hand swinger			Pilot		
Says	*Signal*	*Actions*	*Actions*	*Signal*	*Says*
Fuel 'on' Switches 'off' Throttle Closed	Thumb Down	Stands Clear			
			Checks: Fuel 'on' Switches 'off' Throttle Closed	Thumb Down	Fuel 'on' Switches "off' Throttle Closed
Throttle Set		Positions Propeller			
			Sets Throttle		Throttle Set
Switches 'on' Contact	Thumb Up				
			Switches 'on'	Thumb Up	Contact
		Handswings Propeller			

fuel 'on' and the throttle closed or nearly closed.

If the engine fails to start when using the normal procedure it may be that the mixture is too rich i.e. the engine has been overprimed, in which case, the following procedure can be adopted.

Hand swinger			Pilot		
Says	*Signal*	*Actions*	*Actions*	*Signal*	*Says*
Switches 'off' Throttle 'open' Blow Out	Thumb Down				
			Checks: Switches 'off' Throttle Wide Open	Thumb Down	Switches 'off' Throttle 'open' Blow Out
		Turns propeller backwards through several revolutions and stands clear			
Throttle Set		Positions Propeller			
			Sets Throttle		Throttle Set
Switches 'on' Contact	Thumb Up				
			Switches 'on'	Thumb Up	Contact
		Hand Swings Propeller			

Note: The hand swinger must always treat the propeller as though it were 'live'

RUNNING DOWN METHODS

Although slight differences will occur in the running down procedures between different aero engines, there are several items which
are common to all light aircraft.

Normally, a short period of engine operation at idling RPM is
recommended during which, the various components of the engine
subjected to heat are allowed to cool slowly. During this period, the
pilot should check his engine and systems instrumentation to note
the fuel state, and whether any abnormal condition is present, in
order that he may be able to fill in the 'Aircraft State' column in the
authorisation sheet or technical log.

This check should therefore include (as applicable to type) the
following:

● Fuel state
● Fuel pressure or flow
● Oil temperature
● Oil pressure
● Cylinder head temperature
● Suction
● Ammeter

Since the advent of AVGAS 100 LL which has a higher lead content
than the earlier 80/87 grade, engine manufacturers have recommended that the engine should be run briefly at approximately
1500 RPM immediately prior to shut-down, and not below 1200 RPM
when idling; this reduces the possibility of plug fouling, particularly
after a period of taxying at low RPM. Thus the internal check for
engine and systems integrity should be sensibly accomplished whilst
1500 RPM is set.

The method of stopping the engine is detailed in the particular
flight/owner's manual or pilot's operating handbook and will not be
covered here. Nevertheless, it would be pertinent to point out that for
those aircraft which are equipped with an 'idle cut-off' for engine
stopping, a good procedure is to have the throttle fully closed as the
ICO is operated. This action will ensure that no combustible fuel/air
mixture is left in the cylinders to fire should the propeller afterwards
be turned either inadvertently or deliberately by hand and the
switches have been left 'on' or the magneto system has gone 'live'.

Aircraft Airworthiness

SECTION 5

Aircraft Airworthiness

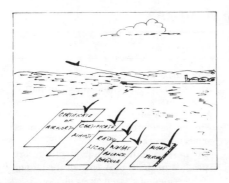

Certification and Documentation

Except for certain specific aircraft (which are issued with a 'Permit to Fly') each new make, type and model of aircraft will initially have to be issued with a document known as a Type Certificate. This will only be issued by the Airworthiness Authority of the country of origin provided it has met a large number of requirements concerning its construction and flight testing in relation to safety and reliability. The Type Certificate is normally retained by the manufacturer and once this is issued the particular aircraft model can be put into quantity production.

When an aircraft made by a foreign manufacturer is imported into the U.K. for which a Type Certificate has already been issued, together with a Certificate of Airworthiness for Export, the Airworthiness Division of the CAA, if satisfied that it meets this country's airworthiness requirements, will issue the particular model with an Airworthiness Approval Note.

Normally one Airworthiness Approval Note will cover any more imported aircraft of the same model, identical in design and performance e.g. the larger aircraft manufacturers normally produce a different model of the same type each year (A Series aircraft). Technically once the approval note for a particular model has been issued, the next step will be to obtain a Certificate of Airworthiness for each individual aircraft.

THE CERTIFICATE OF AIRWORTHINESS

Except under certain conditions all aircraft must be issued with a Certificate of Airworthiness (C of A) which covers a fixed period and has to be in force during the period it is in flight.

Because aeroplanes can operate for different purposes, e.g. public transport of passengers, carriage of cargo, aerial work etc., Certificates of Airworthiness are issued in different specific categories. These categories are defined in the *Air Navigation Order* and are summarised as follows:

Categories of Aircraft

Type of C of A	Aircraft Use
Transport Category (Passenger)	Any purpose
Transport Category (Cargo)	Any Purpose, other than the transport of passengers.
Aerial Work	Aerial work only
Private Category	Any purpose other than public transport or aerial work.
Special Category	Any purpose, other than public transport, specified in the C of A but not including the carriage of passengers unless expressly permitted.

Before issuing or renewing the particular Certificate of Airworthiness, the CAA must be satisfied that the individual aeroplane is fit to fly in the required role, having regard to the design construction, workmanship and materials used including the engine and any equipment which is necessary for the airworthiness of the aircraft.

The results of inspections and flight tests (where required) will also have to be assessed and meet the requirements stipulated in the *British Civil Airworthiness Requirements* (BCAR) document and any other airworthiness division criteria. The BCARs comprise the minimum requirements and constitute the basis for issue of approvals and certificates required by the *Air Navigation Order*.

Figure 7-1 is an example of a typical Certificate of Airworthiness issued in respect of a light aircraft in the transport category (passenger). Item '1' shows the construction and type/model of the aircraft and item '2' shows the aircraft serial number. Item '3' is the aircraft registration and shown at '4' is the category in which the C of A has been issued. Item '5' refers to the conditions which must be complied with during the period of the Certificate of Airworthiness in order to ensure that the C of A remains valid. This condition is on the reverse side of the C of A and refers to a specified Servicing Schedule approved by the Airworthiness Division of the CAA.

THE FLIGHT MANUAL

The last line of the paragraph at item '6' incorporates the particular aircraft's flight manual or pilot's operating handbook with the C of A, and a pilot will have to abide by the particular operating limitations shown in this manual if the validity of the C of A is to be maintained. Item '7' shows the period for which the C of A is issued and this particular C of A would have to be renewed before May 12th 1987.

United Kingdom
Civil Aviation Authority

CERTIFICATE OF AIRWORTHINESS

No. .... **8295** ③ ⑧ ①

Nationality and Registration Marks	Constructor and Constructor's Designation of Aircraft	Aircraft Serial No. (Constructor's No.)
G-BFRV	**Reims Aviation, France** **Reims Cessna FA152**	**0345**

CATEGORY   Transport Category (Passenger)

④   ⑤   ②

This Certificate is issued Subject to the Condition(s) shown overleaf.

This Certificate of Airworthiness is issued pursuant to the Convention on International Civil Aviation dated 7 December 1944, and to the Civil Aviation Act, 1949, and the Orders and Regulations made thereunder, in respect of the above-mentioned aircraft which is considered to be airworthy when maintained and operated in accordance with the foregoing and the pertinent operating limitations. A Flight Manual forms part of this Certificate. **(Reims/Cessna FA152 1978 Flight Manual including CAA Supplement 1)**

⑨   ⑥

Date ..**12th May, 1984**.....................................

....
for the Civil Aviation Authority

This certificate is valid for the period(s) shown below		Official Stamp and Date
From **12th May, 1984**	to **11th May, 1987**	12/5/84
From	to	
From	to	
From	to	
From	to	
From	to	
From	to	

⑦

Fig. 7-1

IMPORTANT POINTS

The aircraft must not be flown after that date on which the C of A expires unless an exemption has been granted by the CAA. An exemption of this nature will normally only be given to enable an aircraft to be flown to an engineering base, or for test flight purposes.

If the aircraft operating limitations are not complied with the C of A will automatically be invalidated and, (if applicable), the manufacturer's warranty will also cease to be in effect.

In relation to the last point a pilot must clearly take all necessary steps to ensure that he complies with the conditions of any insurance policies relating to the aircraft or himself. The consequences of not complying with such conditions could result in an extremely large financial penalty to the individual or the dependants.

In this respect it would be of value to reprint the following paragraphs which are an extract from a typical aircraft insurance policy:

> *General Conditions*
> This policy is subscribed subject to the following conditions all of which shall be deemed to be conditions precedent to the liability of the Insurers.
> 1. At the commencement of each flight, the Aircraft shall have a current Certificate of Airworthiness or permit to fly as may be applicable, and shall to the best of the Assured's knowledge and belief be in every way fit to fly.
> 2. The Aircraft and Pilot shall comply with all relevant international and governmental regulations and civil instructions.
> 3. The relevant log books shall be kept fully entered and up to date and the authorised agents of the Insurers shall be entitled to inspect them at all reasonable times.

At the top of the C of A (item '8') is shown the C of A serial number and this will also be shown at the front of the aircraft Flight Manual (Fig. 7-2 refers). This permits the actual flight manual relevant to the particular aircraft to be identified. This is an essential requirement, as without this information, the pilot will be unable to ensure that he is abiding by the operating limitations for the particular aircraft.

THE FLIGHT MANUAL SUPPLEMENT

Returning to Fig. 7-1, item '9' refers to a CAA Supplement No. 1. To explain the origin and purpose of this supplement, it must be appreciated that the aviation authorities of different countries have different requirements in relation to operation of aircraft.

These differences occur for various reasons which will not be

<u>AIRCRAFT</u>

<u>FLIGHT MANUAL</u>

<u>REIMS/CESSNA FA 152</u>

"This is the flight manual which forms part of
Certificate of Airworthiness Number **8295**"

<u>Manufacturer:</u>   REIMS AVIATION
Aerodrome de REIMS PRUNAY
B.P. 2745   51062 REIMS CEDEX

French Type Certificate No. 38

<u>Serial Number:</u> **O345**   Registration Number **G-BFRV**

Sections: 2-3-5

Pages: 2.1 thru 2.7
3.1 thru 3.7
5.1 thru 5.3

DGAC Visa

This is the exact translation of the FA 152 French Flight manual
approved by DGAC.

This aircraft must be operated in accordance with the limits
specified in this Flight Manual.

THIS DOCUMENT MUST BE CARRIED IN THE AIRCRAFT AT ALL
TIMES.

Aircraft serial No. FA15200337

D 1108-13 GB   0-1

Fig. 7-2

considered in this manual; it is sufficient to mention that when a foreign manufactured aircraft is imported into the U.K. it will be highly unlikely that all the operational procedures detailed in the flight manual or equivalent document will meet with the approval of the U.K. Airworthiness Authorities. Therefore, it is quite normal for supplemental pages issued by the CAA to be inserted in the Manual. Figure 7-3 shows one such page. Note that at the bottom of this page appears the statement: "Page 1 of 3". This enables the pilot to know how many pages are included in the supplement and he can quickly establish if one has been lost.

The reader should carefully study the first paragraph of the example supplement shown in Fig. 7-3 in order to understand the importance of this information in relation to his operating procedures and to maintaining the validity of the C of A, and both the aircraft and his own insurance policies.

In this respect it is worth noting that the placards displayed in the aircraft cockpit have the same status as the information in the aircraft's flight/owner's manual or pilot's operating handbook, and in certain cases may carry additional information to that contained in the appropriate aircraft manual.

THE CERTIFICATE OF MAINTENANCE REVIEW

It will be remembered that item '5' of Fig. 7-1 referred to a maintenance schedule and although a private pilot does not have to understand or even see this document, he will need to know whether the correct maintenance has been carried out before accepting the aircraft as fit to fly.

With regard to aircraft in the transport or aerial work categories this information will be found by examining two documents. These are entitled 'Certificate of Maintenance Review' and 'Certificate of Release to Service' respectively.

For aircraft maintained in accordance with the light aircraft maintenance schedule the maintenance review will normally coincide with what is known as the 'Annual Inspection', and will not be issued unless the engineer concerned is satisfied that the following aspects of maintenance have been carried out:

● All maintenance specified in the approved maintenance schedule has been carried out within the prescribed time period and any extension to limiting periods is in accordance with CAA approved procedures.

● All modifications and inspections deemed mandatory by the CAA have been carried out properly.

Civil Aviation Authority

ADDITIONAL INFORMATION FOR BRITISH CERTIFICATION

CAA Supplement 1 Issue 3 to the Reims/Cessna FA152
1978 Flight Manual.

| Reims/Cessna | Constructor's | Registration |
| FA152 | Serial No. **0345** | Marks **G-BFRV** |

The aeroplane is to be operated in accordance with the following
information in addition to that contained in the Flight Manual
and any additional approved information in the Flight Manual.
The information in this Supplement supersedes any similar
information in the Flight Manual.

LIMITATIONS

1. This type of aeroplane is eligible for certification in the
   Transport Category (Passenger).

   However, this particular aeroplane may be
   restricted to the Special Category and to
   some particular use. This will be stated
   in the Certificate of Airworthiness.

2. When operated in the Transport Category (Passenger)
   the aeroplane is classified in Performance
   Group E.

3. Aerobatic manoeuvres are limited to those
   listed in the Flight Manual. When aerobatic
   manoeuvres are performed the limitations
   associated with the Acrobatic Category in the
   Flight Manual shall be complied with.

CAA Supplement 1
Issue 3   Page 1 of 3   CAA Approved
                                                         8 May 1978

Fig. 7-3

● All defects entered in the technical log* have been rectified or
  deferred in accordance with CAA approved procedures.
● All Certificates of Release to Service have been issued in
  accordance with the correct procedures.

The format of a Certificate of Maintenance Review is shown in Fig.
7-4.

*A technical log, or in the case of light aircraft, a similar document as approved by the
CAA is used to record defects following flight and any corrective action taken by the
ground engineers. When a technical log is used it will contain the valid Certificate of
Maintenance Review and the Certificate of Release to Service.

CERTIFICATE OF MAINTENANCE REVIEW

AIRCRAFT TYPE . . . . NATIONALITY & REGISTRATION MARK . . . .

Certified that a maintenance review of this aircraft and such of its equipment as is necessary for its airworthiness has been carried out in accordance with the requirements of the Air Navigation Order for the time being in force.

The next maintenance review is due on . . . .

Signed . . . .

CAA Approval/Licence . . . .

Date . . . .

Firm . . . .

Fig. 7-4

CERTIFICATE OF RELEASE TO SERVICE

A Certificate of Release to Service will be issued at the completion of any scheduled maintenance inspection required by the appropriate approved maintenance schedule. It is not required for certain scheduled maintenance inspections carried out on aircraft with a private category Certificate of Airworthiness providing the inspection has been carried out personally by the owner or operator holding a pilot's licence.

A CRS will also be issued after overhauls, replacements, and modifications to aircraft in the public transport or aerial work categories. However, certain repairs or replacements may be carried out on aircraft in the private category without the issue of a CRS but, as with scheduled maintenance inspections on aircraft in the private category, this work will have to be done by the owner or operator holding a pilot's licence.

PILOT'S RESPONSIBILITY TO RECORD DEFECTS

It is the pilot's responsibility to check whether the aircraft documentation and serviceability is satisfactory prior to flight, and he is also responsible for entering any malfunction, or unserviceability of the aircraft and its components in the technical log or equivalent document immediately following a flight.

THE MAINTENANCE SCHEDULE

The maintenance schedule which is normally used for aircraft which have a maximum all up weight not exceeding 2730 kg is the LAMS fixed wing schedule. Should an operator decide that the LAMS FW schedule is not suited to his own operation, the provision is made for him to submit an alternative schedule for approval by the CAA.

At the time this manual was printed the LAMS FW schedule listed the maintenance check cycle as follows:

Transport and Aerial Work Category	Private Category
Check A — Prior to first flight of the day.	Check A — Prior to first flight of the day.
50 Hour Check — Not exceeding 50 flying hours, or 62 days, whichever is the sooner.	50 Hour Check — Not exceeding 50 flying hours.
150 Hour Check — Not exceeding 150 flying hours.	150 Hour Check — Not exceeding 150 flying hours.
Annual Check — Not exceeding 12 months, but see Note (2).	Annual Check — Not exceeding 12 months, but see Note (2).
Annual Checks shall be completed only by Organisations approved by the CAA in accordance with British Civil Airworthiness Requirements (BCAR).	The Annual Check which coincides with the Certificate of Airworthiness renewal shall be completed only by Organisations approved by the CAA in accordance with British Civil Airworthiness Requirements (BCAR).

NOTES: (1)   Provided that airworthiness is not impaired, it is permitted to extend the period prescribed for any complete maintenance check, with the exception of the Annual Check, by a maximum of 10%. Extensions are not required to be deducted from the next scheduled period. An extension may only be authorized by persons acceptable as signatories for the prescribed Check. The extension shall be recorded in the appropriate log book.

(2)   The Annual Check may be anticipated by a maximum period of 62 days without loss of the continuity of the maintenance pattern. Thus, for example, where the full 62 days is invoked, the following Annual Check would become due 14 months after the completion of the Annual Check which was anticipated. The period by which the Annual Check was anticipated and the date of the next Annual Check shall be recorded in the appropriate log book.

PILOT MAINTENANCE

Prior to 1st April 1971 legislation required any repairs or replacements of components necessary for airworthiness, even of a minor nature, to be carried out under the supervision of a licensed aircraft maintenance engineer or an ARB approved inspector. As a result of consultation is was decided that this procedure was unnecessarily restrictive and that licensed pilots (other than student pilots) should be allowed to carry out minor repairs, replacements and lubrication on aircraft not exceeding 2730 kg (6000 lb) maximum total weight and which are used for anything *other than public transport*.

At the time this manual was printed, such rectification work consisted of the following: (*Air Navigation (General) Regulations* refer).

PRESCRIBED REPAIRS OR REPLACEMENTS

With reference to Article 11(2) of the *Air Navigation (General) Regulations* the following repairs or replacements are prescribed:
(1)   Replacement of landing gear tyres, landing skids or skid shoes.
(2)   Replacement of elastic shock absorber cord units on landing gear where special tools are not required.
(3)   Replacement of defective safety wiring or split pins excluding those in engine, transmission, flight control and rotor systems.
(4)   Patch-repairs to fabric not requiring rib stitching or the removal of structural parts or control surfaces, if the repairs do not cover up structural damage and do not include repairs to rotor blades.

(5)   Repairs to upholstery and decorative furnishing of the cabin or cockpit interior when repair does not require dismantling of any structure or operating system or interfere with an operating system or affect the structure of the aircraft.

(6)   Repairs, not requiring welding to fairings, non-structural cover plates and cowlings.

(7)   Replacement of side windows where that work does not interfere with the structure or with any operating system.

(8)   Replacement of safety belts or safety harness.

(9)   Replacement of seats or seat parts not involving dismantling of any structure or of any operating system.

(10) Replacement of bulbs, reflectors, glasses, lenses or lights.

(11) Replacement of any cowling not requiring removal of the propeller, rotors or disconnection of engine or flight controls.

(12) Replacement of unserviceable sparking plugs.

(13) Replacement of batteries.

(14) Replacement of wings and tail surfaces and controls, the attachments of which are designed to provide for assembly immediately before such flight and dismantling after each flight.

(15) Replacement of main rotor blades that are designed for removal where special tools are not required.

(16) Replacement of generator and fan belts designed where special tools are not required.

In addition to the above list, pilots are permitted to carry out normal cleaning and lubrication procedures such as:

(a)   Cleaning and greasing of landing gear wheel bearings;

(b)   Lubrication not requiring disassembly other than removal of non-structural items such as cover plates, cowlings and fairings;

(c)   Applying preservative or protective material to components where disassembly of any primary structure or operating system is not involved, and where such coating is not prescribed or not contrary to good practice;

(d)   Cleaning fuel filters.

Important Note: In performing maintenance operations or other procedures, pilots should exercise the utmost discretion and not attempt any work which requires special technical knowledge or technical skill beyond their ability or facilities. All maintenance should be carried out in accordance with the manufacturer's recommended procedures using approved parts and recommended materials, fluids and lubricants.

As a result of these changes, the 50 hour check for aircraft in the private category can be completed by a licensed pilot, who is the owner or operator of the aircraft. The pilot may only sign for the actual check and for rectification work within the scope of that itemised in the *Air Navigation (General) Regulation*. When acting as a signatory, pilots must include their pilot's licence number with their signature. A typical entry format is shown at Fig. 7-5.

```
50 hr/150 hr/Annual Check has been completed to my satisfaction at ...........
total airframe hours
Maintenance Schedule Ref ..............................................
                    Signature            Date            Authority
Airframe ...........................................................
Engine ..............................................................
Radio ...............................................................
```

Fig. 7-5

Note 1. The certification of work or of an inspection made mandatory by an Airworthiness Directive, or its equivalent, is permitted only by appropriately licensed aircraft engineers.

Note 2. Aircraft in the private category do not require a Certificate of Maintenance Review.

Note 3. Aircraft in the private category do not require a Certificate of Release to Service where the pilot/owner carries out the 50 hour check in accordance with the required maintenance schedule.

AIRCRAFT, ENGINE AND PROPELLER LOG BOOKS

In order to maintain a record of any repairs, changes or modifications to the aircraft or its fixed equipment the following log books must be maintained by the aircraft owner or operator:

- Aircraft log book;
- Engine log book;
- Variable pitch propeller log book.

It is also the operator's responsibility to keep these log books up to date in respect of flight times completed by the aircraft.

Note: When an aircraft is equipped with more than one engine a separate log book must be maintained for each engine and when applicable each variable pitch propeller.

These log books must be preserved by the operator or owner of the aircraft until a date two years after the aircraft, engine or variable pitch propeller, as the case may be, has been destroyed or has been permanently withdrawn from use.

Such records will enable the licensed engineer or maintenance organisation to determine what work has been accomplished and to verify that the requirements of the approved maintenance schedule (or any mandatory modifications which may become necessary) have been complied with.

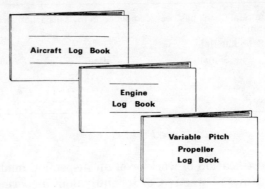

SECTION 8

Aircraft Instruments

Introduction

Although early aircraft had very limited instrumentation, the modern light aeroplane is extremely well equipped with a variety of instruments which basically fall into three groups:

- Flight instruments;
- Engine instruments;
- Ancillary instruments.

The flight instruments are those which are used in controlling the aircraft and they indicate its attitude and performance. This essentially means the airspeed, altitude, air pressure variation, aircraft attitude, direction, rate of turn and balance. They consist of the *airspeed indicator, altimeter, vertical speed indicator, attitude indicator, heading indicator, magnetic compass* and the *turn and balance indicator* or, alternatively the *turn co-ordinator*.

These six instruments provide much essential information and the pilot will need to understand the basic principles of their operation, and to develop the ability to interpret them during flight in order to control the aircraft accurately under various conditions.

Many of the engine instruments have already been discussed in Section 6 of the manual, but it can be said here that they are basically designed to measure the quantity and pressure of liquids (i.e. fuel and oil) and the temperature of liquids and gases etc.

The Flight Instruments

PITOT STATIC SYSTEM

The airspeed indicator, altimeter and vertical speed indicator are all connected into a pitot static system. A typical arrangement is shown in Fig. 8-1.

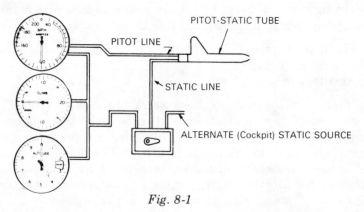

Fig. 8-1

The pitot static system (sometimes called a pressure head) consists of two separate components, the impact tube and the static head, the forward end of the impact tube is open at the front (facing the airflow) and is designed to receive the full force of the air pressure. It has a small hole at the bottom of its forward section to permit moisture to escape back to atmosphere. The impact tube pressure is transmitted only to the airspeed indicator. The second component of the pitot static system can be described as a tube with one or more holes which face at 90° to the airflow. The openings are designed to provide an accurate indication of the ambient air pressure i.e. static pressure. The static pressure is fed to the airspeed indicator, altimeter and vertical speed indicator.

The pitot-static assembly is mounted on the outside of the aircraft in a position where the airflow is least likely to be disturbed. Normally this will be slightly ahead of the wing or in a forward position underneath the wing.

In many aircraft, the system is provided with an alternative static pressure source which is an opening in the cockpit. If for any reason the outside static tube becomes blocked, selection of the alternative source will permit cockpit air pressure into the system. However, because cockpit pressure (in non-pressurised aircraft) is always a little less than that outside the aircraft, the instruments will give less accurate readings. Although this error is normally quite small, most aircraft manuals give information relating to the size of these errors.

Another quite common type of pitot-static system is where a separate static source, in the form of one or two vents, is mounted flush with the fuselage. Nevertheless, the principles outlined in the previous paragraphs will still apply.

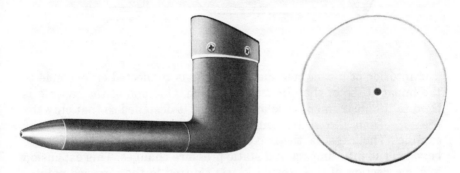

Many pitot static tube assemblies contain a heating element to prevent icing of the tube openings during flight in freezing conditions When this is installed, the pilot should preferably switch the element on prior to entering conditions of heavy rain or before encountering weather and temperatures which are conducive to airframe icing. Care should be taken to ensure that heating elements are only used for short periods when the aircraft is on the ground, due to the risk of the element overheating and burning out when a strong cooling airflow is not present.

THE AIRSPEED INDICATOR

The airspeed indicator is a type of sensitive pressure gauge which measures the difference between the impact pressure and the static pressure. This difference of pressure is indicated by the pointer on the face of the instrument and is calibrated to show the pilot his indicated airspeed.

CONSTRUCTION AND FUNCTION

Airspeed indicators and other instruments are made by various manufacturers and therefore vary in their mechanical construction. The basic construction and operating principles are nevertheless the same for all makes.

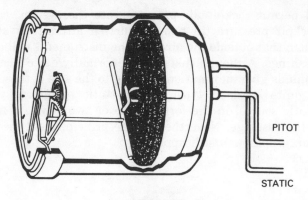

PITOT

STATIC

Fig. 8-3

The interior of a sensitive metal capsule is connected on one side to the impact tube of the pitot/static system. One end of the capsule is fixed to the instrument case and the case is designed so that only the pressure from the static source is exerted on the exterior of the capsule. The capsule then expands or contracts as the difference between the pitot impact and static pressure changes. This expansion and contraction of the capsule is transmitted to the airspeed pointer via a magnification system of levers and gears.

CALIBRATION AND INTERPRETATION OF COLOUR CODING

Airspeed indicators are normally calibrated to show miles per hour or knots or both. Most indicators nowadays are colour coded so that the

Fig. 8-4

pilot can see important airspeeds at a glance. The standard colour codes used with single engined aircraft are white, green, yellow and red.

Referring to Fig. 8-4, the low speed end of the white arc shows the aircraft stalling speed power off, a load factor of 1 and with the flaps lowered. The top end of the white arc shows the maximum speed at which the flaps can be lowered.

The low speed end of the green arc shows the stalling speed power off, and a load factor of 1 with the flaps up. The top end of the green arc indicates the maximum speed permitted to fly the aircraft in turbulent conditions where no specific 'rough air' speed is given in the aircraft manual or placarded in the cockpit.

The yellow arc shows the caution range relative to turbulent conditions i.e. the aircraft should only be flown at a speed within this arc provided that relatively smooth air conditions exist. The red line at or near the high speed end of the airspeed scale indicates the maximum airspeed at which the aircraft is permitted to fly and this should never be exceeded.

One type of airspeed indicator which is becoming quite common has a setting scale marked on the top periphery of the instrument against which temperature and pressure altitude can be set to give the *true airspeed* of the aircraft on a separate side scale.

Fig. 8-5

The manufacturer makes every attempt to minimise errors in construction and positions the pressure head where it will be largely unaffected by the disturbance of the air as the aircraft passes through it. However it is not possible to totally eliminate the errors caused by changes in the aircraft angle of attack to the airflow.

ERRORS

Installation error
It should be appreciated that even if the pressure head were in a position where no air disturbances occurred it could still only be fixed so that it meets the air directly when the aircraft is at one particular angle of attack. When the aircraft departs from this angle a small error will occur. This error is primarily in the static source and is variously known as installation error, pressure error, or position error. The use of static vents placed in a suitable position (usually well back along the side of the fuselage) significantly reduces this error.

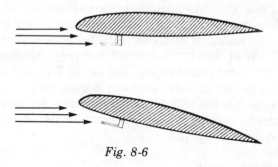

Fig. 8-6

Although the error is small at normal cruising speed, it becomes larger either side of this, and particularly in the lower airspeed range when the aircraft is flying at relatively large angles of attack.

In order that pilots appreciate the magnitude of this error throughout the speed range of the aircraft, a table or graph is normally included in the aircraft manual and Fig. 8-7 shows a typical example.

The letters CAS in this example stand for Calibrated or Corrected Airspeed, which is the indicated airspeed corrected for installation error. In earlier aircraft manuals the term TIAS (True Indicated Airspeed) is used in place of CAS, and in the U.K. the term RAS (Rectified Airspeed) is often used in place of CAS.

AIRSPEED CORRECTION TABLE
(Flaps Up)

IAS	40	50	60	70	80	90	100	110	120	130	140
CAS	51	57	65	73	82	91	100	109	118	127	136

(Flaps Down)

IAS	40	50	60	70	80	90	100				
CAS	49	55	63	72	81	89	98				

Fig. 8-7

It can be seen from Fig. 8-7 that at 100 knots the error is very small, but in the low speed range it increases significantly i.e. when the indicated speed is 40 knots the installation error in this example has increased to 11 knots.

Density error
The standard airspeed indicator is calibrated to give a correct reading when the air density corresponds to the International Standard Atmosphere. This effectively means that it can only accurately measure the true airspeed at sea level and then only when the ISA prevails at sea level. As altitude is gained, the air density reduces and therefore the effect of the impact pressure at any given airspeed is less, i.e. the indicated airspeed (IAS) becomes lower than the true airspeed (TAS) at which the aircraft is flying. Although this effect may seem an added complication, the use of TAS is from a practical point of view generally only necessary during air navigation. For all other purposes it is the IAS which is important, because the air loads on an aircraft are directly proportional to the dynamic pressure acting on it during flight.

Compressibility error
Since air is a compressible fluid it will compress when forced to come to rest in an impact tube. The higher pressure recorded in the

airspeed indicator as a result of this is interpreted in the instrument as a higher IAS.

The effect of compressibility error is however not marked until reaching airspeeds of approximately 200 knots and over, and therefore it is not generally applicable to light single engined aircraft.

PILOT'S SERVICEABILITY CHECKS

Before entering the cockpit the pilot should ensure that the pressure head is unblocked, secure and that any protective cover has been removed.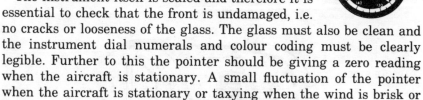

The instrument itself is sealed and therefore it is essential to check that the front is undamaged, i.e. no cracks or looseness of the glass. The glass must also be clean and the instrument dial numerals and colour coding must be clearly legible. Further to this the pointer should be giving a zero reading when the aircraft is stationary. A small fluctuation of the pointer when the aircraft is stationary or taxying when the wind is brisk or strong may occur and this is quite normal.

THE ALTIMETER

This instrument is essential to the operation of the aircraft in that its correct use ensures the pilot is able to operate at precise altitudes and flight levels as well as indicating the aircraft's vertical position in relation to the surface.

SIMPLE PRESSURE ALTIMETERS

These altimeters through the use of a datum setting knob provide the pilot with three basic references.

- Height above an aerodrome;
- Altitude above mean sea level;
- Operation of the aircraft at specific flight levels.

CONSTRUCTION AND FUNCTION

The instrument is similar to an aneroid barometer in that it utilises a stack of two or three pressure responsive capsules which expand or contract with the pressure changes in the atmosphere.

The instrument case is sealed except for a connection with the static tube or static vent (Fig. 8-8). Any changes of static pressure surrounding the aircraft therefore affect the capsule stack.

The expansion or contraction of the aneroid capsule actuates a linking mechanism of levers and gears which indicates the movement by pointers moving around a dial calibrated in feet or metres,

(Fig. 8-9). Altimeters used in U.K. registered aircraft are calibrated in feet (Fig. 8-10).

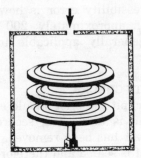

Fig. 8-8

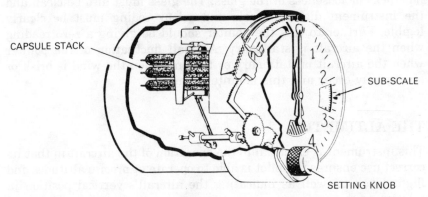

CAPSULE STACK

SUB-SCALE

SETTING KNOB

Fig. 8-9

CALIBRATION AND DIAL PRESENTATIONS

The most common type of altimeter used in light aircraft has a dial and pointer presentation consisting of three needles. These needles sweep the calibrated dial to indicate the altitude of the aircraft. The shortest needle indicates altitude in terms of tens of thousands of feet, the intermediate needle thousands of feet, and the longest needle shows hundreds of feet in 20 or 50 feet increments.

A striped sector is used to provide an additional indication that the aircraft is below 10000 feet. At sea level this striped sector is fully visible and

Fig. 8-10

becomes gradually less so until above 10000 feet when it disappears completely.

Effects of atmospheric density

Under standard atmospheric conditions each level of air in the atmosphere has a specific density, so where non-standard density conditions occur, an error will arise in the altimeter reading. The practical application of this error is in relation to aircraft performance in that the performance data given in aircraft manuals is based on the International Standard Atmosphere. Since this performance data at any level is based on ISA it will not necessarily correspond exactly with the actual altimeter indications.

FUNCTION OF THE SUBSCALE

A barometric pressure scale (which in the UK is graduated in millibars) is located at one side of the instrument face. This scale can usually be adjusted to give any pressure datum within a range from 950–1050 mb.

Since atmospheric pressure continually changes it will be necessary to set the required datum pressure e.g. sea level (QNH) or aerodrome level (QFE) as required in order to measure the aircraft's vertical distance from sea level or the aerodrome surface. Increasing the barometric pressure setting scale will increase the indicated altitude by approximately 30 feet for every millibar.

Fig. 8-11

New altimeter presentations now gradually being introduced into general aviation aircraft have a window through which a digital display gives a read-out of height in thousands of feet whilst a single pointer gives height in hundreds of feet. There are other combinations of digital display but they all have at least one pointer measuring hundreds of feet, in order to give the pilot an instant indication of any tendency for the aircraft to change its height.

ERRORS

Altimeters are subject to small mechanical errors, installation errors and those due to non-standard temperatures.

Mechanical errors are relatively small in a correctly functioning altimeter, and although installation error which is brought about when the static tube is not aligned directly into the airflow is not very large, it can be reduced even further by the use of static vents mounted flush with the fuselage.

Whenever the air temperature varies from that specified in the requirements for the International Standard Atmosphere, an additional error will occur and the altimeter will either under read or over read. For example, an altimeter at sea level will be measuring the weight of a column of air above it. If the aircraft has now climbed to 5000 feet, the weight or pressure on the altimeter aneroid is less by that portion of the column of air below it. If under these conditions the temperature is the same as the ISA then the altimeter will read 5000 feet. However if the lower portion of the column is warmer than ISA then the air will expand and the reduction of pressure will be smaller in this column of air and the altimeter will under read. Conversely if the temperature in the column of air is below that of the ISA the altimeter will over read.

Temperature error is related to density error, and given the pressure altitude and the air temperature at that altitude, the error can be calculated by using a navigation computer.

PILOT'S SERVICEABILITY CHECKS

The pilot must ensure that the pressure head or static vents are secure, unblocked, and any protective covers or plugs are removed before entering the cockpit. As with the airspeed indicator the glass of the instrument must be clean, free of cracks and fit tightly into the casing. The numerals on the instrument dial and subscale must be clear and easily read.

The datum knob should be turned to ensure that it operates freely and that the needles respond correctly in conjunction with the millibar subscale. Once the QFE or QNH setting (as required) has been obtained this should be set and the altimeter indication should not show an error of more than +30 ft to −50 ft.

THE VERTICAL SPEED INDICATOR

This instrument is mainly used to determine the aircraft's rate of climb or descent. However, when flight conditions are calm and the aircraft is in level flight, it can also be used as a trend instrument due to the vertical speed indicator needle being generally more sensitive and so responding more quickly to any variation of altitude.

CONSTRUCTION AND FUNCTION

A vertical speed indicator is essentially a sensitive differential pressure gauge which is connected to the static tube to indicate rate of change in static pressure. A capsule inside the sealed case of the instrument is directly fed with the static air pressure surrounding the aircraft. The static pressure is also fed into the case but through a restricted passage which acts as a metering unit. When the aircraft remains at a constant pressure level the static pressure inside the capsule and the case balance out and cause the indicator needle to show zero on the calibrated dial.

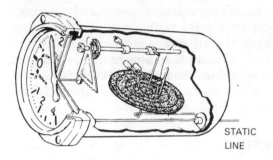 

STATIC
LINE

Fig. 8-12

If the aircraft changes altitude the new static pressure is immediately felt inside the capsule but the change of pressure inside the case is delayed due to the action of the metering unit. Therefore whenever the aircraft climbs, the pressure in the case will remain slightly higher than that within the capsule and the indicating mechanism will cause the pointer to indicate a rate of climb. When the aircraft descends the pressure in the case will remain a little less than that within the capsule and the mechanism causes the pointer to show rate of descent.

ERRORS
The difference in pressure between that contained in the capsule and that contained in the case, takes some 5–10 seconds to stabilise whenever the aircraft commences a climb or descent. Therefore the instrument will not give an accurate indication of change in its vertical direction until this time has elapsed. Sudden or abrupt changes in aircraft attitude will also cause unreliable needle readings due to fluctuating airflow at the open end of the static system.

Another aspect worthy of note is that sudden movements of the elevators will temporarily cause the instrument to indicate a reversed trend, i.e. a sudden backward movement of the control column will cause the VSI pointer to indicate a small rate of descent for a few moments before it gives the correct reading, in this case a rate of climb.

PILOT'S SERVICEABILITY CHECKS

During the pre-flight inspection of the aircraft, the pilot must ensure that the pressure head (or when fitted, the static vents) are unobstructed. The glass of the instrument must be checked to make sure that it is clean, tightly fitting and that there are no cracks. Any leakage of cockpit air into the instru- ment case will cause instrument errors during climbs and descents.

The instrument face must be clearly legible and the indicating needle should show zero when the aircraft is on the ground. If the instrument is showing an error of more than plus or minus 200 feet, it should be reported as unserviceable. The instrument is fitted with a zero setting screw or knob which makes it relatively simple for an engineer to adjust the indicator needle to read zero.

GYRO SUPPLY SYSTEMS

The two types of supply system used to drive the gyroscopic instruments have already been discussed on pages 6-60 and 6-63. Therefore under this heading it is only necessary to explain the pilot's serviceability checks in relation to each type.

Because of the importance of these instruments to the pilot, the Airworthiness Authorities normally require that the gyro instruments are provided with two independent sources of power. In the case of light aircraft this provision is usually met by arranging for the attitude and heading indicators to be driven by a vacuum system, whilst the turn and balance indicator or turn co-ordinator is operated by electricity.

Regardless of which combination of methods or type of power supply is used, a means has also to be provided to enable a pilot to determine that the power source is working satisfactorily.

In the case of a pump operated vacuum system, a gauge is fitted in the cockpit to indicate the vacuum being created when the engine is operating. This instrument may be colour coded with a green sector so that the pilot can obtain a rapid indication if the vaccum is too low.

The normal range of vacuum required to operate the instruments in a particular aircraft will be given in the aircraft manual, but it can generally be stated as being between four and five inches of mercury.

On some aircraft the pipe which vents the suction pressure from the instrument cases back to atmosphere is fitted near the nosewheel access bay, and so can be examined by the pilot during the normal pre-flight inspection to ensure that it is undamaged and clear.

Those systems which use the more modern self-lubricating suction pump have the vent to atmosphere pipe located within the engine cowling and are therefore not normally accessible during a pre-flight inspection. On the other hand, a vent to atmosphere pipe mounted within the cowling is less likely to become damaged.

In the case of those systems which utilise an external venturi system, the venturi is accessible to the pilot, and because they are often fitted underneath the aircraft and in the wake of the propeller slipstream, they should be carefully inspected before flight to ensure they are unblocked and undamaged.

After the engine has been started, the vacuum gauge should be checked to see that the system is operating correctly. At low engine RPM however, the suction indication may be on the low side. The gauge reading should therefore be checked again during the engine power checks prior to take-off.

During taxying, the gyro instruments can be checked by turning the aircraft to the left and to the right to check that each one gives correct indications.

Note: In the case of a venturi operated suction system, it should be appreciated that the system cannot be properly checked until the aircraft has become airborne and a reasonable airspeed established.

The operation of those gyro instruments which are driven by electricity can be checked:

● Aurally e.g. after the master switch has been placed in the ON position it is usually possible to hear the gyroscope rotating and speeding up, and, or;
● By pressing on one corner of the flight instrument panel and noting that the instrument reacts, and, or;
● Noting the instrument reaction during turns whilst taxying.

Note: Current practice is to fit each electrically driven gyro instrument with a warning flag (normally coloured red). This comes into view on the face of the instrument whenever the electrical supply fails.

TURN AND BALANCE INDICATOR

This instrument is used to provide a dual indication – the rate at which an aircraft is turning, and whether it is remaining in balance i.e. no yaw is occurring. Although this latter condition can normally be recognised by the pilot during laterally level flight whenever the aircraft's wings are level and the heading is constant, once a turn is initiated the pilot will have to rely on the ball or balance needle of this instrument to ensure that the turn is being conducted without slip or skid.

It is also an important back-up instrument to the attitude indicator and the heading indicator during manoeuvres, or if either of these instruments should become unserviceable during flight. Although there are several variations of this instrument, the principles of operation of all types are very similar.

GYROSCOPIC PRINCIPLES

A gyroscope is a wheel or disc which when spinning acts in accordance with Newton's first and second Laws of Motion. In essence, the first law states that *a body at rest will remain at rest, or if in motion in a straight line, it will continue in motion in a straight line unless acted upon by an external force.* The second law may be interpreted as stating, *the deflection of a moving body is proportional to the deflective force applied and is inversely proportional to its mass and speed.*

Figure 8-13 is a picture of a typical gyro rotor which is mounted on circular pivoted frameworks called *gimbals.*

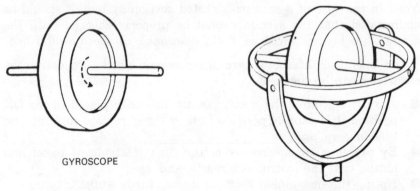

GYROSCOPE

GYROSCOPE WITH GIMBALS

Fig. 8-13

Whilst the rotor is stationary there is nothing unusual about it, in that its axle can be pointed in any direction with no effect on the gyroscope assembly. However when the rotor is spun at high speed the gyroscope exhibits two important characteristics. The first is a high degree of directional rigidity and the second is, that when a force is applied to the rotor, its change in direction will not take place in line with the applied force but at a point 90° removed in the direction of rotation. This second characteristic is known as *precession*.

The degree of rigidity will depend on the mass of the rotor, the speed of rotation and the radius at which the mass is concentrated. This latter factor leads to a method of construction where the mass is concentrated around the rim. Although a pilot is not required to have a detailed knowledge of gyroscopes, the foregoing information should be helpful in understanding the basic principles on which the gyroscopic flight instruments are based.

THE TURN INDICATOR

This part of the instrument is used to determine an aircraft's rate of turn. There are several different ways of presenting this information and Fig. 8-14 shows two common types of turn indicator. The picture at (a) shows an instrument with a needle which moves across a dial painted with calibrated marks to indicate the rate of turn and (b) shows a display used in a similar instrument known as a turn co-ordinator and on which an index aircraft is used in place of a needle.

(a)   (b)

Fig. 8-14

Construction and Function

The turn indicator uses what is known as a rate gyro. This has freedom to move about two of its three axes and is constructed so as to show the rate of aircraft movement about the third axis.

Referring back to the principles of gyroscopes, Fig. 8-15(a) shows a rotor spinning about its axle and mounted in a gimbal thus giving it two planes of movement. If a force is applied, in this case by rotating the base, the applied force will act at 90° in the direction in which the rotor is spinning and so cause it to precess into the horizontal position shown at Fig. 8-15(b).

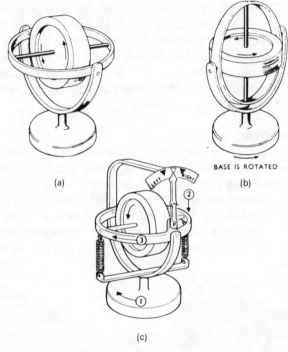

(a)

BASE IS ROTATED

(b)

(c)

Fig. 8-15

If some means of restricting this precesson is fitted to the gimbal assembly such as the springs shown in Fig. 8-15(c) then any given rate of turn will cause a precessing force which will eventually be balanced by the spring tension. The amount by which the precession will overcome the tension in the spring will depend on the rate of angular movement in the plane in which the rotor is fixed and the strength of the spring. A suitable linkage can then be arranged so that a needle can indicate the particular rate of turn against a calibrated dial.

The rotor of the turn indicator is mounted with its axis athwartships in a horizontal gimbal ring. It is rotated by a jet of air impinging on bucket segments cut into the periphery. Figure 8-16 shows this arrangement.

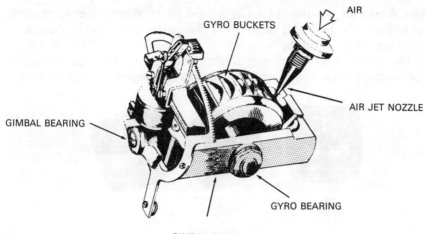

Fig. 8-16

The air used for driving the rotor is drawn in from the top of the casing when the pressure is lowered in the instrument casing by the action of the vacuum system. The instrument requires a suction of about 2.5 inches of mercury which is less than that required for the other gyro instruments. Therefore a reducing valve is fitted to reduce the suction to the required figure. Since the needle of the turn indicator measures the force of precession, too low a vacuum will result in a lower than normal rotor speed and therefore a lesser needle deflection for a given rate of turn, i.e. low vacuum results in the turn needle under reading and a high vacuum will result in an over reading.

THE BALANCE INDICATOR
The most common type of balance indicator in use today consists of a curved glass cylinder filled with kerosene in which is placed a small agate stone, common ball bearing, or some other suitable spherical and dense material. The fluid provides a damping action and so ensures smooth and easy movement of the ball.

A small vertical projection at one end of the glass tube (not visible to the pilot) contains a small bubble of air to compensate for expansion of the fluid during changes in temperature.

The glass container is curved so that when no yaw forces are present the ball will settle at the lowest point, (Fig. 8-17(a)). During turns, the ball will also settle in the centre of the tube when the centrifugal force is equal to the horizontal component of the lift force i.e. when the forces are in balance. If the aircraft is 'slipping in' during the turn, the ball will move from the centre of the tube and in the direction of the turn, (Fig. 8-17(b)). When the aircraft is 'skidding', the ball will move from the centre towards the outside of the turn, (Fig. 8-17(c)).

The older types of balance indicator use a needle presentation in conjunction with a dial which is marked in degrees of slip or skid.

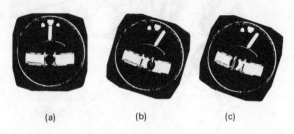

(a)   (b)   (c)

Fig. 8-17

DIFFERENT DIAL PRESENTATION
Figure 8-18 shows the various types of dial presentations used in turn and balance indicators.

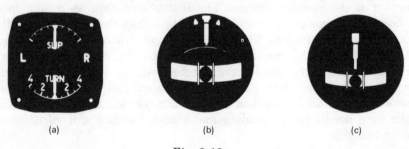

(a)   (b)   (c)

Fig. 8-18

The instrument shown at (a) is found in a number of older type aircraft, the top needle showing the degree of slip or skid, whilst the bottom needle indicates various rates of turn up to rate 4.

Turns are classified by numbers from 1 to 4 which correspond to turning rates measured in degrees per minute, for example:

- Rate 1 = 180° in 1 minute
- Rate 2 = 360° in 1 minute
- Rate 3 = 540° in 1 minute
- Rate 4 = 720° in 1 minute

The instrument presentation shown at (b) is one which is commonly used today and displays balance information through an inclinometer at the bottom of the instrument. The rate of turn is presented by the two marks either side of a central pointer on the dial. These two marks represent a rate 1 turn to the left and right respectively.

The presentation shown at (c) differs from that shown at (b) in that the turn needle and dial calibration is such that a rate 1 turn will be indicated when the turn needle is displaced to the edge of the central index mark.

A fairly new instrument known as a turn co-ordinator has now come into widespread use (Fig. 8-14(b)). The marks on the periphery of the dial indicate turns from nil to a particular rate of turn, and due to differences in manufacture the rate of turn marks may represent rate $\frac{1}{2}$, rate 1 or rate 2. The pilot will therefore have to establish the actual rate of turn relative to a particular mark on the instrument during flight in order to interpret the instrument correctly.

An additional point to bear in mind when using a turn co-ordinator is that the small aircraft which replaces the vertical pointer of earlier instruments *only indicates rate of turn*. However, it is sometimes mistaken as presenting angle of bank.

For example, if the aircraft were placed in a banked attitude and opposite rudder is used to hold the aircraft heading constant, the index aircraft will remain with its wings level because no rate of turn would be occurring. Alternatively if the aircraft's wings were held level and the aircraft was yawed by use of rudder, a rate of turn would occur and the index aircraft would tilt to show the particular rate of turn.

PILOT'S SERVICEABILITY CHECKS

  When powered by electricity, the pilot can usually hear the rotor winding up to speed after the master switch has been placed in the 'on' position. Many electrically driven instruments of this type also have a flag display which disappears if the instrument is electrically serviceable.

Regardless of whether the power source is electricity or suction, another useful check is to press the adjacent corner of the instrument panel when the instrument has reached its normal rotor speed (about one to two minutes after starting). This action will produce a precessional force to the rotor and cause the instrument to give a small turn indication.

A check of the instrument's state of serviceability in relation to both the turn and the balance indications should be carried out by turning the aircraft from side to side during taxying. This will clearly show whether the instrument is indicating properly i.e. a left turn should produce a left indication of the turn indicator and the balance indicator will move out of balance in the opposite direction to the turn.

During flight, the calibration can be checked by turning through a specific number of degrees and timing this with a stop watch or the second hand of the aircraft clock.

THE ATTITUDE INDICATOR

This instrument which is variously known as an attitude indicator, gyro horizon or artificial horizon depending on its year of manufacture and limitations, is used to present the pilot with a pictorial display of the aircraft's attitude.

Fig. 8-19

CONSTRUCTION AND FUNCTION

The instrument is constructed about a gyroscope, the spin axis of which is mounted vertically, and maintained in this position by a gravity sensing device in the form of a pendulous unit. Utilising the properties of a gyro to maintain a constant position in space, the rotor is mounted in a gimbal assembly consisting of an inner and outer ring.

The inner gimbal forms the rotor casing and is pivoted parallel to the athwartships axis of the aircraft. The outer gimbal is pivoted parallel to the aircraft's fore and aft axis. The pivot points of the outer gimbal are located at the front and rear ends of the instrument case. Figure 8-20 shows a typical vacuum operated instrument.

The indications of the aircraft's pitch and bank attitude are presented by the relative position of a miniature aircraft symbol (index aircraft), and a stabilised bar which remains parallel to the earth's horizon. This bar is called the *artificial horizon*. Additional indications to show the degree of bank and sometimes pitch are marked out on the face of the instrument.

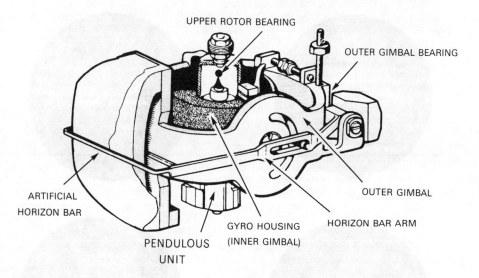

UPPER ROTOR BEARING

OUTER GIMBAL BEARING

ARTIFICIAL
HORIZON BAR

OUTER GIMBAL

PENDULOUS
UNIT

GYRO HOUSING
(INNER GIMBAL)

HORIZON BAR ARM

Fig. 8-20

INTERPRETATION OF INDICATIONS

Because the rotor retains its rigidity in space whenever the aircraft's attitude is changed, it is the case of the instrument (attached to the aircraft) which moves relative to the rotor.

Typical presentations of aircraft attitude are shown in Fig. 8-21. In (a) the aircraft is in level flight and the wings of the index aircraft are laterally level in relation to the artificial horizon line. The fore and aft pitch of the aircraft is also shown to be level with the horizon, as the index aircraft's attitude in pitch is such that it is superimposed over the artificial horizon line.

In Fig. 8-21(b), the aircraft is banking to the left and the degree of bank is indicated by the position of the pointer at the top of the instrument relative to the angle of bank marks on the dial.

Figure 8-21(c) shows the aircraft to be in a nose high attitude and Fig. 8-21(d) shows the aircraft is in a low nose attitude and banking to the right.

It must be clearly understood that the attitude indicator shows a direct picture of the aircraft's attitude and not of its performance e.g. climbing or descending. Information in relation to performance has to be obtained by using the other flight instruments.

DIFFERENT DIAL PRESENTATIONS

The information given by the instrument is displayed by different methods depending on the period of manufacture and the specific make. However some earlier models have a bank pointer which indicates degrees of bank in the opposite sense to the actual direction

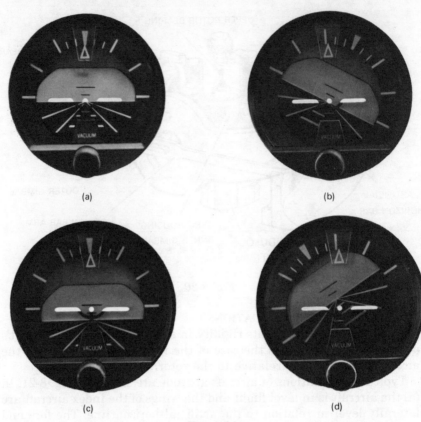

(a)   (b)

(c)   (d)

Fig. 8-21

of bank being applied. This can be confusing as shown by Fig. 8-22(a). In more recent presentations this indication is reversed so that when the aircraft is in a bank to the right, the bank pointer indicates a bank to the right and vice versa, Fig. 8-22(b). This later type of presentation reduces the possibility of the pilot misreading the instrument.

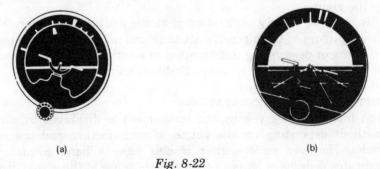

(a)   (b)

Fig. 8-22

ERRORS AND OPERATING LIMITATIONS

Errors in the indications given by the instrument will occur if the power source fails to operate correctly. In vaccum operated instruments it will be necessary to maintain the correct amount of suction for the rotor and the filters must therefore be clean.

Friction caused by worn bearings will also create errors and faulty indications. Because of the design and construction principle involved certain errors can be induced during normal operation but generally they are small and quickly disappear when the aircraft is flown accurately. For example a skidding turn will cause the pendulous erection mechanism to cause a small precession effect, as will the effect of centrifugal force during balanced turns. Both of these effects may result in a temporary one wing low indication when the aircraft is returned to straight and level flight. Small pitch errors are also induced, as are acceleration and deceleration errors, when the aircraft commences turning, however, in a serviceable instrument these errors are fairly small and of a transient nature.

If the bank and pitch limitations of the particular instrument are exceeded, the gimbals will topple, and it may take up to five or ten minutes before the erection mechanism returns the rotor and gimbals to the operating position.

Another error inherent in the instrument occurs when the aircraft experiences an acceleration, the effect of this on the pendulous erecting unit results in a small pitch and bank error, the amount and degree of which will vary slightly depending on the particular make of instrument.

The pilot must appreciate that an acceleration error of this type will be produced during take-off and initial climb, however, this is not always evident in light aircraft because of their relatively low rates of acceleration.

In earlier instruments driven by vacuum, the geometry of their construction limits the freedom of the gimbal system, and as a result, the instrument will topple and give erratic indications when the aircraft exceeds about 60° in pitch and 110° in roll. Later instruments however have a greater freedom of movement and those operated by electricity are considered to have complete freedom from toppling in both pitch and roll.

Earlier instruments incorporate a manual caging device which can be used to cage the instrument before carrying out manoeuvres which are known to be in excess of its limitations. It can also be used as a quick erection device should these limitations be inadvertently exceeded. When uncaging the instrument it is however necessary to ensure the aircraft is in straight and level flight, otherwise erroneous indications will be given until the normal erection mechanism has had time to act.

PILOT'S SERVICEABILITY CHECKS

After starting the engine, the instrument should be checked to see that it has erected properly and that the artificial horizon is laterally level. Some instruments have an adjustable index aircraft which can be raised or lowered by a setting knob. When this facility is fitted, it is important to align the index aircraft over the artificial horizon bar so that a presentation of level flight is more clearly shown when airborne.

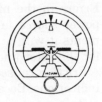

The normal suction required for this instrument is between $4\frac{1}{2}$ to $5\frac{1}{2}$ inches of mercury and this can be ascertained from the vacuum gauge. Whilst taxying, the aircraft should be turned left and right during which, the artificial horizon line should remain stable. On earlier instruments, the action of turning the aircraft will affect the pendulous vanes which are part of the pendulous erection device and it will be normal to note a slight change in the lateral level of the artificial horizon line.

THE HEADING INDICATOR

This instrument, also known as the directional gyro was designed to give the pilot dead beat indications of the aircraft's heading. Although the magnetic compass is the master instrument for determining the heading of an aircraft, it oscillates and cannot be damped sufficiently to overcome the fluctuations and erroneous readings arising from air turbulence and the errors associated with turning and changes of airspeed.

Fig. 8-23

CONSTRUCTION AND FUNCTION

The construction and operation of the heading indicator is based on the principles of gyroscopic rigidity. The rotor is mounted vertically and is normally driven from the suction created by the vacuum system.

Air enters the instrument case, passes through channels in the vertical gimbal ring and impinges upon buckets cut into the periphery of the rotor. The rotor is enclosed in a case and supported in an inner gimbal ring which is free to turn about a horizontal axis. This inner gimbal is mounted in an outer gimbal, the bearings of which are located at the top and bottom of the instrument case, permitting the gimbal to pivot about a vertical axis.

Fig. 8-24

The rotor is maintained in vertical alignment by arranging for the air jets which strike against the rotor grooves to apply a precessional force whenever the rotor starts to tilt from the vertical. This precessional force automatically re-aligns the rotor into a vertical position with its axis horizontal.

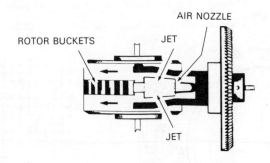

Fig. 8-25

A second type of erection device is incorporated in the mechanism which is used to set the instrument's heading to that of the magnetic compass. This mechanism which is operated by an external knob below the glass case of the instrument is also used to cage and uncage the gimbal assembly. Whenever the knob is pressed in, it operates a caging arm which re-erects the rotor to its correct position should it

have toppled due to the limitations of the gimbal assembly being
exceeded.

USE WITH THE MAGNETIC COMPASS
Although the instrument provides a stable heading reference, it has
no power of seeking magnetic direction. Therefore it can only be used
in conjunction with a magnetic compass.

ERRORS AND RE-SETTING IN FLIGHT
The main errors which occur in the heading indicator are caused by
friction in the bearings, the gimballing, and the apparent drift due to
the earth's rotation.

Bearing friction is fairly small in a well serviced and clean
instrument but increases markedly if the bearings are worn, dirty or
improperly lubricated. Gimballing error occurs because of the
geometry of the gimbal system in that, unless the gyro frame (the
aircraft) is rotated about only one of the gyro axes, the outer gimbal
ring will move if the direction of the rotor axis is to remain
undisturbed. The net effect of this is to cause small transient errors in
a combination of pitch and roll on all headings and whilst turning
between cardinal headings when the aircraft is changing its attitude.
These small errors are quickly reduced to zero as soon as normal
straight and level flight is resumed.

Apparent drift is caused by the effect of the earth's rotation and
also whenever the aircraft changes its longitude. In Fig. 8-26(a), three
heading indicators are shown, one at the equator and one at each of
the poles.

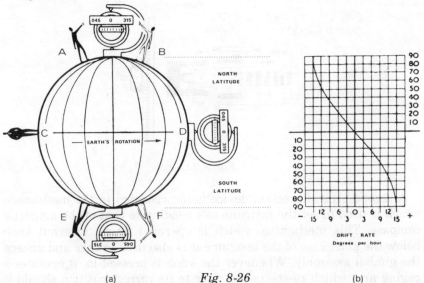

(a)   *Fig. 8-26*   (b)

A person standing at 'A' (the North Pole) at 0600 hours and reading the heading scale as 090° would be at point 'B' at 1800 hours. Due to the rotation of the earth at this time he would read the heading scale as 270° although the heading indicator will not have moved. Therefore the earth's rotation during the 12 hour period would have caused an apparent drift of 180° i.e. 15° per hour.

A person standing at 'C' (on the Equator) at 0600 hours and reading the heading scale as zero would be at 'D' at 1800 hours, but in this case would still read the heading scale as zero because no apparent drift has been experienced.

Finally, a person standing at 'E' would be inverted relative to a person at 'A'. Therefore he would read the heading scale as 270° at 0600 hours and 090° at 1800 hours 'F' – the same amount of apparent drift will have been observed but in the opposite direction.

This apparent drift of minus 15° per hour at the North Pole and plus 15° per hour at the South Pole varies proportionately in the intermediate latitudes and is zero at the Equator, (Fig. 8-26(b)). Because of these various errors, a pilot will have to reset the heading indicator at periodic intervals during flight.

DIFFERENT DIAL PRESENTATIONS
Earlier heading indicators use a compass ring marked in degrees which are shown through a glass window relative to a vertical reference (*lubber*) line, (Fig. 8-27).

Later models use a dial presentation consisting of an azimuth display as shown in Fig. 8-28. The gyro assembly is similar to that used in the earlier model, but instead of the horizontally mounted compass card, an azimuth card is mounted on the front of the instrument which is easier to read and facil-

Fig. 8-27

itates the pilot's orientation. This card, which is geared to the vertical gimbals rotates as the aircraft turns and the aircraft heading is shown under the pointer of the index aircraft inscribed on the glass cover of the instrument face. Indices are also usually marked out on the glass cover to show the 45°, 90° and 180° points relative to the aircraft heading.

OPERATING LIMITS
Earlier models had a geometric limitation to the gimbals which caused the instrument to topple when 55° of pitch or bank were exceeded. Later models, with improved geometric gimbal design permit the instrument greater freedom in pitch and bank and like

certain attitude indicators some of these models are considered as *topple free.*

CAGING AND RE-SETTING PROCEDURE
The earlier models of this instrument are equipped with a caging knob below the instrument face, which can be pushed in locking the whole gyro assembly until pulled out again. This facility can be used to avoid strain and wear on the gimbal bearings when carrying out manoeuvres known to be in excess of the gyro's limitations. The same caging mechanism is also used to re-synchronise the heading card with the magnetic compass.

Later instruments incorporate a spring loaded knob which when pushed and held in this position can be rotated to re-synchronise the instrument with the magnetic compass.

When re-synchronising any type of heading indicator, it is important to maintain an accurate heading with the aircraft wings level and in unaccelerated flight before noting the compass heading and setting it on the heading indicator. Failure to do this will result in an erroneous reading from both instruments.

Fig. 8-28

PILOT'S SERVICEABILITY CHECKS
Prior to starting up the engine, the instrument should be checked to see that the glass front is intact and the numerals are clearly legible. The power source supply should be checked after engine starting to ensure that it is functioning correctly and when a vacuum operated instrument is used, the correct minimum amount of suction must be obtained.

Fig. 8-29

During taxying, the heading indicator should increase its heading reading when the aircraft is turned to the right and decrease its reading when turned to the left. The heading card should also give a dead beat reading.

The instrument should be synchronised with the magnetic compass before leaving the parking area and re-checked again during the pre-take-off checks. Small errors of 5° to 10° incurred during taxying will normally be acceptable but larger errors will indicate a faulty instrument.

During normal flight, errors of up to 3° per 15 minutes are considered normal, but significantly larger errors are a pointer that the instrument needs servicing.

THE MAGNETIC COMPASS

The magnetic compass utilises the inherent qualities of magnetism to indicate direction. It is a simple self-contained instrument which has a single or multiple bar magnet freely suspended to allow it to rotate in the horizontal plane. The bar magnet will assume a position in which one of its ends points towards the earth's magnetic pole. This is known as the north seeking pole of the magnet.

Earlier compasses were constructed to give a horizontal display (Fig. 8-30(a)) but later models use a vertical heading display. In both cases the principle of operation is closely similar.

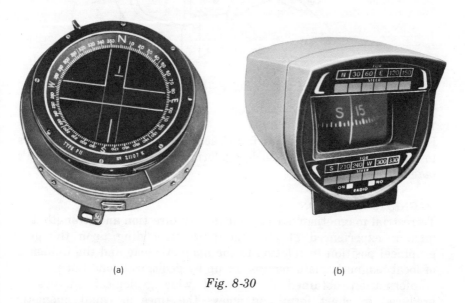

(a)   (b)

Fig. 8-30

CONSTRUCTION AND FUNCTION

The instrument consists of a liquid filled bowl containing a pivoted float element to which the bar magnets are attached. The liquid is normally an acid free white kerosene which is used to dampen the oscillations of the float assembly during flight and also to decrease the friction of the pivot and support some of the weight of the compass heading card or ring.

In order to provide for contraction and expansion of the fluid during temperature changes, an expansion chamber is an integral part of the assembly.

A compass card graduated in degrees is attached to the pivot assembly and in the case of the vertical type compass, a fixed reference marker is attached to the compass bowl. The horizontal type compass uses a moveable grid ring which can be set to the heading required.

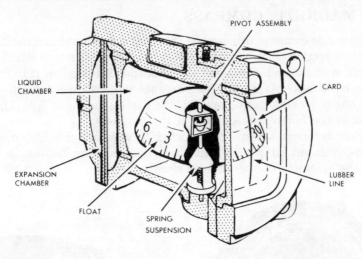

Fig. 8-31

THE EARTH'S MAGNETIC FIELD

Lines of magnetic force flow from each of the earth's *magnetic poles* towards each other and by so doing, form what is known as the *earth's magnetic field.*

MAGNETIC VARIATION

Terrestrial magnetism is irregular in both direction and strength, the amount experienced at any one place depending upon the geographical position in relation to the magnetic pole and the influence of local magnetic disturbances set up by geological conditions.

Information obtained from world wide geological surveys is produced in chart form and shows the lines of equal magnetic variation and their value in relation to latitude and longitude. These lines, known as *isogonals*, are overprinted on pilot navigation maps to show the pilot the amount of variation he has to allow for when calculating headings from *true* to *magnetic.*

Although the amount of variation at a given place on the earth's surface will vary, the change is relatively small (at the present time over the UK it averages about 0.1 of a degree annually) and an aeronautical chart will become obsolete for many other reasons long before any significant changes in variation occur.

To sum up, variation can be defined as being the angular difference between the direction taken up by an aircraft compass needle (when influenced only by terrestrial magnetism) and the direction of *true north.*

It is said to be easterly variation if the magnetic north lies to the east of true north and westerly variation if the magnetic north lies to

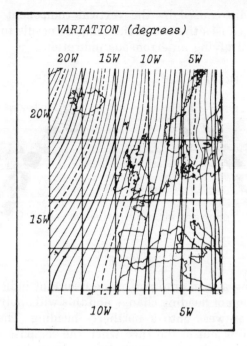

Fig. 8-32

the west of true north. Depending upon the aircraft position in relation to the *true pole* the variation at that place will therefore be westerly or easterly.

The method of applying variation in relation to navigating an aircraft is given in technical manual two of this series.

THE DIP ANGLE

If an aircraft was flying over the North Pole the compass needle would attempt to tilt vertically downwards, whereas at the equator this *angle of dip* would be much less. The problem of minimising the effect of this angle is of more concern to the instrument manufacturer than the pilot. However, even though the instrument manufacturer is able to construct a reliable compass in which the effect of the dip angle is minimised, the secondary effect of compensating for this leads to two basic errors in the instrument and the pilot will have to appreciate these effects during flight.

TURNING, ACCELERATION AND DECELERATION ERRORS

Turning error is the most pronounced of the in-flight errors to which the magnetic compass is prone. This occurs because when an aircraft is banked, the compass heading ring and needle are also banked, and the angle of dip caused by the vertical component of the earth's magnetic field causes the end of the compass needle to dip to the low side of the turn giving an erroneous indication.

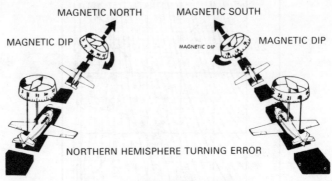

Fig. 8-33

When making a turn onto north, the resultant indication is a lead into the direction of heading change and this will apply when turning through east or west onto a northerly heading. The correction is applied by rolling out of the turn when the compass reading is still some 30° from north when operating in latitudes covered by the United Kingdom. This correction is however based on the aircraft making a rate 1 turn (bank angle approximately 15°).

When turning onto a southerly heading the error is reversed in relation to the readings of the compass card and the correction will be to roll out some 30° after the compass has indicated a southerly heading. Turning error is maximum when turning onto north or south and nil when using a rate 1 turn onto east or west. Therefore if the heading required is 045° or 315° the turn error correction will be approximately 15°

Acceleration and deceleration errors occur on easterly and westerly headings, and when accelerating on east or west an apparent turn towards north will be indicated when the aircraft is actually maintaining a constant heading. When decelerating on easterly or westerly headings the apparent turn will be in the opposite direction, i.e. to the south.

There is little point in memorising the direction of the acceleration or deceleration errors, but whenever a positive acceleration or deceleration occurs, the aircraft should be kept on a constant heading by use of an outside visual reference, or when, under instrument flight conditions, kept on a constant heading by using the heading indicator.

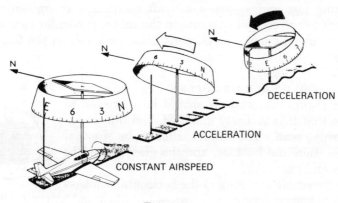

DECELERATION

ACCELERATION

CONSTANT AIRSPEED

Fig. 8-34

MAGNETISM IN AIRCRAFT

The compass needle is not only affected by the earth's magnetic field, but also by any magnetic fields set up by ferrous metal components in the aircraft and/or generated when the aircraft electrical equipment is operated.

The effect of magnetic disturbances created within the aircraft is called *deviation*, and they also deflect the compass needle so that it is out of alignment with magnetic north.

DEVIATION AND USE OF DEVIATION CARDS

To reduce the effect of deviation, aircraft compasses are regularly calibrated (known as a compass swing) at periodic intervals (which are normally every six months), to ascertain the value of deviation and to compensate for it as much as possible by making adjustments to the magnets. It is also necessary to calibrate magnetic compasses when certain components are added or removed from the aircraft.

Following the compass being swung, the residual errors are recorded on a compass deviation card and mounted near the instruments. Further information on deviation and the use of the compass deviation card is given in technical manual two of this series.

PRECAUTIONS WHEN CARRYING 'MAGNETIC GOODS'

Apart from using the information on the deviation card correctly, a pilot must take care to keep any magnetic materials which may be carried in the aircraft well away from the magnetic compass or large erroneous readings may occur during navigation flights.

The effect of large unpredictable errors produced by the carriage of magnetic materials near the compass can easily lead to a pilot becoming lost and as many aircraft compasses are mounted on or adjacent to the cockpit coaming in the cabin, particular care must be taken to avoid placing metal pens, clipboards etc. on the facia panel or shelf.

PILOT'S SERVICEABILITY CHECKS

Before flight, the compass should be inspected to ensure that it is securely installed, and that it can be easily read. The liquid should be free of discoloration and bubbles, and the glass should be secure and uncracked.

The moveable grid ring of the horizontal compass (if fitted) should rotate easily when unlocked and be rigid when it is locked.

A check should be made to ensure that it is indicating an approximately correct direction and this can be done by noting the direction of runways or buildings relative to magnetic north. Runways, it may be recalled, are always numbered according to the magnetic direction (to the nearest 10°) to which they are aligned.

During taxying, the aircraft can be turned to the left and right to check that the compass responds correctly.

Progress Tests

Progress Tests

This section contains a series of progress tests designed to enable you to test your level of knowledge in the subject material included in this manual. You should bear in mind the following points when completing the tests:

- They are designed to enable you to monitor your progress. Their objective is to provide a means whereby you can assess your knowledge and understanding at various stages in your learning task. If you can score good marks (75% or above) in these tests you will be able to sit the CAA written examination with a high degree of confidence.
- The test items are not trick questions, each statement means exactly what it says. Therefore read each question, response or statement carefully and do not look for hidden meanings.
- Be sure that you understand what the test item asks, and then review the alternative responses. Following this, decide which response is the correct one or work out the problem to obtain the correct answer.
- Always select the response which gives the most complete and correct answer, the others will be responses which are totally wrong, partially wrong or those which you might select if you lack sufficient knowledge of the subject.
- After completing each test, check your answers against those shown on pages Q49-50. Questions which give you difficulty or which you fail to answer correctly will give you an indication of those areas in which you lack understanding, and you should therefore review the appropriate parts of the subject before proceeding with your next stage of study.

Quiz No. 1

1 A symmetrical aerofoil section which is moved through the air at a zero angle of attack:

  (a) Will cause the air passing over the top of the aerofoil to travel faster than the air passing below it.

  (b) Will produce a low pressure above the wing and a high pressure below the wing.

  (c) Will cause an acceleration to the airflow passing round it and the speed of the airflow above and below the wing will be the same.

  (d) Will produce a high pressure above the wing and a low pressure below the wing.

2 An asymmetric shaped aerofoil as shown in the diagram below will, on being passed through the air at sufficient speed create:

  (a) An upward lift force, but only provided the angle of attack is more than zero.

  (b) A negative lift force when placed at an angle of attack of zero degrees.

  (c) An upward lift force at a zero degree angle of attack.

  (d) Will produce an equal reaction both upward and downward when at a zero degree angle of attack.

3 Which of the following statements is correct?

  (a) The total reaction of a wing acts at 90° to the relative airflow.

  (b) The camber of a wing is the imaginary line between the leading and trailing edges.

(c) The angle of attack is the angle between the chord line and the relative airflow.

(d) All the above responses are incorrect.

4 If the angle of attack of an aerofoil in a given airflow is increased, the:

(a) Lift and drag will decrease.

(b) Lift will increase and the drag will decrease.

(c) Drag will increase and the lift will decrease.

(d) Lift and the drag will increase.

5 Which of the following statements is correct?

(a) As the angle of attack is increased the centre of pressure will move rearward.

(b) There will be a change in the pitching moment of the wing.

(c) As the angle of attack is decreased the centre of pressure will move forward.

(d) None of the above statements are correct.

6 Induced drag is caused by the:

(a) High pressure area over the wing moving outwards to the tips.

(b) Air below the wing moving outwards towards the tips.

(c) Turbulence produced by the joining of the wing root to the aircraft fuselage.

(d) Frictional effect of the air passing over the wing surface.

7 During flight the wing will produce 'profile drag' and 'induced drag'. In relation to induced drag, which of the following is true?

(a) It increases with increase of airspeed.

(b) It remains constant regardless of variation in airspeed.

(c) If the speed decreases and level flight is maintained, the induced drag will increase.

(d) Induced drag is least at high angles of attack.

8 The term 'lift/drag ratio':

   (a) Can be used to illustrate the aerodynamic efficiency of the wing.

   (b) Can be defined as the ratio of the amount of lift to drag produced from an aerofoil.

   (c) Is obtained by comparing the amount of lift and drag produced from an aerofoil at different angles of attack.

   (d) All the above responses are correct.

9 A wing of high 'aspect ratio' will:

   (a) Be less efficient than one with a low aspect ratio.

   (b) Produce a larger drag force at any angle of attack than that of a low aspect ratio wing.

   (c) Be more efficient than one with a low aspect ratio.

   (d) Have a long chord and a short span.

10 Which of the following statements is correct?

   (a) The curvature of the aerofoil from its leading edge to its trailing edge is known as 'camber'.

   (b) Thicker wing sections will in general produce more lift for a given airspeed and angle of attack.

   (c) The wing is normally attached to the fuselage at a particular angle known as the 'angle of incidence'.

   (d) All the above responses are correct.

ANSWER SHEET QUIZ NO. 1

Q	A
1	
2	
3	
4	
5	
6	
7	
8	
9	
10	

Quiz No. 2

1 Load factor is expressed in multiples of gravitational pull or 'gs', and in normal straight and level flight the load factor will be:

(a) +1

(b) −1

(c) +2

(d) +3

2 The limiting load factors to which an aircraft can be safely subjected are:

(a) Determined by the manufacturer.

(b) Shown in the particular aircraft manual.

(c) Measured in positive and negative load factors.

(d) All the above responses are correct.

3 The limiting load factors normally applicable to any light aircraft:

(a) Cannot be exceeded by the pilot.

(b) Can be exceeded by the pilot's handling of the controls.

(d) Will only be shown on the placards fitted in the cockpit.

(d) Can be guaranteed to apply to any aircraft regardless of age.

4 In relation to the structural design of aircraft wings:

(a) The applied lifting loads are arranged primarily to be taken by the skin, thence transmitted to the stringers and ribs to the wing spars.

(b) They are constructed of frames and rings with the applied loads being taken directly by the bulkheads and rings.

(c) They are designed to withstand both torsional and bending stresses.

(d) Both responses (a) and (c) are correct.

5 The range of control surface movement is limited by:

(a) The length and tension in the control cables.

(b) Adjustable stops fitted to both the cockpit controls and in a region adjacent to the control surface.

(c) An arrangement of turnbuckles.

(d) A system of pulleys and fairleads.

6 Loss of pressure from a shimmy damper fitted to a nosewheel will result in:

(a) The nosewheel castoring through 180° during take-off or landing.

(b) Loss of brake fluid.

(c) The nosewheel castoring a few degrees either side of its centreline resulting in vibration.

(d) None of the above responses are correct.

7 In relation to creep marks painted on the wheel and tyre assembly.

(a) If a gap occurs between the marks painted on the wheel and the tyre, it can be considered as serviceable but should be reported to a ground engineer as soon as possible.

(b) The tyre and wheel assembly can only be considered serviceable providing both marks remain dead in line with one another.

(c) If any gap appears between the mark on the tyre and that on the wheel, the aircraft must be considered unserviceable and a report made to a ground engineer.

(d) Creep marks are only used when tubeless tyres are fitted.

8 The limit of wear in tyres varies with the type of tread used. In the case of tyres with a patterned tread, they

(a) May be used until the tread is worn to the depth of the tread pattern.

(b) Must be considered as unserviceable if the depth of the pattern is less than 2mm.

(c) Must be considered as unserviceable if the pattern of tread has worn unevenly.

(d) Can be safely used until the grey cushion fibres are showing.

9 Although various makes of tyre and patterns of tread are used on aircraft, they can all be assumed to be:

(a) Impervious to oil and fuels.

(b) Designed to have no harmful effects from over or under inflation.

(c) Susceptible to damage from contact with oil and fuels.

(d) Capable of safely withstanding deep cuts and scores to their casings.

10 When baggage is carried in an aircraft the pilot should ensure that:

(a) The weight carried in the baggage area is such that it does not exceed the limitations given in the aircraft manual.

(b) It is safely secured.

(c) It does not foul any control systems.

(d) All of the above responses are correct.

ANSWER SHEET QUIZ NO. 2

Q	A
1	
2	
3	
4	
5	
6	
7	
8	
9	
10	

Quiz No. 3

1 In relation to the aircraft axes and the flying controls:

   (a) The ailerons are used to control the aircraft about its longitudinal axis.

   (b) The rudder is used to control the aircraft in pitch.

   (c) The elevators and ailerons are used together to control the aircraft about the lateral axis.

   (d) The elevators are used to control movement about the normal axis.

2 The use of a differential aileron movement (which is often combined with the use of 'frise' aileron) is to:

   (a) Reduce the tendency for the aircraft to pitch whenever the ailerons are operated.

   (b) Reduce adverse yaw.

   (c) To give greater dynamic stability.

   (d) To increase static stability.

3 In order to reduce any tendency for the controls to flutter during flight it is usual to:

   (a) Design the control surface with a horn shaped tip.

   (b) Arrange the hinge line to be ahead of the centre of gravity of the control surface.

   (c) Incorporate some form of mass balance.

   (d) Attach a fixed tab to the trailing edge of the control surface.

4 An anti balance tab will:

   (a) Move in the same direction as the movement of the main control surface.

    (b) Move in the opposite direction to the movement of the main control surface.

    (d) Remain in a fixed position whenever the control surface is moved.

    (d) Reduce any tendency of the control surface to flutter.

5 Which of the following responses is correct?

    (a) During the approach to a landing, the use of flaps on a light aircraft is primarily to steepen the approach path and permit the pilot a better view along the approach path.

    (b) When flaps are lowered, both the lift coefficient and the drag coefficient increase.

    (c) The lowering or raising of the flaps will usually induce a pitching movement.

    (d) All the above responses are correct.

6 If an aircraft has a lift drag ratio of 10:1 which of the following responses correctly quantifies the amount of lift and drag when the aircraft is in level flight?

    (a) 1500 lb of lift to 150 lb of drag.

    (b) 750 kg of drag to 750 kg of lift.

    (c) 150 kg of lift to 1500 kg of drag.

    (d) None of the above responses are correct.

7 Which of the following responses is correct?

    (a) The centre of gravity will remain at a constant fixed point on the aircraft during flight.

    (b) The centre of lift (centre of pressure) is arranged by the designer so that if the aircraft is loaded correctly, it will always remain ahead of the centre of gravity.

    (c) The couple formed by thrust and drag will balance out the couple formed by lift and weight.

    (d) None of the above responses are correct.

8 Concerning the various factors which relate to dynamic stability it could be said that:

    (a) Neutral dynamic stability will exist if the aircraft once disturbed, returns to its original condition.

(b) If the aircraft is displaced and returns to its original position of equilibrium it will have a degree of dynamic stability.

(c) If the aircraft is displaced and continues its movement without any increase or decrease in its rate it is said to possess positive dynamic stability.

(d) To be considered as having neutral dynamic stability, the aircraft should immediately return to its original position in equilibrium.

9 If the centre of gravity of an aircraft is moved aft the 'tail lever arm' will be:

(a) Increased and the longitudinal stability is increased.

(b) Decreased and the longitudinal stability is increased.

(c) Decreased but this will not affect the degree of longitudinal stability.

(d) Decreased and the aircraft's longitudinal stability will decrease.

10 Which of the following responses are correct.

(a) If the weight of the aircraft is increased the wing loading will be increased.

(b) The greater the weight of the aircraft the greater will be the stalling speed.

(c) A change in aircraft weight will have no effect on the stalling speed.

(d) Both responses (a) and (b) are correct.

ANSWER SHEET QUIZ NO. 3

Q	A
1	
2	
3	
4	
5	
6	
7	
8	
9	
10	

Quiz No. 4

1   In relation to spinning, which of the following responses is correct?

(a)   A forward position of the centre of gravity will make spin recovery more difficult.

(b)   If the centre of gravity is well aft, it may be impossible to effect a recovery from a spin manoeuvre.

(c)   An aft centre of gravity will make the spin become very steep and the airspeed will rapidly increase.

(d)   Both responses (a) and (c) are correct.

2   When the aircraft is in a balanced turn during which altitude is being maintained:

(a)   The load factor is decreased.

(b)   The stalling speed will increase with increase in bank.

(c)   The stalling speed is decreased.

(d)   All the above responses are incorrect.

3   The term V_a in relation to an aircraft is defined as:

(a)   The maximum speed for operation of the flaps.

(b)   The never exceed speed.

(c)   The stalling speed with power off and flaps up.

(d)   The maximum speed at which the pilot can make abrupt and extreme control movements involving their maximum deflection.

4 The load factor is an important consideration during man-
oevures. Which of the following statements is correct?

(a) Load factor is the ratio between lift and weight and is
determined by $n = L/W$ where n is the load factor.

(b) Load factor is the result of the high increase in drag at steep
angles of bank.

(c) When a sudden backward movement of the control column
is made during normal level flight, a negative g force will
result.

(d) Both responses (a) and (b) are correct.

5 If an aircraft is placed in a 60° banked turn at a constant
altitude, the load factor will be:

(a) 3.0

(b) 1.5

(c) 2.0

(d) 4.0

6 The V code for the stalling speed with flaps up, power off and a
load factor of one is:

(a) V_{fe}

(b) V_{s0}

(c) V_{s1}

(d) V_{ra}

7 Which of the following responses is correct?

(a) Propeller blades undergo very high centrifugal, twisting and
bending forces.

(b) Twisting forces on a propeller are caused by aerodynamic
and centrifugal twisting moments.

(c) It is important to carry out engine run-ups in an area where
the ground is free from stones and similar loose material,
because any damage to propeller blades causes imbalance.

(d) All of the above responses are correct.

8 The power developed from a normally aspirated aero engine, will:

   (a) Decrease with an increase of air density.

   (b) Increase with an increase in temperature.

   (c) Increase with an increase of air density.

   (d) Increase with an increase of humidity.

9 When an aircraft is fitted with a fixed pitch propeller:

   (a) The RPM will remain constant for a fixed throttle position regardless of any change in airspeed.

   (b) The RPM will increase if the airspeed increases regardless of the position of the throttle.

   (c) The pilot can adjust the RPM lever to give a constant RPM regardless of any change in throttle position.

   (d) The propeller blades will automatically be at their most efficient angle during take-off.

10 In relation to propeller design:

   (a) The maximum thrust force will occur at the blade tips.

   (b) The maximum thrust force will occur at the blade roots.

   (c) The magnitude of the thrust it creates is equal to the mass of air moved per unit time, multiplied by the slipstream velocity, minus the speed of the aircraft.

   (d) None of the above responses are correct.

ANSWER SHEET QUIZ NO. 4

Q	A
1	
2	
3	
4	
5	
6	
7	
8	
9	
10	

Quiz No. 5

1 The fundamental principle of operation of an aero engine is:

(a) The conversion of heat energy into mechanical energy.

(b) The utilisation of fuel and air which through the process of combustion creates pressure in a cylinder which does work against a piston.

(c) To burn fuel and create an explosion. This moves a piston in a linear direction which is then converted into a rotary action to turn a propeller.

(d) Both responses (a) and (b) are correct.

2 A piston engine undergoes a cycle which involves pistons moving linearly in cylinders. This cycle comprises the following.

(a) Four strokes, which in order are named, intake, expansion, compression and exhaust.

(a) A sparking plug ignites the fuel which is then compressed to produce a power stroke after which the cylinder is exhausted to atmosphere.

(c) Four strokes, which in order are named, intake, compression, expansion and exhaust.

(d) None of the above responses are correct.

3 During the four stroke cycle, the sparking plug ignites the mixture:

(a) Just prior to the intake stroke.

(b) During the exhaust stroke.

(c) Just prior to the exhaust stroke.

(d) Just prior to the end of the compression stroke.

4 The term 'valve overlap' is given to the method of opening and shutting the inlet and exhaust valves. The use of this method is to:

   (a) Ensure that all the exhaust gases are removed from the cylinder after the intake stroke.

   (b) Delay the period of the compression stroke.

   (c) Close the intake valve earlier to prevent a backfire.

   (d) Improve the volumetric efficiency of the engine.

5 Magnetos are used to provide an electric current which creates:

   (a) Heating for the air drawn through the intake system.

   (b) An electric spark from the sparking plugs in each cylinder.

   (c) Electrical power for the starter motor.

   (d) The power which is harnessed to the aircraft electrical system for the operation of lighting, radio and similar services.

6 The purpose in having a dual ignition system is:

   (a) To provide for greater safety.

   (b) To provide electric current to the sparking plugs and aircraft radio.

   (d) To provide for a more efficient combustion of fuel/air in the cylinder.

   (d) Both responses (a) and (c) are correct.

7 In relation to float type carburettors:

   (a) It is not always possible to deliver the same strength of fuel/air ratio to all cylinders.

   (b) It utilises the principle of a venturi to produce a drop of pressure in the system and cause fuel to flow through its jets.

   (c) Most float type carburettors used in small aero engines are of the updraught type.

   (d) All the above responses are correct.

8   With regard to the ratio of fuel to air:

(a) All reciprocating aero engines are arranged to have a slightly lean fuel/air mixture which will be enriched after take-off.

(b) The mixture is pre-set to be rich under idling, medium power and high power conditions and the pilot should adjust the fuel/air mixture in accordance with his flight conditions, and the manufacturer's recommendations.

(c) The mixture control is only used to shut down the engine after flight.

(d) The mixture control should never be adjusted below 5000 ft unless the engine is at idling power.

9   The cruise performance graphs or tables, shown in flight manuals, owner's manuals or pilot's operating handbooks:

(a) Show range and endurance figures based upon operating the engine in rich mixture.

(b) Give range and endurance figures based upon the use of correct mixture leaning techniques.

(c) Allow for headwinds of up to 20 knots.

(d) All the above responses are incorrect.

10 Which of the following responses are correct.

(a) The use of correct mixture leaning technique increases both range and endurance but is harmful to the life of an engine.

(b) Detonation can be incurred by using fuel of a lower grade than recommended.

(c) The use of correct mixture leaning technique increases an aircraft's range and endurance and is also beneficial to the engine.

(d) Both responses (b) and (c) are correct.

ANSWER SHEET QUIZ NO. 5

Q	A
1	
2	
3	
4	
5	
6	
7	
8	
9	
10	

Quiz No. 6

1 The definition of 'range' is:

(a) The longest time an aircraft can remain airborne with the fuel carried.

(b) The furthest distance an aircraft can fly on the amount of fuel carried.

(c) The furthest distance an aircraft can fly with an arbitrary fuel load and tailwind component.

(d) The longest time an aircraft can remain airborne in a headwind of 30 kts.

2 The correct method to use in determining an aircraft's range is:

(a) A simple rule of thumb procedure from knowledge gained during previous flights in an aircraft of the same type.

(b) To increase the IAS by 10 knots for every 20 knot increase in a headwind component.

(c) To refer to the 'Performance Section' of the specific aircraft flight manual or equivalent document. Your calculations should include such factors as, the planned altitude to fly, the air temperature and the BHP for the intended airspeed.

(d) Both responses (a) and (b) are correct.

3 The best rate of climb speed will be:

(a) Shown on the ASI by a yellow radial line.

(b) That airspeed which gives the greatest excess of power available over that required to maintain level flight.

(c) That airspeed which gives the maximum height gain for distance flown.

(d) Both responses (b) and (c) are correct.

4 Using the figures given in the table below, what will be the 'take-off distance' under the following conditions:

Aircraft Weight	2300 lbs
Pressure Altitude	Sea level
Outside Air Temperature	10°C
Tailwind Component	4 knots
Runway	Level, Paved and Dry

TAKEOFF DISTANCE

CONDITIONS:
Flaps Up
Full Throttle Prior to Brake Release
Paved, Level, Dry Runway
Zero Wind

NOTES:

1. Decrease distances 10% for each 9 knots headwind. For operation with tailwinds up to 10 knots, increase distances by 10% for each 2 knots.

2. For operation on a dry, grass runway, increase distances by 15% of the "ground roll" figure.

WEIGHT LBS	TAKEOFF SPEED KIAS		PRESS ALT FT	0°C		10°C		20°C	
	LIFT OFF	AT 50 FT		GRND ROLL	TOTAL TO CLEAR 50 FT OBS	GRND ROLL	TOTAL TO CLEAR 50 FT OBS	GRND ROLL	TOTAL TO CLEAR 50 FT OBS
2300	60	70	S.L.	775	1380	835	1475	895	1575
			1000	850	1510	915	1615	980	1725
			2000	930	1650	1000	1770	1075	1895
			3000	1020	1815	1100	1945	1180	2085
			4000	1125	2000	1210	2145	1300	2305
			5000	1235	2210	1330	2375	1430	2555
			6000	1365	2450	1470	2640	1580	2850
			7000	1505	2730	1625	2955	1750	3190
			8000	1665	3065	1800	3320	- - -	- - -

(a) 1475 ft.

(b) 1770 ft.

(c) 1327.5 ft.

(d) 1622.5 ft.

5 Using the figures given in the Cruise Performance table shown below, what will be the range in still air (nil wind) if the aircraft is flown at 4000 ft pressure altitude at 64% BHP with an outside air temperature of 35°C, and a total of 40 gallons of useable fuel?

CRUISE PERFORMANCE

CONDITIONS:
Recommended Lean Mixture
2300 Pounds

PRESSURE ALTITUDE	RPM	20°C BELOW STANDARD TEMP			STANDARD TEMPERATURE			20°C ABOVE STANDARD TEMP		
		% BHP	KTAS	GPH	% BHP	KTAS	GPH	% BHP	KTAS	GPH
2000	2550	80	114	8.8	75	113	8.2	71	113	7.8
	2500	76	111	8.3	71	111	7.8	67	111	7.5
	2400	68	107	7.5	64	107	7.2	61	106	6.9
	2300	61	102	6.9	58	101	6.7	55	99	6.5
	2200	55	96	6.4	52	95	6.2	49	93	6.1
4000	2600	80	116	8.8	75	116	8.3	71	116	7.8
	2500	72	111	7.9	68	111	7.5	64	110	7.2
	2400	65	107	7.3	61	106	6.9	58	104	6.7
	2300	58	101	6.7	55	100	6.5	53	98	6.3
	2200	52	95	6.3	49	93	6.1	47	92	5.9
6000	2650	80	118	8.8	75	118	8.2	71	118	7.8
	2600	76	116	8.3	71	116	7.9	68	115	7.5
	2500	69	111	7.6	65	110	7.2	62	109	7.0
	2400	62	106	7.0	59	104	6.7	56	103	6.5
	2300	56	100	6.5	53	98	6.3	50	97	6.1
	2200	50	94	6.1	47	92	5.9	45	91	5.8

(a) 781 nm.

(b) 770nm.

(c) 611 nm.

(d) None of the above responses are correct.

6 Using the cruise performance table shown in question 5, what will be the aircraft endurance at a pressure altitude of 2000 ft using 52% BHP at standard air temperature conditions with 35 gallons of useable fuel?

(a) 5 hours 39 mins.

(b) 6 hours 42 mins.

(c) 4 hours 11 mins.

(d) 6 hours 11 mins.

7 Using the 'Landing Distance' table shown below, what will be the landing distance, under the following conditions?

Aircraft Weight	2300 lbs.
Pressure Altitude	1000 ft.
Outside Air Temperature	10°C.
Headwind Component	18 knots

LANDING DISTANCE

CONDITIONS:
Flaps 40°
Power Off
Maximum Braking
Paved, Level, Dry Runway
Zero Wind

NOTES:

1 Decrease distances 10% for each 9 knots headwind. For operation with tailwinds up to 10 knots, increase distances by 10% for each 2 knots.

2. For operation on a dry, grass runway, increase distances by 45% of the "ground roll" figure.

WEIGHT LBS	SPEED AT 50 FT KIAS	PRESS ALT FT	0°C		10°C		20°C	
			GRND ROLL	TOTAL TO CLEAR 50 FT OBS	GRND ROLL	TOTAL TO CLEAR 50 FT OBS	GRND ROLL	TOTAL TO CLEAR 50 FT OBS
2300	70	S.L.	495	1205	510	1235	530	1265
		1000	510	1235	530	1265	550	1300
		2000	530	1265	550	1300	570	1335
		3000	550	1300	570	1335	590	1370
		4000	570	1335	590	1370	615	1410
		5000	590	1370	615	1415	635	1450
		6000	615	1415	640	1455	660	1490
		7000	640	1455	660	1495	685	1535
		8000	665	1500	690	1540	710	1580

(a) 1358.5 ft.

(b) 1111.5 ft.

(c) 1012 ft.

(d) 1518 ft.

8 In relation to an aircraft's weight and balance schedule, which of the following responses is correct?

(a) The basic weight is the weight of all the basic equipment and fuel load which are required for the flight, but it does not include the weight of the aircraft.

(b) The variable load includes the weight of the crew and their baggage and equipment.

(c) The disposable load consists of the weight of all persons, and baggage, but does not include the fuel.

(d) None of the above responses are correct.

9 In relation to the weight and balance of an aircraft, it can be assumed that:

(a) If all seats and fuel tanks are filled, the aircraft's weight and balance will remain within the specified limits.

(b) If all seats and fuel tanks are filled and the baggage limit is not exceeded, the weight and balance will be within limits.

(c) A weight and balance calculation need only be carried out prior to flight when it is intended to fill all seats and fuel tanks.

(d) All the above responses are incorrect.

10 Using the centre of gravity moment envelope shown below and the following conditions:

Item		Weight (lbs)	Arm	Moment
Basic Weight	Aircraft	1500	37.5	56250
Variable Load	Pilot	160	40	6400
Disposable Load	Fuel	140	41	5740
	Oil (included in basic weight)			
	Passengers (2)	320	45	14400
	Baggage	40	48	1920

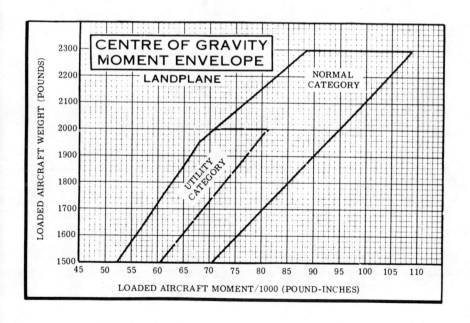

Which of the following responses is correct?

(a)   The aircraft is within the weight limit but the centre of gravity is outside the envelope.

(b)   The aircraft can be operated safely in the utility category.

(c)   The weight and balance is within limits for the normal category only.

(d)   The aircraft is overloaded but within the centre of gravity limits.

ANSWER SHEET QUIZ NO. 6

Q	A
1	
2	
3	
4	
5	
6	
7	
8	
9	
10	

1   In relation to carburettor icing, this can:

(a)   Only occur when the aircraft is flying in cloud or precipitation in outside air temperatures of 0°C or below.

(b)   Form when the outside air temperature is below −8°C.

(c)   Form at the engine air intake, throttle butterfly and walls of the carburettor passages.

(d)   Both responses (a) and (b) are correct.

2   During flight, an aircraft with a fixed pitch propeller suffers a drop in RPM at a fixed throttle setting. Following this, the engine begins to run roughly. In determining the cause, the pilot should first suspect:

(a)   Fuel starvation.

(b)   A faulty tachometer.

(c)   Fouling of the sparking plugs.

(d)   Carburettor icing.

3   After a period of engine rough running (which is gradually worsening) the pilot selects 'carburettor heat'. Immediately following this action, the rough running worsens. In these circumstances the pilot's next best course of action should be to:

(a)   Enrich the mixture.

(b)   Select 'cold air'.

(c)   Remain in 'hot air' for a short while to see if the rough running ceases.

(d)   Weaken the mixture and open the cowl flaps (if fitted).

4 Which of the following responses are correct:

   (a) The grade of oil recommended for use in a particular aero engine will normally vary according to whether the engine is being operated in hot or cold climatic conditions.

   (b) Filters are fitted in the oil system to remove the products of 'oxidation'.

   (c) The grade of oil recommended for use in a particular aero engine will always be the same regardless of whether the engine is being operated in hot or cold climatic conditions.

   (d) All of the above responses are incorrect.

5 In relation to the construction of fuel tanks:

   (a) Tank vents are incorporated to ensure that the fuel pressure increases as the aircraft climbs.

   (b) Baffles are fitted to ensure that when the aircraft climbs, the change of pressure within the tanks varies the fuel flow.

   (c) Tank vents are fitted to ensure that as fuel is used, a reduced pressure area does not occur above the fuel level in the tank and cause a reduction in fuel flow to the engine.

   (d) All the above responses are correct.

6 If the cylinder head temperature gauge shows abnormally high readings during flight, the pilot should:

   (a) Enrich the mixture and use a higher power setting.

   (b) Decrease airspeed, close the cowl flaps, increase the power, enrich the mixture.

   (c) Enrich the mixture, increase the airspeed, close the cowl flaps.

   (d) Ensure the cowl flaps are fully open, enrich the mixture, reduce the power, increase the airspeed (if possible).

7 In a vacuum system which is operated by a suction pump, any restriction in the master filter will cause:

   (a) An increased suction within the system which will result in erroneous instrument indications.

   (b) The relief valve to become inoperative.

(c) A reduced vacuum within the system, which will result in erroneous instrument indications.

(d) An increased suction which will be compensated for by the normal action of the pressure relief valve.

8 Which of the following responses is correct?

(a) A voltage regulator controls the rate of charge to the battery from the alternator/generator.

(b) Aircraft electrical systems are normally of the direct current single wire negative ground type.

(c) Aircraft electrical systems normally use alternating current which is earthed through the battery.

(d) Both responses (a) and (b) are correct.

9 If the fuse protecting a particular circuit blows, the pilot should:

(a) Immediately reset the appropriate circuit breaker.

(b) If the circuit is equipped with a cartridge fuse it should be replaced with another fuse, but of higher amperage.

(c) Wait at least 2 minutes before re-setting the appropriate circuit breaker or inserting a fresh cartridge fuse.

(d) All the above responses are incorrect.

10 In relation to the electrical systems used in aircraft.

(a) The presentation of 'charge state' is the same for all aircraft ammeters.

(b) An excess voltage output from the alternator or generator is prevented by the use of a voltage limiting device known as a voltage regulator.

(c) A 12 volt battery will normally be used in conjunction with a 14 volt electrical system.

(d) Both responses (b) and (c) are correct.

ANSWER SHEET QUIZ NO. 7

Q	A
1	
2	
3	
4	
5	
6	
7	
8	
9	
10	

Quiz No. 8

1 In relation to the operation of an engine equipped with a variable pitch propeller, which of the following responses is correct?

  (a) The throttle lever will vary the RPM at cruising and higher power settings.

  (b) The pitch lever will vary the manifold pressure.

  (c) Once cruising power is set, the throttle position will control both the manifold pressure and the RPM.

  (d) During flight, the throttle is used to control the manifold pressure and the RPM is controlled by use of the pitch lever.

2 The correct sequence of operating throttle and pitch levers when increasing engine power is:

  (a) To move both the throttle and pitch levers forward at the same time.

  (b) To smoothly push the pitch lever forward to obtain the required RPM and then increase the manifold pressure by use of the throttle lever.

  (c) Reduce the manifold pressure and then increase the RPM.

  (d) None of the previous responses are correct.

3 During the engine run-up period in an aircraft fitted with a variable pitch propeller, (non-feathering type) the pilot should:

  (a) Occasionally operate the pitch lever from climbing to cruising RPM.

  (b) Ensure that the propeller blades are exercised through their full range of pitch travel.

  (c) Ensure that the propeller is kept in fully coarse pitch throughout.

  (d) Keep the propeller in fully fine pitch throughout the complete run-up period.

4 If a pilot takes off with the propeller blades set in coarse pitch he will experience.

  (a) An increase in thrust.

  (b) A reduction in thrust.

  (c) The same value of thrust as for a fine pitch setting.

  (d) All of the above responses are incorrect.

5 The use of carburettor heat during ground running operations should be:

  (a) Kept to a minimum because sparking plug temperatures remain fairly low at idling RPM.

  (b) Used as freely as possible particularly during high ambient air temperatures.

  (c) Reduced to a minimum because carburettor icing cannot occur at low RPM.

  (d) Kept to a minimum because the induction air filter is normally by-passed when 'hot air' is selected.

6 In relation to the indications shown by engine instruments, these:

  (a) Can be used individually or collectively to determine the operating condition of an engine.

  (b) Must always be used individually to determine the operating condition of an engine.

  (c) Cannot be used to provide early warning of any engine malfunction.

  (d) All the above responses are incorrect.

7 In relation to the use of mixture control:

  (a) Mixture leaning can be carried out at any altitude when more than 80% power is being used.

  (b) Regardless of the power being used, the minimum altitude to use the mixture control technique is 5000ft.

(c)   Mixture control techniques can normally be used at any altitude providing the engine is being operated at not more than 70% power (subject to the recommendations contained in the aircraft manual).

(d)   In low wing aircraft, mixture control techniques can only be used when the electric fuel pump is in the 'on' position.

8   In the event that a pilot experiences significant and continuous engine vibration:

(a)   He should increase power to maximum and climb to the highest possible altitude compatible with the cloud base.

(b)   He should switch on the electric fuel pump and/or select another fuel tank.

(c)   If the fault does not lie with carburettor icing, the fuel supply or ignition system, he should make preparations to land as soon as it is safely possible.

(d)   Either response (b) or (c) could be the correct course of action.

9   When using chocks during the starting up of a nose-wheel aircraft:

(a)   They should be placed in front of the main wheels only.

(b)   Only one should be used and this should be in front of the nose-wheel.

(c)   Chocks should be placed in front of both mainwheels and the nose-wheel.

(d)   All the above responses are incorrect.

10   If a propeller has to be hand swung to start an engine, the safety precautions must include:

(a)   The aircraft being positioned so that the person who swings the propeller can obtain a firm foot-hold for both feet.

(b)   The person swinging the propeller must have had sufficient training.

(c)   The propeller should not be handled initially until both the pilot and the person handling the propeller have established that the ignition switches are 'off'.

(d)   All the above responses are correct.

ANSWER SHEET QUIZ NO. 8

Q	A
1	
2	
3	
4	
5	
6	
7	
8	
9	
10	

Quiz No. 9

1   A Certificate of Airworthiness is issued in a particular 'category'. In respect of light aircraft, which of the following categories may apply:

(a)   Transport category

(b)   Utility category

(c)   Permit to fly category

(d)   Normal category

2   A Certificate of Airworthiness is issued:

(a)   For an indefinite period.

(b)   For a specific period.

(c)   To cover several aircraft of the same type and model.

(d)   Only in respect of aircraft in the transport category.

3   The number which is recorded at the top of a particular Certificate of Airworthiness is an identification number which will also appear on the:

(a)   Certificate of Maintenance Review

(b)   Certificate of Release to Service

(c)   Certificate of Authorisation

(d)   Flight/owner's manual or pilot's operating handbook.

4   The aircraft flight manual for a specific aircraft:

(a)   Forms part of the aircraft's Certificate of Airworthiness.

(b)   Must be used to determine the pertinent operating regulations for the particular aircraft.

(c) Will include information in respect of the aircraft's operating limitations.

(d) All of the above responses are correct.

5 When an aircraft flight manual includes a CAA Supplement:

(a) The pilot must abide by the contents of this supplement.

(b) The pilot must abide by the information given in the flight manual as supplements of this nature contain advisory information only.

(c) The aircraft will only be issued with a 'permit to fly'.

(d) It cannot be operated with passengers on board.

6 Placards which display information in the aircraft cockpit:

(a) Do not have the same status as the flight manual.

(b) Have the same status as the aircraft's flight manual.

(c) Only display information of a transient nature.

(d) All of the above responses are incorrect.

7 The Certificate of Maintenance Review gives information whereby the pilot can determine:

(a) Whether or not the flying hours carried out by the aircraft are within the specified check cycle.

(b) The number of flying hours remaining to the next maintenance inspection.

(c) Whether the calender period between maintenance checks has been exceeded.

(d) All of the above responses are correct.

8 The list of maintenance items which can be conducted by a licensed pilot who is the owner or operator of the aircraft is given in the:

(a) Air Navigation Order.

(b) Pilot Regulations Order 1978 (as amended).

(c) Flight manual.

(d) Air Navigation (General) Regulations (as amended).

9 Aircraft engine and propeller log books:

(a) Are raised at the time the aircraft receives its Certificate of Airworthiness.

(b) Must be used to maintain a record of any repairs, changes or modifications to the aircraft or its fixed equipment.

(c) Must be preserved by the aircraft's owner or operator for at least two years after the aircraft engine or variable pitch propeller, as the case may be, has been destroyed or permanently withdrawn from use.

(d) All of the above responses are correct.

10 In relation to a pilot's responsibilities:

(a) He must *personally* check whether the aircraft documentation and serviceability is satisfactory prior to any flight he undertakes.

(b) He can accept another person's assurance that the aircraft documentation is satisfactory but must physically check for himself as to whether the aircraft is serviceable prior to any flight he undertakes.

(c) He can accept the assurance of the owner or operator as to whether the aircraft's documentation is correct and the aircraft is serviceable.

(d) He need not record any aircraft unserviceability following a flight provided he has reported the defect to a ground engineer.

ANSWER SHEET QUIZ NO. 9

Q	A
1	
2	
3	
4	
5	
6	
7	
8	
9	
10	

1 If the impact source of a pitot static system becomes blocked during flight, which of the following instruments will give an erroneous reading?

(a) The altimeter.

(b) The turn and balance indicator.

(c) The vertical speed indicator.

(d) The airspeed indicator.

2 In relation to the altimeter, which of the following responses is correct?

(a) The aneroid capsule is sealed and affected by changes of air pressure fed through a static tube into the instrument case.

(b) If the datum scale is correctly set to read the current QFE, the altimeter will indicate the aircraft's height above the particular aerodrome.

(c) Part of the pilot's serviceability checks will be to ensure that the instrument glass is secure and unbroken.

(d) All the above responses are correct.

3 Referring to the diagram below, the altimeters shown indicate

    A   B   C

(a) A   7800 ft.   (c) A   8800 ft.
    B   1800 ft.   B   880 ft.
    C   2420 ft.   C 12420 ft.

(b) A   8700 ft.   (d) A   9800 ft.
    B 18800 ft.   B   1880 ft.
    C 12400 ft.   C   2400 ft.

4 Referring to the altimeter indications illustrated below, select the correct response.

          A   B   C

(a) A   8880 ft.
    B   1140 ft.
    C   1150 ft.

(b) A   7880 ft.
    B   1130 ft.
    C   1500 ft.

(c) A   8900 ft.
    B   1380 ft.
    C 15500 ft.

(d) A   7880 ft.
    B   1380 ft.
    C 15500 ft.

5 One millibar is approximately equal to:

(a) 60 ft.

(b) 30 ft.

(c) 40 ft.

(d) 50 ft.

6   In relation to the turn and balance indicator, which of the following is correct?

   (a) It is a gyro operated instrument which utilises the principle of a gyro having rigidity in space and affected by precession.

   (b) The gyro assembly will not topple, regardless of aircraft attitude.

   (c) It is constructed so that it has freedom to move about two of the three axes, and shows rate of aircraft movement about the third.

   (d) All the above responses are correct.

7   In relation to the attitude indicator, which of the following is correct:

   (a) Regardless of the type and year of manufacture, the dial presentations are exactly the same.

   (b) All of these instruments are topple free.

   (c) They give a direct indication of the aircraft's rate of turn.

   (d) None of the above responses are correct.

8   Regardless of the different dial presentations used in various types of heading indicators, it can be assumed that all types will:

   (a) Have to be checked and re-synchronised with the magnetic compass approximately every 15 minutes.

   (b) Remain synchronised with the magnetic compass for at least one hour after synchronisation.

   (c) Initially, need to be set to the magnetic compass heading once the gyro is operating at the correct RPM.

   (d) Both responses (a) and (c) are correct.

9   The normal operating errors to be found in any aircraft magnetic compass are:

   (a) An erroneous indication whenever its gyro is running too fast or too slow.

   (b) Latitude errors due to the earth's rate of rotation.

   (c) Acceleration, deceleration and turning errors.

   (d) All of the above responses are correct.

10 In relation to carrying magnetic (ferrous) materials on board an aircraft:

(a) They should be stowed as far away from the magnetic compass as possible.

(b) They will have no effect on the magnetic compass.

(c) Unless they are stowed well away from the magnetic compass, they will cause a change in variation.

(d) They will have no effect on the value of deviation.

ANSWER SHEET QUIZ NO. 10

Q	A
1	
2	
3	
4	
5	
6	
7	
8	
9	
10	

Answers To Progress Tests

Quiz No. 1	
1	c
2	c
3	c
4	d
5	b
6	b
7	c
8	d
9	c
10	d

Quiz No. 2	
1	a
2	d
3	b
4	d
5	b
6	c
7	c
8	a
9	c
10	d

Quiz No. 3	
1	a
2	b
3	c
4	a
5	d
6	a
7	d
8	b
9	d
10	d

Quiz No. 4	
1	b
2	b
3	d
4	a
5	c
6	c
7	d
8	c
9	b
10	c

Quiz No. 5	
1	d
2	c
3	d
4	d
5	b
6	d
7	d
8	b
9	b
10	d

Quiz No. 6	
1	b
2	c
3	b
4	b
5	c
6	a
7	c
8	b
9	d
10	c

Quiz No. 7	
1	c
2	d
3	c
4	a
5	d
6	d
7	c
8	d
9	c
10	d

Quiz No. 8	
1	d
2	b
3	b
4	b
5	d
6	a
7	c
8	d
9	a
10	d

Quiz No. 9	
1	a
2	b
3	d
4	d
5	a
6	b
7	d
8	d
9	d
10	a

Quiz No. 10	
1	d
2	d
3	c
4	d
5	b
6	d
7	d
8	d
9	c
10	a

Index

Index

Index

Index